The Filmmaker's Craft:

16mm cinematography

Philip R. Courter

Van Nostrand Reinhold Company

New York   Cincinnati   Toronto   London   Melbourne

for Gay

Copyright © 1982 by Philip R. Courter

Library of Congress Catalog Card Number 81-11689

ISBN 0-442-21708-0

Printed in the United States of America

Designed by Ben D. Kann

Published by Van Nostrand Reinhold Company Inc.
135 West 50th Street
New York, NY 10020

Van Nostrand Reinhold Publishers
1410 Birchmount Road
Scarborough, Ontario M1P 2E7, Canada

Van Nostrand Reinhold Australia Pty. Ltd.
480 Latrobe Street
Melbourne, Victoria 3000, Australia

Van Nostrand Reinhold Company Limited
Molly Millars Lane
Wokingham, Berkshire, England

16 15 14 13 12 11 10 9 8 7 6 5 4 3 2 1

Library of Congress Cataloging in Publication Data
Courter, Philip R.
    The filmmaker's craft.

    Includes index.
    1. Cinematography.   2. Moving-pictures—
Production and direction.   I. Title.
TR850.C59   778.5'3   81-11689
ISBN 0-442-21708-0   AACR2

Contents

Acknowledgments

I would like to express my sincere gratitude and give recognition to the following people: my wife Gay for the years of encouragement, organization, editing, typing, phone calls, and corrections; "T," "P.C." and Lisa Thompson for numerous photos, time, energy, and advice; Jem Cohen, who deserves equal credit with me for creating the illustrations; Fred Huffman for the special illustrations in the lighting chapter; Jac Yager for his advice and research; Josephine Imhoff for the massive job of typing all materials into the word processor; Marie Breeden for reading and correcting the text; Three Tyler of the *American Cinematographer* magazine for her cheerful and speedy photo research; Marylee Lander of Florida's Dade County film and television department for additional pictures; Ruth and Sandra Mandel for photo research; Leo Rosenberg of Camera Mart and Joy Sorensen of Brenner Photo for advice and equipment photos; Jean Koefoed for his initial faith in the project and Nancy Green for ultimately producing the book; John and Carrie Staples for their long and faithful advice and encouragement; Katherine Stenholm, Wade Ramsey, and the excellent staff of Unusual Films, Bob Jones University, for much of the knowledge contained herein; and finally, to my Mom and Dad for a list longer than all these pages.

Introduction

To be a filmmaker is the goal of many of today's brightest and most creative talents, all of whom face an amazing array of new production hardware, systems, and methods. But there has been a widespread shift toward the teaching of video production techniques in the schools and colleges, and those who wish to utilize film find their educational quest increasingly difficult to attain. Yet film techniques have, in the eighties, emerged as the highest quality, visual information-capturing system available to producers. The image record stored on motion picture film has the best resolution, color accuracy, and detail of all existing information storage and retrieval systems now known. When the potential for future program distribution exists in so many different formats (such as video cassette, disc, and theatrical release) the safest choice for many productions continues to be film.

Today it is both possible and popular to be an almost self-sufficient filmmaker: to write, shoot, edit, direct, and produce a film singlehandedly. Such a filmmaker must certainly learn the skills of all the specialists in the industry, but the filmmaker who chooses instead to rely on a complete staff of technicians must also study these skills.

The director, more than anyone else, must fully understand every aspect of producing a motion picture even if he never touches the film materials himself. Traditionally directors have commanded the respect of the entire crew because they understood all facets of filmmaking and knew virtually as much as the cameramen, editors, and the rest of the staff combined.

Beginning filmmakers sometimes try to start as directors but soon become frustrated because they lack the technical proficiency that would enable them to realize their ideas. At the same time, professionals in the industry are frustrated when they hire a person with a master's degree in cinema and find him unable to handle even the simplest editing or shooting jobs because he had only studied film history, film criticism, and film as art.

Today's novice filmmaker faces many problems learning the craft created by the increased specialization of the film industry. If lucky enough to get a job as an assistant editor, for example, he may never go out for any of the shooting and may never view the finished film. Even if he is able to watch a good cameraman at work, observation alone will not teach him why the scene is shot in a certain manner or why a light is placed in a given position. Without persistence and luck, it may be impossible for the beginner to get a well-rounded film education on the job.

Learning filmmaking is difficult even for the cinema student enrolled in a course, because the subject is so very complex. Making a film is not a simple sequential process, and therefore film courses cannot have a sequential relationship. Courses in editing, lighting, photography, and script writing are so interdependent that it is difficult to understand one without previous knowledge in another. It would seem impossible to plan a curriculum that would properly meet the needs of the filmmaking student.

By looking at many case histories, I have found that "learning by doing" is the technique most likely to lead to success in establishing a career in film/video. There are at least three advantages to spending major amounts of time and money producing a marketable film as a learning experience. First, the hands-on work is invaluable. Second, as with all artistic endeavors, it is absolutely necessary to demonstrate to teachers, your prospective employers, and yourself what kind of filmmaking you can produce. Third, when students apply their efforts to sensible and useful as well as creative and interesting subjects, more often than not a market exists for the finished product. Thus, production costs are recovered and a career may be simultaneously embarked upon.

This book is designed to fill the gap for those caught between the seemingly impossible job market where experience is required but not given, and the university that may not provide enough practical courses. Previously existing books on this subject fall roughly into two categories: reference works, which are very useful if you thoroughly understand the process; and texts, which cover all aspects of production, editing, laboratory, sound, and so on, but, because of space requirements, cannot give any real depth.

Limiting this volume to the shooting but not the editing or postproduction of films creates the opportunity to combine three important aspects of many other separate works. First, the book provides the most background material, which gives depth and answers the question of why a particular technique is used. Second, major sections are devoted to the practical application or "how to," which in this book are compiled from the experiences of many cameramen. Third, reference charts list all kinds of tools and techniques, which provide much needed information in a highly concentrated form.

Today films can be produced in Super 8mm, 16mm, super 16mm, 35mm, 65mm, and 70mm. Super 8 is generally used by amateurs for home movies, but it is finding its way into professional circles because Super 8 cartridge prints are easily made from films originally produced in 16mm. Super 8 is also fast becoming a production medium, and many nontheatrical films have already been produced in the Super 8 format. Super 8 prints, whether reduction prints from 16mm or from films originally produced in that format are used in cassette projectors such as the Fairchild Mark IV, the Technicolor Super 8, and television players. They are becoming widely accepted for classroom, sales, and training purposes.

Problems with the Super 8 format as the original production film stock are its small size, which makes it difficult to handle in editing, and its low-quality sound reproduction. Also, the size of the projected Super 8mm picture makes it useful only for small groups. It is interesting that all of these things were being said about 16mm only a few years ago.

Sixteen millimeter began as the amateur format, but technical improvements have perfected the picture and sound quality. Professional results are possible because it is easily edited and the sound is reproduced on a relatively high-quality track. It can be shown to larger audiences and can be used for television transmission. It is the obvious choice of the student filmmaker, for the nontheatrical market, television, and—to a growing extent—for low-budget feature film production. Sixteen millimeter is less expensive to work with than the old professional standard 35mm because film stock, cameras, processing, and related equipment are all less expensive to start with.

Thirty-five millimeter is the standard for theatrical film production because its larger

I-1. Scale drawing with dimensions of current film formats.

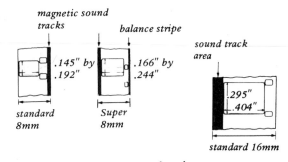

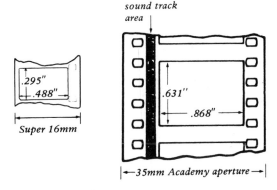

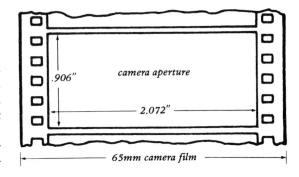

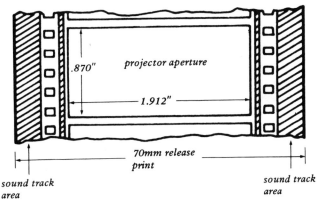

size allows it to be shown on screens that may be more than sixty feet wide while maintaining a high-quality image. Some common variations on 35mm include Cinerama, where three cameras simultaneously shoot one scene later projected by three synchronous projectors; Cinemascope, which uses a lens that squeezes the image horizontally to about half the normal size and thus records a wide-angle view on regular 35mm film; and Techniscope, which uses only half the standard four-perforation height image and thus provides an economical wide-screen process. The 65mm and 70mm formats are extremely expensive to work with, but they produce a picture that has an unusually high degree of fidelity.

It is necessary to set limits to the scope of any book. This book concentrates on the 16mm format and its production methods. But it is important to remember that all the film sizes can be reproduced in different formats. A film produced in one gauge can be reduced in a laboratory process to a narrower gauge or enlarged to a wider one. A film originally produced in 16mm can, and frequently is, enlarged or blown up for theatrical release in 35mm or reduced to Super 8 for use in cartridge projectors. Sixteen-millimeter film goes through all of the production processes of 35mm film, and any special exceptions will be pointed out as they arise. Thirty-five millimeter is, in fact, a more forgiving format than 16mm, and those who handle 16mm materials successfully will certainly be able to step up to 35mm without any significant adjustment problems.

By studying this book, the novice filmmaker will learn a tremendous amount regarding the capturing of images. Although 16mm film is utilized as the format for discussion throughout the book, other formats and media are being taught here as well: the chapters on film exposure and lighting apply directly to still photography; the directing and lighting chapters are almost totally applicable to video; and Super 8 and 35mm formats represent a very simple substitution of hardware from those 16mm cameras and accessories illustrated in the text. Thus 16mm is the ideal teaching medium for the filmmaker who aspires to produce creatively everything from television commercials to feature films.

chapter 1

Production methods and film directing

Because this book is primarily about 16mm nontheatrical filmmaking, the subjects contained in this chapter fall mostly into the directing category. If this were a book about 35mm feature filmmaking, the material on selecting camera angles and maintaining screen direction might be listed with the cinematographer's responsibilities. In both the 16mm and 35mm fields, the text concerning selecting a production approach could probably be listed with the producer's tasks. In a way, these conflicts are typical of the differences not in the substance, but in the variations in style that occur between specialties and areas in filmmaking.

The material that follows is so important to all beginning filmmakers that it has been included here despite the above-mentioned conflicts.

The role of the director

A most important underlying characteristic of all art forms is premeditation. The successful artist embarks on a piece of work only after he knows exactly what it is he intends to do and understands completely the techniques of the chosen medium that can transform this idea into something communicable.

In most art forms the artist is responsible for both the original conception and the technical execution. The painter chooses his subject, selects the size and shape of the canvas, and applies the chosen paint with the chosen tool in a manner compatible with his chosen style.

But these generally accepted principles of creation are not always completely appropriate to the film producer/artist/director. The original conception is often handed over to the director in the form of a script or contract, a novel, or some other form of treatment. The actual technical completion of the ideas may be left in the hands of other creators, each with his own talents, inputs, and perceptions. But the basic characteristics of artistic creation nonetheless must not be totally violated. The massive number of alternatives and choices available to the director demand close adherence to creative guidelines. If he does not know exactly what he intends to do and does not understand the techniques that can transform the idea into a communicable form, only confusion and chaos will be seen both during production and during review of the work.

Following is a brief list of the responsibilities normally assumed by a motion picture director:

Work on the script with the writer and client.

Select the production approach and the production unit, estimate budgets, and set up shooting schedules.

Pick location sites, sets, costumes, props.

Work out a solid continuity of action, the directions, entrances, movements.

Plan the pace, rhythm, and mood.

Choose the actors, their appearance, their voices, their makeup.

Figure out the camera angles and microphone positions.

Work out the production format, choose the stock, plan the lighting.

Direct the actors—their movements, deliveries, style, and their presentations.

Decide on all elements for the soundtracks, dialogue, voiceovers, music, effects.

Supervise the editing, the mixing, the negative cutting.

Supervise the laboratory timing and printing, check the prints.

Help put together and supervise promotion and distribution.

In a small production unit, the director may also do the shooting and cutting. In addition, some directors use their own special abilities, such as the director who also acts, animates, or writes, or who can perform the music, do the free falls or scuba dives.

Since the director has all these responsibilities and makes all these decisions, the ultimate product will reflect the director's personality. His feelings, experiences, knowledge or lack of it, straightforwardness, honesty, courage, insecurities, and phobias affect every filmmaking decision and are visible to those who analyze his work. But a director without distinct personality and recognizable character will produce little personality or character in his work.

The director is also required to persuade people of diverse interests and personalities to work as a team toward a common goal through many demanding and difficult days. He must be able to make quick, sure decisions, inspire his cast and crew, communicate abstract ideas, persuade without embarrassing or intimidating, give orders inoffensively; he must also be knowledgeable in many technical areas, patient, and able to operate effectively under pressure.

Three of the most important areas that every director faces on each production are (1) *the production approach,* (2) *pictorial continuity,* and (3) *building a story.*

The production approach

The production approach is chosen early in the hierarchy of film planning. It follows the initial decision to make a film and the understanding of what the film is about. The production approach is the sum total of a whole group of decisions where the input consists of numerous bits of data, some simple and some complex. An example of simple data would be the budget where the ceiling is known. A more complex item might be the choice of lighting style. When all known requirements have been reduced to the most logical form of input, the computer in the brain of the filmmaker must output a list of crew members, equipment, locations, and all the elements that will hopefully deliver the inputted requirements.

But the problem is that the definition has been vastly oversimplified. Part of the method involves the creative use of existing resources; it takes innovative thinking to help solve the problem of skimpy budgets by substituting simplicity and improvisation.

There is always more than one "right way" to make a film about a given subject. Ideally the style for a film is selected strictly on the basis of what is most likely to communicate the idea to the chosen audience in the most powerful manner. But film styles are often determined by such forces as the location, the season, date of product announcement, availability of actors and crew, and schedules of completion for the production. Ultimately the production approach is a composite of the central theme as modified by restrictions, requirements, producer/client suggestions and demands, availabilities, and dozens of other variables.

As the director begins to analyze his filmic needs he must answer the following questions. Do I need a large or small crew? Can the cameraman work alone? Are multiple cameras necessary? Should I use cinéma vérité, stills, or animation? Does the film call for prescore and playback or postsync voice dubbing? While it is impossible to set rules to answer these questions, the following discussions will help foster the kind of thinking that can lead the filmmaker-director to sensible production solutions.

Determining crew size

No two shooting situations are alike in terms of setup and production needs, and it is impossible to set rules for personnel requirements. Simply adding together the number of people required to accomplish each production operation is not the answer unless the work is being done within the strictest union rules. The most efficient crew is made up of versatile people who are willing and able to haul in the equipment, tie in the electric feeds, set lights, dress sets, smear on the makeup, coddle actors, run the camera and sound, operate the teleprompter and clapstick, and break down at wrap time. Under certain circumstances, a versatile crew of four can do the work of a dozen rank and file; at other times, much larger crews will be necessary. As with any kind of hiring, it is important to review what a potential crew member has done, with what kind of help and supervision, and at what cost.

Though there is no rule of thumb to determine crew sizes, certain factors almost always increase the number of people required.

Interiors, both locations and studio, usually require extensive lighting. (Shooting in 16mm color requires about 100 footcandles or more.) The cost of studio rental and restrictions on the use of some locations often means the lighting must be accomplished in a short time. The task of simply moving the hundreds of pounds of cable, trunk lines, power boxes, luminaries, stands, and associated lighting gear can quickly overwhelm an inadequate crew. Extra hands are the forces that can get this work done quickly. Two or three competent assistants are required for quickly lighting small setups with one or two actors; more crew members must be added as the scenes get bigger and the time gets shorter. When large sets with several actors and considerable movement within the scene are called for, a competent team of electricians and gaffers and a skilled director of photography are needed.

While any good person is willing to put forth a special effort in an emergency, it is a mistake for the director to demand extra heavy labor and long hours on a continuing basis throughout many days of shooting. Bad crew morale makes for mistakes and costly reshoots.

When sync sound is being shot, one or two crew members minimum should be added. With documentary subjects it is possible for a recordist equipped with a portable synchronous quarter-inch recorder and hand-held microphone to handle the whole sound recording job, but when consistent, clean sound is demanded, the recordist is best left to do careful recording level and tape monitoring while an assistant handles the microphone. Often the microphone is used on a boom or fish pole, and this equipment requires a full-time operator.

The recordist often needs to see the action, hear the lines, and listen to the acoustics before he can choose the best possible microphone techniques. A lavalier mike almost takes care of itself once it has been securely clipped to the speaker's lapel or collar, and its use will free the sound man to run the recorder. A highly directional cardoid or supercardoid microphone, on the other hand, needs to be very carefully aimed at all times to keep proper presence in the recording, and its use requires an additional crew member. Careful planning of the shooting, a visit to the location prior to setup, and a certain amount of experience are needed to predict what the many actual shooting requirements will be.

When the cast is large or when children or animals are needed, a larger production staff is called for. Depending on the child's age, it is not unusual to assign one adult to see to each child's physical and psychological needs. This helps keep children in the best possible shape throughout the tedium of filming. Animals require trainers and caretaking personnel.

When schedules are tight and deadlines immovable, as in the production of TV news material, multiple crews are sometimes the best answer. Despite the advances of modern transportation, schedules that look fine on paper often bog down on snowy Mondays. When ten setups in each of three cities must be pushed through the camera, dragged to the lab, and shoved into the editor's hands in less than a week, you may need three directors, three crews, and quadruple budgets.

The construction of sets, buildings, props, and so forth, is an obvious staff sweller, and short schedules multiply the problems. It is often difficult to find reliable and competent mechanics and carpenters to do this critical work, and one well-paid expert can accomplish more than three inexperienced helpers.

The absence of lights, sync sound, heavy construction, and large cast can free the film-maker from all but his camera and subject. Obviously, when costs must be held to a minimum, the choice of subject and location are the most important factors to be considered.

With documentary subjects, the possible disruption of a delicate scene can be a critical factor, and extra personnel usually results in less spontaneity from nonprofessional actors. By using fast films to negate the need for lights indoors and with a portable recorder and directional microphone, a crew of two can handle many documentary subjects, especially where multiple cameras are not needed to cover important never-to-be-repeated action. The results obtained in this way by Fred Wiseman in his documentaries are more than adequate evidence that cinéma vérité methods can produce excellent results with the right subjects. New lightweight cameras such as the Arriflex 16SR or the Eclair NPR are *self-blimped* (noise-less when running), have *reflex viewing* (allow instantly accurate composing and focusing), and utilize *crystal sync* (provide cordless synchronization with the sound recorder); they provide enormous flexibility and great convenience for this kind of filming.

1-1. Typical feature film crew on location. Approximately 16 staff needed to shoot medium shot of actress. (Memory House)

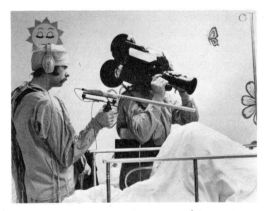

1-2. Two-person documentary team (author and soundman) on location in hospital. (Gay Courter)

The use of simultaneous multiple cameras (multicam)

The most important use of multiple cameras is to cover an uncontrolled event or action from different angles. There is no other way to get the best shots of the action and provide the needed material for controlled editing. Sports events are examples of that kind of action. In this area of documentation, specialized television crews using multiple cameras have achieved amazing technical success. Multiple cameras are also advantageously employed for news stories, concerts, quiz shows, panel discussions, talk shows, and theatrical presentations.

The second major use of several simultaneous cameras is in the filming of expensive action. When an auto crash is supposed to cascade down the mountainside as the star leaps from a window and goes to heaven in his rocket belt, or when a chariot race starts up with fifty chariots and a hundred horses, or Moscow is burning, the extra camera rentals and cameramen are insignificant in cost compared to recreating the scene to establish an extra angle or close-up.

The filming of what are essentially stage presentations, such as television situation comedies, is one of the largest areas of multiple camera use. The fact that this "TV-style" coverage has had a direct effect on film production methods is substantiated by the various kinds of combination film and video camera systems being designed and used with increasing frequency. Multiple-purpose distribution can still demand production in two media, but usually the combined TV/film cameras serve to apply television-style production methods to making edited-in-the-camera film versions. The use of video viewfinders and instant replay simply facilitate multicam motion picture production.

Some producers seem to think that all action is expensive and call for the use of second cameras on every scene. Although there are examples that show this approach can be useful, it is sometimes merely a product of someone's insecurity. Unless a very specific and important kind of shot (angle) or use (slow motion, reactions) can be defined for the second or additional cameras, efficiency will be greater if the necessary action is repeated and one camera concentrates on getting what is needed.

Uncontrolled action and multicam use can easily be construed to include all sorts of documentary subjects, but in some situations a heavy crew can destroy spontaneity. Classrooms are a good example of places where numerous filmmaking intruders can upset a fragile balance. By shooting an adequate number of alternate close-ups and cut-aways with a single camera, most editing problems and the need for a second camera will be eliminated.

Special production methods

There are a few special production methods that warrant paticular mention since they are used to solve many filming problems. The following are the five most commonly employed.

Cinéma vérité
There is great beauty in the unadorned, and no film presentation rings of truth quite like pure cinéma vérité (as its name suggests). To those who are able to see deep meaning in the commonplace, the so-called

vérité format holds a special and exalted place. The freedom of filming created through the use of highly portable equipment and the absence of special lighting, combined with the public's high tolerance of the technically inferior, make this an attractive production approach given the right choice of subject. The cinéma vérité style has been successfully applied in feature films, commercials, documentaries, and many kinds of subject films.With unscripted action, the vérité method is most likely to be successful.

The latest tools for vérité production are portable self-blimped (silent) cameras that can be hand held, shoulder held, or mounted on a body brace. They include the Aaton 7, Eclair AC, Eclair NPR, Arriflex BL, Arriflex 16SR, and "news" cameras such as the Frezzi cordless, and C.P. 16, Bolex Pro 16, Beaulieu News 16, and many others. Ideally these cameras should be equipped with both a crystal sync motor and electronic slate to allow freedom from interconnecting cables and clapsticks. These versatile cameras are used in conjunction with crystal-sync-controlled portable quarter-inch tape recorders. These in turn are equipped with high-quality directional microphones, to complete the production package.

Single-system sound

Both single- and double-system sound recording methods need to be described at the outset.

Double-system sound recording refers to the most commonly used method for all kinds of professional synchronized picture and sound shooting. The camera captures only the picture while the sound is recorded on a separate machine. The recording machine is usually a precision quarter-inch magnetic portable recorder that can be synchronized to the camera in several ways, discussed further in the camera chapter. Until recently 16mm magnetic sound recorders that utilize fully coated 16mm magnetic sound film were commonly used for double-system shooting. In any case, the sound is edited as a separate entity in the 16mm magnetic film format on such machines as the Moviola, the flatbed editor, or an editing bench set up with a picture viewer and separate sound reader.

Single-system sound recording utilizes a specially equipped camera that contains a sound recording module and recording amplifier and can capture the sound directly on the raw stock as it is being exposed during shooting. The early (pre-1950s) single-system cameras used optical sound modulators in the camera. The resulting developed original film would play directly on any standard optical sound projector. The problems with these units (almost exclusively Auricon equipment) centered around, first, obtaining exactly the right exposure for the sound track, and second, the fact that existing emulsions never had enough density and contrast to reproduce sound properly. Today these problems have been eliminated with film that has been prestriped with a magnetic track along its edge. The camera is equipped with a magnetic recording head that can produce an excellent-quality simultaneous sound recording at the time of shooting. The biggest remaining problem is that there are so few magnetic sound projectors available, not to mention the two steps required to print a copy.

Whereas double-system sound provides for the maximum quality and versatility via separate recording, single-system sound modules are available for many self-blimped cameras. Talented news cameramen have proven that acceptable coverage of many events can be had with a self-contained single-system camera with attached microphone.

Single system is the less expensive method of recording sync sound motion pictures because only one roll of film need be purchased, exposed and recorded, developed and projected.

Although TV news cameramen are the chief users of single-system sound, it can often be useful to the documentary and feature producer as well. By recording a single-system "scratch track" on all the original film, a built-in sync reference track is instantly and inexpensively procured. This reference track can be very helpful in syncing footage from many cameras to a master sound track, such as is done when filming rock festivals. The sound-on-film can be transferred to a regular double-system mag track and edited double-system style, and the single-system scratch track can also be used as a guide in dialogue dubbing when the voice is added later by actors in the studio.

Prescore and playback
Chiefly employed for filming musical numbers, the prescore and playback technique is easy to use and allows for the greatest freedom and control in both recording and filming phases.

The orchestra and vocalists record the music in a studio with all the microphones and electronic support needed to produce a high-quality recording. Care is taken to equalize the musical voice tracks so that

1-3. Auricon Pro-600 single-system sound camera on location.

presence and quality will closely match the sound that will be heard in the film's adjacent dialogue. The final mix of the music tracks is transferred to a monaural tape, which can be played back synchronously on location, usually through the use of a portable quarter-inch recorder equipped with a playback synchronizer and loudspeaker. The Nagra recorder and Nagra SLO playback synchronizer are frequent choices for this purpose.

During shooting, the soundman plays back the synchronous tape on cue and the actors mouth the prerecorded words while performing in front of a sync-driven camera. Professional actors with experience in prescore and playback can do a very convincing job, particularly when they did the original voice recording themselves and have carefully memorized the words and timing. Practice makes perfect, and skillful editing of alternate angles as well as good safe long shots make for smooth performances.

An alternate technique frequently used in TV variety shows is to prescore and play back the background music and then add to this signal a live mike of the vocals for the video tape. This allows the performer to do a totally convincing vocal for the camera with full orchestral support. Hand-held mikes usually provide excellent voice quality under studio conditions.

But for filming and taping location exteriors, dramatic presentations, and dance numbers, where microphones cannot be used for technical and physical reasons, the complete prescore and playback method is the only satisfactory answer.

Post-sync or voice dubbing

Sometimes, because of location noise, acoustical problems, or the nature of the action, lip sync recording during shooting is simply impossible. When the budget is tight, this can mean shooting itself is impossible. But with adequate funds, the dubbing studio "door" can be opened. In actuality, the time and effort saved during shooting goes a long way toward offsetting the additional actors' fees and studio rental time needed for dubbing a clean track.

A sync sound "scratch track" is made during shooting to provide a cue track for the dubbing session. Traditionally the edited version of the cue track and workprint picture is broken down into short loops for the dubbing session. In the dubbing studio (similar in every way to a film mixing studio), the picture and scratch track loops are synchronously projected for the actors, who wear headphones to hear their cues. Sitting in front of a microphone, the actors can watch, rehearse, and record repeated sections.

The looping method is still in common use, but the latest technology in backup recorders with pickup recording capabilities has opened the way for films to be dubbed straight through in unbroken reels. These systems, which utilize preset electronic controls to back up quickly to any given point, allow the actors to rehearse again and again, and then each segment is laid down onto an unbroken master tape. When the dubbing session is over, a clean, synchronous dialogue track exists for the entire reel and is ready for mixing with the other sound elements. This new technology eliminates the piecework editing involved in breaking the show into loops and then rebuilding it when taped. The cue track also helps the actors retain the spontaneous quality of the on-location sound, rather than lapse into a stiff studiolike performance that fails to match the drama on screen.

Stills and animation

In addition to the times when only animation can be used to tell an imaginary story, still photos of live subjects and graphics of every description can be used to illustrate different or expensive visual subjects. Pans, zooms, dissolves, wipes, and other optical devices help provide eye-stimulating movement with the benefit of a dynamic sound track. This technique, called *photomation, pixilation, pseudoanimation,* and many other terms, is being used today with increasing frequency.

Since many still photos are available of every conceivable subject and can often be procured for the asking or for a small licensing fee, this inexpensive wealth of visual material is being used to teach, sell, persuade, inform, entertain, and otherwise stimulate viewers.

When precise pans and zooms on artwork must be shot to specific lengths, use an animation stand. Material can be shot in separate pieces and edited later. A good fluid-head tripod supporting a camera equipped with a zoom lens and supplementary lenses to allow close working distances can produce smooth pans and zooms at a reasonable cost. Shoot faster and slower movements on alternate takes to give the editor maximum choices for a well-paced cutting job. The extra footage is cheaper than the animation costs if the job was shot on a stand.

Full animation is an art form unequaled in terms of visual variety— and production requirements. Many delightful films have been created by children with a minimum of technical know-how, yet a fully animated Disney-style film requires unbelievable experience and professional achievement.

A few well-known TV spots illustrate animation's use in nontheatrical films. An oil company has produced several "pencil-drawing" ads to explain difficult concepts about the creation and exploitation of oil deposits; the animation's seeming simplicity serves the company's purposes well. But the creation of even so straightforward a piece requires extensive animation experience, not to mention an enormous number of drawings. The parts of drawings that are to move independently are often prepared on different layers of clear celluloid and "sandwiched" to create the full drawing. If a sandwich consisting of ten layers must be changed every two frames, a one-minute spot requires 6200 cels. Quite understandably, full-scale animation is produced almost exclusively on the professional level by a handful of specialty houses.

Computers give filmmakers an ever-expanding list of options in at least two ways. A fabulous new tool for shooting stills and graphics (photomation, mentioned above) has been created by equipping the animation camera stand with computerized controls. Camera raising/lowering, north/south/east/west artwork movements, shutter, motor

1-4. Quick cut (two frames each) sequence of stills from pseudo-animated IBM Coffee Break *film.*

speed, fade/dissolve, and every other aspect of stand control is under the command of easily written computer input. The classic Star Gate sequence in *2001: A Space Odyssey* as well as the beautiful TV title logos that "bloom," "tunnel," and splash color across the screen in a seemingly unlimited number of variations, are photographed in hours instead of weeks on such machines as the Cinetron; the technique is called *slitcan*.

Computer-generated graphics is another special technique. Many microcomputers equipped with high-resolution color graphics can be used to generate titles, patterns, plots, and abstractions. New machines for slide/AVs can produce a graphic and, with a push of the button, copy the visual onto a slide. Other machines soon to be marketed will record a whole series of computer-generated visuals on videotape and play them back with a synchronized sound track (Matsushita Electric Co.). At the time this book was written, most film projects involving computer graphics have been experimental; we have only begun to explore the exciting possibilities in this new area.

Pictorial continuity

Pictorial continuity in motion pictures applies to the joining of individual shots to form a scene, the joining of scenes to form a sequence, and the joining of sequences to form a coherent motion picture story. When there is a breakdown of the logical progression within any of these units, the audience is left in confusion; whatever ideas, feelings, moods, or concepts have been established are at least temporarily lost.

The directors of fully scripted films have the advantage of advance planning. Continuity between sequences, scenes, and shots can be thoroughly visualized beforehand, revised, strengthened, and built into the shooting script. But the makers of documentary and unscripted films must develop techniques to build continuity into the shooting as it progresses. Logical sequences built out of smoothly flowing shots must be sought and procured even when advance planning and foreknowledge of events is impossible. Success comes not just from luck and quick thinking, but also from procedures and filming techniques that will guarantee the film footage needed to edit into a logical, communicative film.

Pictorial continuity can be divided into two separate aspects: time and space.

Time continuity

Continuity of time in a film can be roughly divided into two different types: the chronological time—the sequence of events to be depicted—and the overall time frame.

Chronological time
In a dramatic film, the chronological sequence of events is embodied in the plot or storyline. For example: Mr. X gets up in the morning;

Mr. X goes outside to empty the garbage; the garbage men kidnap Mr. X and throw him in the back of the garbage truck. It is important, particularly in stories that have *parallel action,* that each step in the disclosure of facts and events is given in the proper order for story clarity. Parallel action refers to the crosscutting of two or more related stories, such as showing in this sequence:

Mr. X getting up in the morning

The garbage men preparing their disguises

Mr. X taking the garbage out

Cutting back to the garbage men waiting at the corner

When plots and subplots overlap in several levels of parallel action, as in a film like *The Godfather,* the clearly worked out chronology of events is crucial to story effectiveness.

Overall time frame

The overall time frame of any story can fall into four categories: present, past, future, and conditional.

Present time continuity depicts action that appears to be occurring now. The settings, props, and costumes are contemporary, and the plot unfolds for the audience in much the same way it unfolds for the characters within the story. By being kept in suspense about future events, the audience is also kept involved in the action as it happens. Even historical films can benefit from present time continuity, especially if the outcome of the story is not a well-known or completely predictable event.

Past time continuity is often introduced with a flashback. This commonly used technique can show an event that occurred before the present story began or show an important event that has bearing on the current state of affairs. The advantages of flashbacks are numerous. They help the audience understand a character by telling how past actions and events shaped him, offer different viewpoints of the same story, quickly bridge time spans of many years, and tie historical and other background material into the story. But flashbacks also have disadvantages. If a viewer misses the introduction of the flashback, he may become confused about where the story suddenly seems to be going. The important introduction may be a visual or verbal cue ("When I was a boy things were different. . . ." Dissolve to actor as a boy.) If the flashback is too lengthy, the return to present time may also be confusing.

In future time continuity, the viewer is transported into the future and sees an event as it will or could happen. This is often accomplished with a flash forward, which was done several times in *2001: A Space Odyssey.* After the flash forward the balance of the film takes place in the future, and future time becomes the "present" in the minds of the viewers.

Conditional time continuity applies to imaginary or dream sequences within a story film where someone's fantasized or dreamed chronological sequence of events is made to apply to the "real" events depicted. The filmmaker can play freely with the order of events and build continuity on the meaning of the events rather than on the direct connection of one event with another. Fellini and others have used conditional continuity to strip away unnecessary plot lines and explore meanings on a second level of interaction between characters, both real and imaginary. Many good industrial, promotional, and educational films can also be considered as conditional in time as the narrator strings together past, present, and future events in whatever manner necessary to communicate a particular presentation.

The filmmaker's task is to use the elements of time continuity to excite, challenge, and involve his viewers while being careful not to confuse or muddle the basic story. To succeed, a clear, carefully worked-out plan must be set down on paper or firmly embedded in the consciousness of the director before the cameras roll.

Space continuity

The second important aspect of motion picture continuity is the continuity of space—the actual positions and movements of characters within individual shots, within scenes, within whole sequences, and within the combined sequences of a complete story. The terms for the technique used to resolve the difficulties are interchangeably *stage line, screen direction,* and *action axis.* In this book, the last term, action axis, will be used. The principles involved must be totally understood by all film directors. Space continuity itself has two major categories: static and dynamic.

Static space

Static space continuity is concerned with people and objects that essentially do not move about, but must be kept in their proper relationship from shot to shot.

The rules for filming static space tell the director how actors must face for various shots so that when the shots are intercut the relationships between the actors will seem real and continuous. The simplest example is that of two people talking.

Groups of Two: The two people are established with a medium long shot to show their positions and then the camera cuts to close-ups to show their faces during the delivery of their lines.

In the establishing shot, camera position 1, actor A is looking to the right and actor B is looking to the left. (*Establishing shot,* as used here, refers to the all-important first shot of a scene when, usually, the relative positions of people and objects are introduced to the viewer. Although it may be preceded by a few mood-building close-ups, the establishing shot orients the audience.) In the close-ups that follow the establishing shot, these "eye directions" must be maintained if the two are to appear still to be facing one another. Camera position 2, a close-up of actor B, shows the actor looking screen left as seen in the establishing shot. But if the camera were to shift to position 5, the actor would be seen looking to the right. This shot would make actor B appear to be talking to someone not seen at all in the long shot. Similarly, camera position 3, the close-up of actor A, shows the actor looking screen right, which is how he was established and how he must continue to look if the shots are to cut together properly. But camera position 4 gives a close-up of actor A looking screen left, the same direction as actor B from the correct camera position 2. Since they were facing each other in the establishing shot, something went wrong in the cut to camera position 4.

The key to finding proper camera positions lies in drawing an imaginary line, or *action axis,* through the two actors. All camera positions on one side of the line will give shots that can cut together smoothly. This applies to camera positions right up to the very edge of the imaginary line. As long as each actor's eyes can be detected looking even slightly toward the established direction, the shot will intercut smoothly. If the

1-5. Shooting typical two-shot from side. (Memory House)

1-6. Action axis.

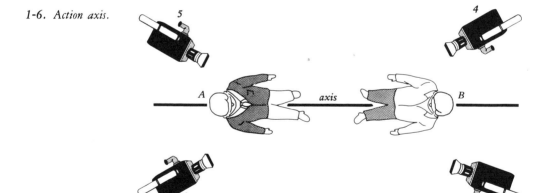

actor's eyes seem to be looking right into the camera, this *neutral angle* will be confusing in normal dialogue scenes. The neutral angle works much better if the actor looks above or below the camera lens, as if relating to the off-camera person who might be standing or sitting at a level above or below the on-camera actor's eye level. It is always best, even when the actors are established at different heights, to preserve the established screen direction by having them look to the correct side of the camera.

Once this basic principle is understood, the director can be confident about shooting close-ups even when the actors must be shifted about to allow for inadequate backgrounds. Figure 1-7 shows how this common problem is solved. The axis, rather than the camera, is shifted, but the camera remains on the same side of the axis to preserve screen direction.

Neutral angles usually show people or groups facing the camera directly (the *head-on shot*) or facing directly away from the camera (the *tail-away shot*) and can be used under certain circumstances discussed later to help change the action axis when necessary.

The principle of the action axis also applies to individuals as they relate to specific objects, such as a man operating a machine. In cases

1-7. Shifting action axis.

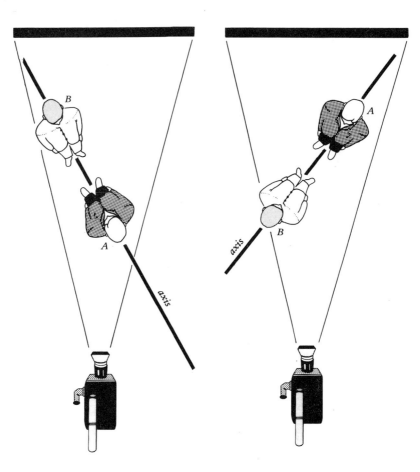

like this, the imaginary line passes through the operator and the object to which he relates. If camera 1 faces camera left, the close-ups made from camera position 2 will show the machine facing in the established direction; the resulting shot will intercut smoothly and be easy for the audience to comprehend. A shot made from position 3 will make it seem as though the operator has suddenly shifted to the other side of the machine; this kind of mistake can be disastrous in training films and the like where clarity is vitally important.

For the purposes of these illustrations the terms "camera 1" and "camera position 1" are being used interchangeably; under actual production conditions one or more cameras could be used to film the scene as described.

Groups of Three: There are essentially two possibilities when groups of three are to be filmed in conversation. In some cases one person nearly always relates to the other two, such as a clergyman and a young couple getting married, a teacher and two children, or a married couple and their doctor. In these cases, either of the two subordinates relate frequently to the dominant figure, but rarely do the subordinates relate to each other. In other cases all actors are of equal status during the scene, and each actor converses with both of the others.

In cases with one dominant and two subordinate players, there are two imaginary lines across which the camera must not be placed. In figures 1-10 and 1-11, the two action-axis lines run through the teacher and each child. The establishing shot (camera 1) places the teacher opposite the children to strengthen their interrelationship. Camera positions 2 and 3 provide close-ups of the children and are safe because they are made from the same side of both imaginary lines. Camera position 4 is always satisfactory for the teacher's close-ups because it too is on the established side of the action axis. Camera position 5 would be a suitable close-up of the teacher if it is used directly after a shot of the teacher relating— listening—to child B. But if this shot followed a close-up of a child talking, it would seem as if the teacher were looking at some third

1-8. *Person holding object follows same rule as man and machine. Over-shoulder shot must be made from same side of action axis as establishing shot. (*American Cinematographer, October, 1979, *reprinted by permission)*

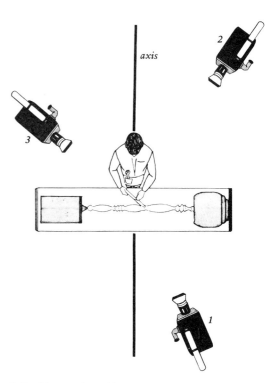

1-9. *Man and machine.*

unseen child. Camera position 6 crosses both stage lines and would never be acceptable.

Scenes with three characters of equal status have three imaginary lines. To make sure that the characters are always facing in the proper direction, the camera should essentially work from within the three imaginary lines. In figure 1-12, if character A speaks first and all three are established with camera 1, it is possible to cut to a close-up of character A with camera position 2 and his glances can cross back and forth from camera left to camera right as he addresses characters B and C. If character A ends his speech expecting a comment from character B and looking left, the proper shot of character B must show him looking camera right (the opposite direction) and can be made from camera position 3. Then if he should swing his glove past the camera to character C, we would be ready for an opposing shot of character C made from camera position 4. In actual production, the camera can be placed at positions such as 3A for attractive over-the-shoulder shots of C. The important factor is the direction of each actor's glance *at the point where a cut is made.*

In other words, if character B is being filmed from camera position 3 or 3A while facing camera right and speaking to character A, a cut to a close-up of character A made from position 2 or 1 should show his eyes looking in the opposing direction (camera left) at the point of the cut. If his next comments are to character C, a cut to his close-up while still facing character D should see his head turn past the camera before addressing the next character.

Groups Larger than Three: A large group of people naturally presents the greatest difficulties in filming so that intercut close-ups always show opposing players looking in opposing directions. When possible the skillful director of controlled action filming will place his players so that the ones who do the most interacting will have opposing positions for the camera and can be filmed from relatively few positions. But imaginary lines must be drawn between all players who interact, and the direction of their glance at the point of

1-10. Shooting establishing shot for group of three. (Memory House)

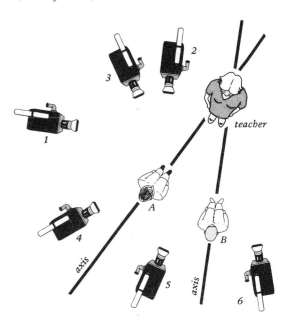

1-11. Axis for three.

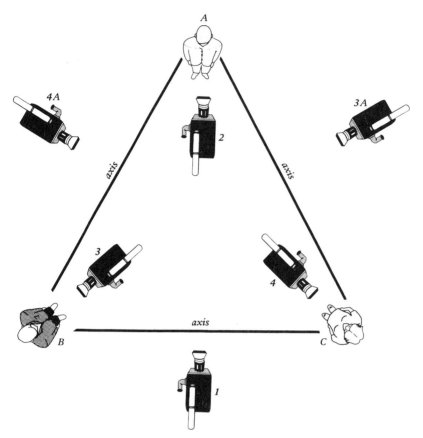

cut is the key to smooth intercutting of close-ups. To make the most of these complicated scenes the director can diagram the action ahead of time, make a sketch not unlike the illustration in this section, and find suitable camera positions in spite of the ever-changing action axis.

In figure 1-13, a card game is set up in which player D is the dealer and the whole table is established with camera position 1. A and G are the main opposing players who place most of the bets and are positioned around the table to form a convenient triangle. Then, as with other groups of three, close-ups of main character G can be made with camera 3. The importance of a professional actor's ability to repeat scenes over and over in precisely the same manner becomes evident if a director is going to get close-ups in which all the glances match those made by the camera from other angles. If in the course of the game an argument develops between B and E and the argument is established in the long shot made from camera 1, the close-ups of B can be satisfactorily made from camera position 2, as this camera is on the same side of the new action axis as camera 1.

But camera position 3 crosses the action axis and would show E's eyes looking camera right, the same direction as the shot preceding

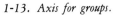

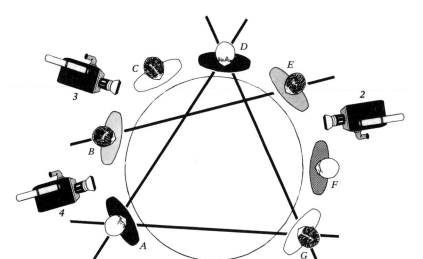

and obviously wrong if he is supposedly addressing B. A new camera position (4) would have to be set up to maintain the necessary opposing balances that would be consistent with correct continuity.

Speaker and Audience: The filming of a single speaker and a large audience is one of the more flexible directorial situations because the individual shots are usually easily recognized for what they are, regardless of screen direction. A shot of several members of the audience always looks like "audience"; the speaker, because he stands alone, has different lighting, and is speaking or performing, always looks like the on-stage person. There is little chance for the film audience to be confused, no matter what the sequence of shots presented. But since avoiding confusion is not the only directorial consideration, diagraming a speaker and audience can help make the most of the cutting opportunities.

The usual approach is to draw an imaginary line through the interacting elements; in this case the axis runs through the speaker and audience. If the speaker and audience are established from the right side, as from camera 1, all further shots should be made from that side of the axis. Speaker close-ups are made from position 2 showing the

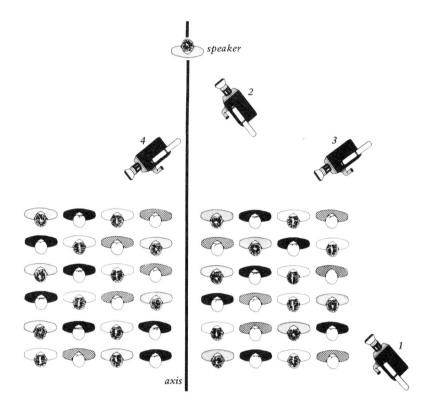

character facing camera left. All audience shots are made to show the audience looking in the opposing direction, as from cameras 3 or 4. This kind of consistency is particularly useful when the speaker is in conflict with the audience; the opposing glances support the dramatic content.

But it is also possible to establish the speaker from a neutral angle (camera 1) and draw imaginary lines much as if the sides of the audience and speaker formed a triangle. When the speaker's glance shifts to the right, as seen from close-up camera 2, cut to an opposing audience reaction shot as made from camera 3. Then, as a cut back to the speaker shows his glance shifting to camera left, an audience shot can be made from position 4. If cameras cannot be placed in positions 3 and 4 for physical or "political" reasons (such as blocking the audience view in documentary filming), shots from positions 3A and 4A will also work nicely. The speaker and audience can also be filmed from position 5 to give another neutral audience shot. This kind of directing strengthens the unity and rapport of speaker and audience beyond what is possible with the strict audience-speaker axis previously described.

Since the images of speaker and audience are easily recognizable, both types of axis can be intermixed in a single sequence. This kind of directing can add variety during long sequences and can further develop dramatic goals. If the filmmaker is producing a film for an evangelist or politician and wants to show that during the course of

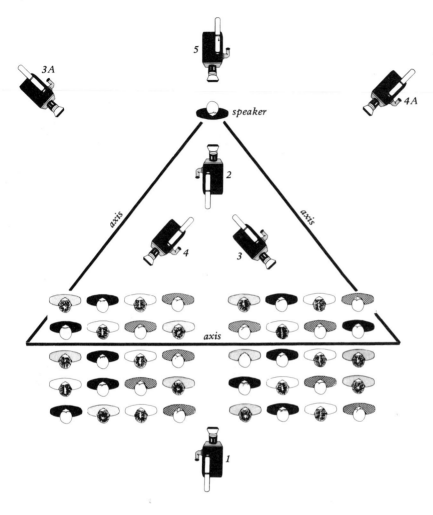

the speech the audience is won over, he could begin with the speaker-audience axis and show clearly opposing shots early in the sequence. Then, as a turning point is reached in the speaker's presentation, he could use the neutral angles and perpendicular action axis to give stronger unity and common direction to the audience and seemingly persuasive speaker.

Shifting the Action Axis: There is essentially just one way to change the screen direction of shots and not confuse the audience: *show the change*. It can be accomplished in several ways.

The camera can dolly past the action axis to establish a new one. In figure 1-16 actor A is established from position 1. The axis is through the two opposing players, the reaction shots to camera 1 are made from camera 3. To shift the axis while shooting, a dolly over to position 2 keeps the audience, which has observed the shift, clear as to the new position of the characters. From position 2 actor A looks screen right and actor B must be filmed from position 4 to give the necessary screen left opposing look.

The second way the action axis can be shifted is to have the players walk around. In other words, when the actors move about, the action axis is shifted automatically.

If, as in figure 1-17, actor A is being shot from position 1, camera position 2 is on the correct side of the axis for filming actor B when he is on the right of camera 1. When he walks past camera 1 to sit down, the axis shifts past camera 1 and a new position (3) must be used for subsequent close-ups of actor B (when he is sitting in the chair).

Another way the action can be shifted is by showing actor A move his eye direction from camera right to camera left (while close up from position 1). In figure 1-18 it appears his eyes are following the movement of actor B behind the camera, and it is an easy cut to actor B as he sits down from camera 2. In this way the shifting eyes cue the audience that a move is occurring and the actual move, which may be clumsy or difficult to film for a variety of reasons, need not be shown in its entirety.

Dynamic space
Dynamic elements—people, cars, moving objects—all create an action axis the moment they

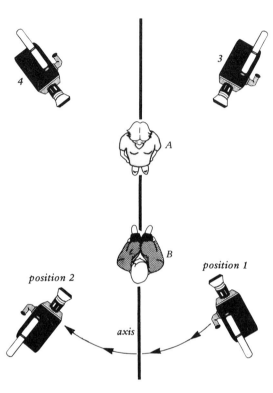

1-16. *Changing the axis, dollying.*

1-17. *Changing axis by shifting actors.*

1-18. *Changing axis by shifting eyes.*

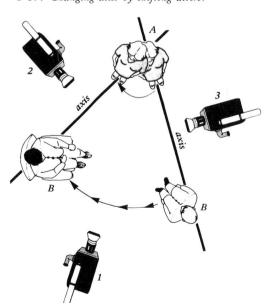

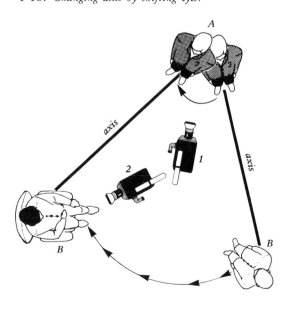

begin to move in any specific direction. *The axis is the line of travel,* the tracks of a train, the road on which a car travels, the sidewalk for people walking.

When people or objects are moving, the goal is usually for them to arrive somewhere. If their progress is to appear consistent and continuous, the film director must maintain the established direction; he can do so by *keeping the camera on the established side of the acting axis in every camera angle.* This means that if the train pulls out of the station going from left to right, the camera should stay on the same side of the tracks and the train should be shown entering the left side of the screen, exiting the right side of the screen, or passing from left to right in any following shots. This rule applies after a brief intercut, such as the interior of the train as the passenger finds a seat, or after longer story sequences. Whenever there is a cut back to the train on its way, the train should still be traveling in the established direction, or the audience will feel that the railroad engineer is up to some kind of a trick.

It is sometimes important that map direction be established correctly as well. If the audience has been told that the passenger is taking the train from Chicago to New York, the well-known easterly direction will strongly suggest left to right in the audience's mind. Consistent screen direction can and should be maintained even if the persons or vehicles are shown going around a corner. The camera must be placed on the same side of the original and new action axis. In figures 1-19 and 1-20 the car enters from the left and continues to travel toward the right throughout the turn and exits on the right as it heads away from the panning camera.

The dramatic content helps suggest how carefully and to what extent this rule should be followed. If the story is about a singleminded murderer who goes directly to the scene of the crime, his determination will be supported visually by shots showing strong consistent direction. What if the story is about a confused mental patient who slips out into the woods and eventually wanders into a nearby town? His progress, though unsteady, still results in an arrival at a specific destination. In this case the director may choose to use angles consistent with the action axis from shot to shot, but within which direction changes also take place. For example, the actor staggers in from screen left, wanders toward screen right, turns back and almost exits screen left, then stumbles out to the right. Or the actor enters left and exits again on the left but in the next shot enters right and exits again on the right. Careful planning helps the director use movement to indicate the players' problems and motivations.

Changing Screen Direction: There are at least four ways screen direction can be changed within a given sequence. Each method has advantages for given types of filming.

First, simply *show the change.* The object or actor begins moving in one direction (or enters one side of the screen) and is shown turning and moving in the other direction (and exiting on the same side of the screen that was entered). This technique is generally useful only

1-19. Crew films moving train. To maintain screen direction, all shots must be made from same side of tracks.

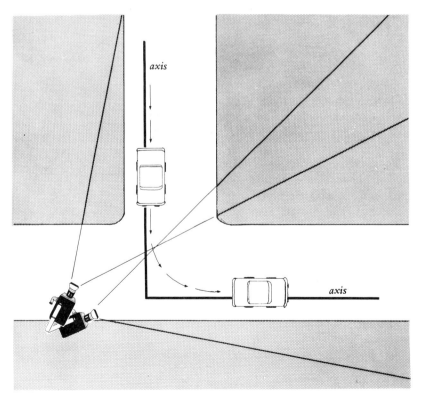

1-20. Maintaining screen direction.

axis

axis

when the character or object is actually to start heading back the other way. Remember that the rule of continuity is that the direction of travel should not change simply by cutting. A person can be seen to turn around six times within the shot, but when he exits screen right (moving left to right) the next shot must pick him up entering screen left (still moving left to right) or the audience will begin wondering what happened while he was offscreen.

Shooting across a curve accomplishes a change in direction and keeps the moving object headed toward the previously established goal. A curve in the tracks can be used to reverse the screen direction of a train and a corner of a street can change the direction of cars or people walking. It can always be assumed that even the most direct path has a few curves and corners along the way.

When the path of the moving object cannot be chosen but shots are needed from both sides of the action axis, a dolly from one side of the axis to the other can be made. If a parade

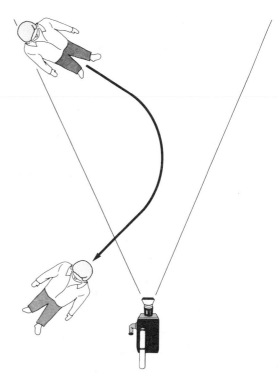

1-21. Change in direction—curve.

1-22. Screen direction of group could be changed by dollying from one side of walkway to the other. (Memory House)

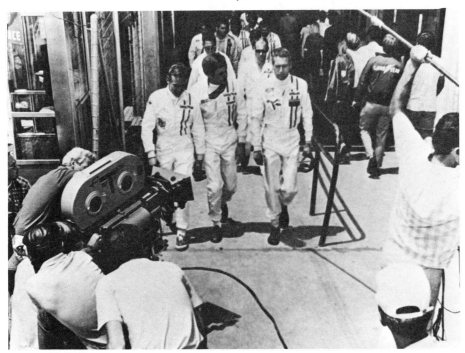

is being filmed and the marchers have been established as moving from left to right, a dolly shot moves the camera from one side of the street to the other as the group approaches. In figure 1-23, when the camera is on the left side of the street the parade is moving from left to right. When the dolly is to the center of the street the movement becomes neutral, and when the dolly moves to the right side of the street the direction of the movement has changed from right to left. A few interesting dolly shots of this kind in both directions make it possible to shoot montage material from both sides of the parade. Later, when the dolly shots are inserted to bridge changes in direction, the film

1-23. Change in screen direction—dolly.   *1-24. Changing screen direction by shifting camera.*

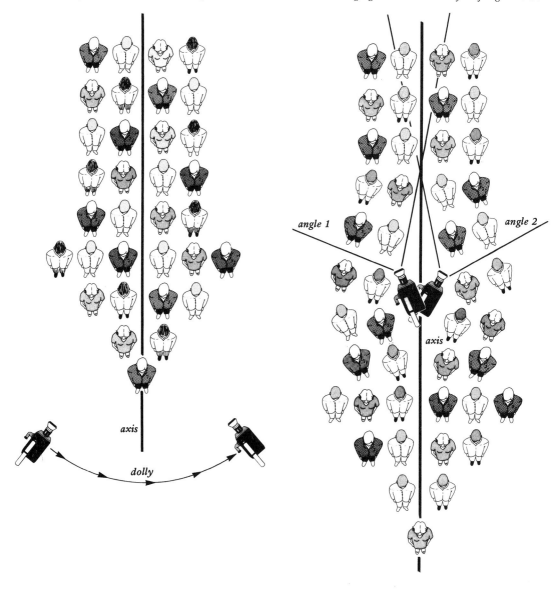

will still maintain the feeling that the marchers are actually going somewhere.

A similar way to change the direction of crowds is for the cameraman to stand in the midst of the moving group and shoot toward the side moving past the camera in the direction consistent with that of the previous shot, then pan over to the side of the mob that is moving past the camera in the other direction.

Neutral angles, which are usually either *head-on shots* or *tail-away shots,* can also be used to smooth over a change in direction. Sequences about moving objects that do not lead to a specific arrival point lend themselves to showing the object moving in any and all directions. But as mentioned earlier, a direct cut from a person or vehicle moving one way to a shot moving the other way can be visually disturbing. Invariably a cut directly to the same vehicle moving in the opposite direction makes the audience think a second vehicle is suddenly approaching. By inserting a neutral shot between two opposing directions, a much smoother series of shots is created. Auto commercials are good examples of films where the client wants to see both sides of the car but may wish to avoid any jarring cuts that could distract from the smooth-flowing narration.

Contrasting Screen Directions: Consistency in screen direction is also important when the subjects must not only get to their goal but also be brought back again to their starting point. To be sure that the audience is always clear about where the subjects are headed, one direction must be established for the journey forth and the opposite direction must be reserved for the return trip.

Furthermore, it is often necessary to show the dynamic interrelationship of two individuals or groups. Again, consistent screen direction can make or break such sequences. Battle scenes are the classic examples of the need to show opposing forces moving in opposing directions. If the director should fail to maintain contrasting screen movement, the audience would become confused as to who is fighting whom, which players are loyal, and which have turned on their own forces or have begun to retreat. As two lovers reunite at the train station, opposing screen direction will bring them ever closer, while mixed screen directions will show mixed feelings at the least and certainly will result in a mixed-up audience. When football teams switch directions at the quarter, a little confusion may result for uninitiated audience members, but think of the confusion for even the most ardent fans if cameras were placed on both sides of the field and were freely intercut.

In action sequences of all kinds, consistent screen direction is so much a part of what makes the action work that even the slightest directorial switches can make the entire story fail.

Neutral Screen Direction: Neutral shots are those that show the action moving toward or away from the camera. They may be any of the following: *head-on* or *tail-away shots* from the same level as the moving object; *overhead* shots from above the action that show the moving subjects passing directly under the camera; *low angle shots,* which often utilize a buried camera and allow the subjects to pass directly overhead; and *tracking shots,* when the camera dollies *on* the action axis and either leads or follows the moving subjects.

There is an obvious physical problem of starting a strictly neutral tail-away shot or ending a neutral head-on shot. When the camera is on the same level as the subject, the person or vehicle must begin or end the shot by coming in contact with the lens, or else pass by one side of the camera or the other at the last moment. There is, of course, a limited use for neutral shots that actually do begin or end with the subject coming in contact with, and thereby blocking out, the lens. But when a head-on shot ends with the subject passing by one side of the camera, or when a tail-away shot begins with the subject entering one side of the frame, the shot loses its neutral value. To keep the shot strictly neutral the entrance or exit must be cut off and only the portion of the shot in which no sideways action can be detected may be used.

Double Action Axis in Moving Two Shots: Moving shots, such as a dolly shot made alongside a moving vehicle from a camera car or traveling crane, must be consistent with the established direction. Trying to analyze the direction of the foreground subject as opposed to the moving background is asking for confusion. If the camera is kept to the established side of the action axis, all the footage obtained will be consistent.

There is, however, one exception to crossing the action axis of moving subjects. It applies to groups of two or more players that interact in conversation during a traveling shot. These shots could be of two people walking down the sidewalk or riding in a car while talking. If there's a cut to close-ups for conversation intercutting, the

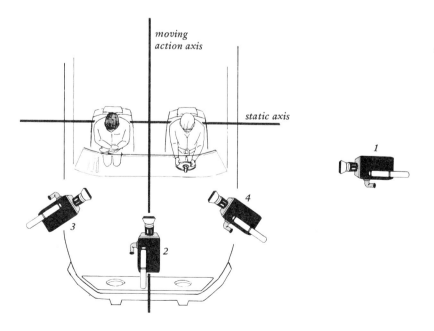

1-25. *Axis in moving car.*

static axis between the two becomes predominant for the duration of the scene. In figure 1-25, showing two people talking in a moving car, camera position 1 has established the car moving right to left and sets the screen direction for the moving vehicle. Camera 2, mounted on the hood, is a neutral head-on tracking shot that establishes our players in conversation. Camera position 3 crosses the moving action axis, but it is acceptable because it is following the rules of the static action axis between the two opposing players. The alternate close-up is, of course, made from camera position 4. When the conversation has ended or if a "breather" shot is called for, any successive shots of the car should return to the previously established dynamic action axis.

Building a story: selecting the shots

The makers of all kinds of films—theatrical features, nuts-and-bolts industrials, news and documentary films—all have at least one common goal: to come away from the shooting session with enough material so that a clear, purposeful, communicative sequence can be edited from the footage secured. To accomplish this goal the experienced filmmaker has learned that he must be sure to get several kinds of footage, the key visual elements that will later be pieced together in such a way that those who watch will understand the intended story. These key visual elements, or *shots,* are used to accomplish an important number of duties.

There is no need to improve upon the suggestion that a filmmaker, when choosing shots, should simply rely on his own eye to satisfy the needs of the camera and audience. For example, if you found yourself suddenly awakening in some new and strange surrounding, you will surely want to take a good look around and see where you are, who else is with you, and what the new location looks like. Film audiences are subjected to new and strange surroundings with each new scene, and if their consciousness (and subconsciousness) is to feel comfortable with each new place, the filmmaker will have to give their eyes what his own eyes would demand: a *long shot.*

The *long shot* (LS), or establishing shot, should be used to give answers to the following questions: Where are we? What is going on? What people or elements are involved? Where are the key people or elements located in relation to each other and their surroundings? The actual size and scope of long shots can vary greatly from one kind of scene to another. In a medical film dealing with identifying viruses in the microscope, the long shot could be a piece of tissue less than one mm across. In a commercial the long shot might include only three competing bottles of ketchup. In *The Sound of Music* it could be a sweeping pan of the Swiss Alps.

Exterior long shots are usually bigger and wider than interior long shots for an obvious reason: the walls of the rooms set definite limits to how wide the shot can be.

Establishing shots do not have to come first in the series of elements that tell a story. In fact, some sequences are exceptions to the rules of filmic clarity and never include long shots at all. A scene that is to show a player waking up in the morning can be directed so that the audience is shown a series of slowly expanding views of the dimly lighted room as the character begins to open his eyes. Soft close-ups of bed linen patterns, medium shots of clothes on a nearby chair, a wider shot of the dripping faucet in the bathroom, all could easily precede the long shot which shows us that a gunman sits and waits for a final confrontation. As the heroine gropes about in the haunted basement and is unaware of the monster which lurks just beyond the next doorway, there is no need to tip off the audience with an unnecessary long shot. But in most scenes, in most films, about most subjects, an early establishing shot is the all-important frame of reference that helps the audience understand and feel comfortable with the shots that follow.

Medium shots (MS) combine many of the advantages of both long shots and close-ups, and therefore the MS is by far the most widely used cinematic element.

Compare a film sequence with an evening at a party. Once inside with your coat removed, you take a look around to see who is there and what is happening. This is the long shot. Within the shot, you notice a few friends talking near the buffet. You walk over and greet them, and spend the following conversation in a series of medium shots. As you greet and kiss an old girl friend you may get a quick close-up of her low neckline, but mostly you are seeing her in nice, comfortable, not-too-far, not-too-close medium shots. Only when you decide to look about to see who else is there do you return to a long shot, and only for some small detail of special interest do you use any close-ups.

Medium shots are the stuff of motion pictures. They can single out special objects, people, or groups without getting intimately involved. They show both the detail and the background elements closely related to the detail. They bridge the large and possibly disturbing gap between the long shot and close-up.

Many beginning filmmakers try to create a cinematic appetizer out of each camera angle and use ultrawide long shots or super-maxi-close-ups for everything they shoot. But a disorientation problem can quickly develop for the audience, because the close-ups are not clearly established with long shots.

Imagine that after you enter a large room full of people someone places a blindfold over your eyes, leads you to a distant corner, and places you on a seat near the wall. When the blindfold is removed you find that your face is three inches from another face you have never seen before. Chances are you would like to grab a quick look around. But no, the blindfold is put back and you are taken to another place. When the blindfold is removed, you find your face not three inches from a window through which cars can be seen going by on the street outside. While this may be an interesting experience, it does not lend itself to your feeling comfortable in the room or finding out what is going on around you.

In the same way, shots forming a film sequence will leave the viewers disoriented and uncomfortable unless there is a visual bridge to hold the shot relationships together and make the relationships recognizable. The medium shot is the building block between the long shot and the close-up, because the MS can be recognized from the LS and the CU can be recognized from the MS.

Medium shots also lend themselves to interesting compositions. Good pictorial composition depends upon the careful selection and arrangement of the lines, forms, and masses in the scene to be photographed. Long shots often include so many elements that simplicity, unity, harmony, and contrast (the building blocks of strong composition) cannot be attained from any available camera position. Close-ups, on the other hand, are often made of single simple forms and are often compositionally frozen for the photographer. But medium shots, since they often contain just one or two or three important elements, lend themselves to an easy selection of forms and their arrangement for the most pleasing and useful compositions. Flexible, interesting, versatile, and useful are adjectives easily applied to medium shots.

Close-ups (CU) are one of the primary secrets of cinematic power. Close-ups of people's faces can reveal even the slightest hint of emotion. The tiniest twitch or tear is blown up to gigantic proportions for all to see. While the long shot shows the arrangement of moving objects within vast spaces, the close-up reveals the subtle detail of single elements. The power of the close-up separates motion pictures from all previous forms of visual presentation.

But the eye is quickly bored. An everlasting series of close-ups becomes uninteresting and monotonous. Life and all forms of art contain pulses, rhythms, highs, lows, intense close-ups, and vast long shots. The filmmaker potentially can combine an unlimited number of angle selections; to fail to take advantage of the infinite variety is to miss out on the best of movie magic (figure 1-26).

Close-ups, since they intensify and magnify all movements and actions, tend to exaggerate the meaning of shots. This can be an advantage when exaggeration is needed, but using ultraclose-ups in places where no special emphasis is called for leads to viewer confusion. Once an audience realizes that the close-up is being used repeatedly to emphasize unimportant details, the filmmaker has given up much of its potential power.

A *dolly shot* properly refers to takes where the camera moves during shooting but the subject, for the most part, does not. The dolly shot can replace the entire sequence of long, medium, and close-up shots by starting at some distance from the subject and moving from the long shot all the way to a close-up. This movement simulates the viewer walking or otherwise moving closer and closer to the subject, and this action has strong psychological power. For example: the camera dolly begins at the entrance to a church sanctuary; as the clergyman

1-26. Long shot, top, establishes locality and position of subject. Medium shot, middle, singles out subject within background. Close-up shows details of expression.

speaks from a pulpit in the center of the front section, the camera slowly but steadily rolls forward until it stops two feet from his nose at the climax of his most convincing point. In such a scene, the viewer's being compelled to move closer and closer to the subject lends an ever-increasing feeling of importance to the subject. The dolly shot not only can be used to give added strength to scenes, but it also may be used to extract viewers slowly from close involvement (by pulling the camera backward).

The *zoom shot,* which uses the zoom lens, optically expands the image to fill more of the screen during a zoom-in and reduces the image size during a zoom-out. It also can eliminate the need for long, medium, and close-up shots. This is useful when a close-up is needed without interrupting a take, when a special kind of emphasis is desired, when the punctuation of direct cuts from one shot to another is not wanted. But the zoom does not provide the same visual power as a dolly shot. The zoom image does not change in perspective while changing size; this somewhat subtle difference is important psychologically to the viewer. In a dolly shot the feeling of movement is created through the visual record of objects passing by the edges of the screen; in a zoom shot no real sensation of movement is created because the center of the image simply expands outward. When the scene calls for the added visual emphasis that a camera movement toward or away from the image can give, the whole camera should be moved, not just the zoom lever.

The biggest advantage of the zoom lens in modern film production is not its ability to zoom; that is most definitely an overused visual device. The zoom lens enables the cameraman to set up for a particular field size very quickly without a lot of tripod shifting and releveling. A 9.5mm to 95mm or 12mm to 120mm zoom lens is equivalent to a very large turret full of fixed focal-length lenses. It is always in place on the camera, has only one focus ring to be worried about and only

1-27. Dolly shot with moving subjects.

one aperture ring to be set. Creatures of laziness, filmmakers with zoom lenses tend to move the camera from position to position far less frequently between takes than filmmakers without them. This often results in shots that will not cut together smoothly. The slightest mismatch of action, actor position, hand position, and facial expression are most obvious and distracting in these zoomed-in close shots.

Tracking shots, another camera technique, follow moving subjects with a moving camera, such as one moving car from another moving car. They may be made from in front, behind, or alongside the subject. They are interesting visually because of the background movement seen all around the subject, which itself remains rather stationary in the frame. A well-executed trucking shot can give the viewer the feeling that he is experiencing much of the same kind of movement as the player on the screen.

Walking shots, which are often made by news cameramen who need to begin filming an event from the very moment they arrive on the scene, are seldom steady enough for inclusion in general purpose films. But ultra—wide angle lenses and careful camera balancing can produce walking shots that very nicely duplicate the feeling of walking for the viewer. These shots can follow moving subjects (usually other people walking) or give a"walking tour" of a new place, building, or room. It is possible to use a constantly shifting and walking camera to simulate a person's movements and glances, thereby eliminating the need for the standard LS, MS, and CU in point-of-view shots. But it is very obvious technically, and may psychologically stand in the way of the interesting action happening in front of the camera for the viewer. In other words, a radical technique, such as walking with the camera, may make a stronger impression on the viewer's mind than the important action of the scene itself.

Panning the camera is probably the most common of all camera movements, and properly refers to a pivotal movement of the camera in the horizontal plane. Panning is a little like zooming in that many filmmakers become unduly attracted to the swirl of shifting images produced. But panning shots, like all moving shots, can present editing difficulties. It is impossible to cut from a static image directly to a moving image without producing a visual jolt. While visual jolts are sometimes desirable, all too often these jump cuts are disrupting to the flow of ideas; they should be reserved for moments when their effect is genuinely needed. Panning shots cannot easily be cut short to fit a particular narration or line of dialogue. If the head portion of the pan is cut off, the start is abrupt and disturbing. If a portion of the middle is cut out, there is a jump cut again. Chopping off the end of the shot does not work either. The only way to shorten a pan smoothly is to dissolve. This solution usually creates a stronger visual transition than desired.

Nevertheless, pans are very useful in following moving subjects; in covering a scene wider than the widest available lens; in connecting two elements in a scene that, again, cannot be connected by the widest lens. Pans should be used only when they are really needed.

Shooting when the action is controlled

In theatrical films, TV shows, commercials, public relations films, and many kinds of educational and nontheatrical productions, the actions of the players and other visual elements are totally under the control of the director. In these cases the action can be "blocked out" for the camera. It can be staged, set up, and rehearsed to get the most natural, practical, dramatic, visually interesting, and suitable setup possible prior to shooting. Obviously, successful shooting with controlled action requires actors capable of delivering sustained performances; such devices as cue cards and teleprompters are helpful in this regard.

The technique known as *overlapping the action* is a most important editing consideration, and one most easily fulfilled while shooting controlled action. When the cameras are stopped and restarted for any reason, the last part of the filmed action should be repeated in the next take so that the shots will cut together smoothly without any clumsy breaks in the action.

The camera, recorder, crew, and cast are now ready to begin shooting. What should be shot first? Within this general category of film production, the answer is most often the *master shot* or *master take*. The master shot is usually a long shot that covers all the action and gives the editor a usable, safe, wide shot which can be used any time during a given scene. Not only does the master take give an establishing shot, it also gives a reestablishing shot that can always be used to introduce a new element into the scene.

Imagine a soap commercial that begins with Sue and Madge talking about their dingy laundry while seated on a bench at the laundromat. After each of them has made a few comments, Ellen comes in with some whiter, brighter clothes and a box of "New Super Blitz." After rehearsal, a wide master take of the entire commercial would be shot. It allows a good opportunity to "shake down" the cast and crew, eliminate any pauses or slow cues, and see how the timing is working out. The editor will probably use the master shot just twice: to establish the laundromat and the characters, and to reestablish everyone's position when Ellen enters. After getting a good take of the master shot, each actor's lines and reactions can be repeated in medium shots and again in close-ups, and lots of footage of the Blitz box can be included as well.

Say the scene is a sales demonstration being made by a single expert salesman. His personal delivery is of special concern, and most of this segment is to be shown in a crucial medium shot. The medium shot might, in this case, be the master shot because the establishing shot and close-ups are to be used only briefly in the edited version.

The master take is usually made as a long shot and has the following advantages:

It gives the editor a duplicate of all action, which can be used at any time.

It allows the editor to "pull back" and establish new story elements and other elements as well, also at any time.

It allows the editor to shift emphasis on characters by using the long master shot for one character's lines and medium or close-up shots for another character's lines.

The shooting of the master gives the cast and crew a safe angle in which to settle into their roles while rehearsing under shooting pressure.

It allows actors to get through a section without interruption prior to breaking the action apart for the close shots.

It eliminates the need for precise editorial planning before shooting. In essence, two shots of every piece of action are being made and cutting can be done freely later.

The master take technique, backed up by close-ups and medium shots that repeat all important actions and reactions, gives the filmmaker the widest number of editorial choices possible and is the best method of shooting controlled action subjects. Single cameras can shoot master shots from several positions if that is desired.

There are, however, some disadvantages to the master take method. First, there is a tendency to shoot a lot of film. Careful planning and advance visualization of the finished sequence may reveal that very little of the master take will be used and it could be a waste of film and time.

Second, the cast will have to memorize all their lines. This is not too much to ask of professionals, given enough time, but it usually cannot be expected of amateurs and children and so the making of a perfect master shot becomes an exercise in frustration. Sometimes it pays to shoot the close-ups first: this gives the cast a chance to go over their lines several times, and when the master is done later everyone is more familiar with the script.

Third, after a good master take is "in the can" the director may realize during the shooting of the close-ups that some changes are needed in the action. If the changes are at all significant, the shots made will no longer match the master, and additional shooting and expense become necessary.

This leads to the important alternative to the master take method. It is used for filming partially controlled and not totally predictable action of the kind found in many documentary and industrial films: the *linked series of shots*. This is the solution when the filmmaker cannot tell the subjects what to do or when the players are incapable of sustained performances; the filmmaker can ask them to repeat portions of the actions they have already completed.

Usually beginning with a wide shot, the filmmaker shoots and observes the action until he feels a cut is necessary. He stops the camera, asks the players to wait a moment while he changes the lens or camera position or both, then rolls the camera as he asks the players to repeat their last piece of action. In this way a linked series of shots is made which will cut together smoothly because each shot contains *overlapped action* with the adjacent shots.

This kind of filming allows the subjects to cover their mistakes easily and inconveniences them very little, and both the filming and the acting are simplified because they take place in sequential order. But the lack of planning can cause the filmmaker to come away with a very odd assortment of shots and take lengths. If time and circumstances permit, a few extra takes or master shots to back up the most critical pieces of action would undoubtedly make the editor very happy.

Shooting when the action is not controlled

In documentaries, unrehearsed talk shows, quiz shows, panel discussions, conferences, nature filming, and in movies with children and nonprofessional actors, it can be impossible to use the single-camera master shot technique. The most difficult filming situations are those about which the filmmaker has no advance knowledge, such as an unfolding news event or a sudden disaster. But previously announced events such as concerts and parades, while uncontrolled by the director, at least allow for some planning and predictably good camera positions.

The master take approach can be applied to uncontrolled action only through the use of multiple cameras. One camera constantly records a very useful wide angle shot and the second or other cameras get medium shots and close-ups of important action. This approach is used in television production for many kinds of shows; it is also useful in filming management conferences, sporting events, costly scientific experiments, public events, space shots, and ceremonies.

But when a single camera must be used with uncontrolled action, there are two important techniques that will minimize editorial headaches later.

First, the camera angle should be changed every time the camera is cut. Lens focal length or the camera position—or best of all, both—can be changed. Arthur Gaskill and David Englander, in their little book *How to Shoot a Movie Story,* call this "The General Rule" for all types of filming when the action cannot be fully repeated.

A typical problem is one of shooting the subject in such a way that the editor can shorten the sequence and make it seem as though the action or process has been shown in its entirety. If the camera remains in the same position relative to the subject, any later change in the positions of the visuals will quickly and disturbingly reveal all attempts to cut out portions of the action. But if the camera is moved during natural pauses (often people can be asked to wait a moment before continuing) to a new position or if the lens focal length is shifted (which takes only a fraction of a second with a zoom lens), these pieces of film can later be shortened to the desired length and joined without terribly obvious jump cutting.

Changing the lens and camera angle with every possible break benefits all kinds of filming. The new angles not only mask action changes, they also constantly present the audience with a fresh view. The fact that each successive shot contains something different and new distracts the viewer's attention from the unimportant details within the action.

The second method of sustaining editorial versatility in shooting is to get lots of *cut-ins, cut-aways, inserts,* and *reaction shots.* These shots can even be made after the primary action is over or during some pause in the event of interest. Football cameramen, for example, often pick up crowd shot cut-aways and scoreboard inserts between plays to bridge lapses in action. During a concert or performance, a second camera can sometimes be deployed to pick up "wild" shots of audience reactions for later use to create continuity and help the cutting.

Here are the definitions for these important bridging shots:

A *cut-in* is a close-up within the established action that may have been invisible in the wide shot. A hand reaching into a pocket, a close-up of the note being written, an object being taken from a drawer, all qualify as cut-ins.

A *cut-away* is a shot of any object or person not included in the main action. Cut-aways are usually shots of people who are supposedly reacting to the main action, such as the audience or the innocent bystander.

A *insert* is an isolated shot of some usually static item that is related to but not included in the action. A map shot, an illustrative picture, a close-up of a model shot separately, a title diagram, or a scoreboard, all can qualify as insert shots.

Reaction shots are similar to cut-aways, but they are often established within the main action. They are used to give the audience clues about how that player and the film audience itself might be reacting to the action of the moment.

These shots, which should be made whether the action is controlled or not, give the editor a wide range of advantages. A few of them follow.

Cut-aways or reaction shots are a natural and easy way to bridge huge gaps in continuity. The shot of a speaker saying, "Good evening ladies and gentlemen," cuts to an audience reaction shot, and then cuts smoothly back to the same shot of the speaker as he says, "Thank you very much," and sits down.

Insert shots bring in supplemental information, numbers, facts, dates, directions, diagrams, instructions, and so forth.

Reaction shots guide the film audience as to the intended meaning of a previous shot. If, during a series of shots of a medical operation, one of the doctors is seen reacting with a confident nod, everyone will assume things are going well. But if the reaction shot shows a serious slow shake of the head, the prognosis is negative.

Cut-away shots point out important or interesting pieces of action that might otherwise go unnoticed. During the preparation, count-down, and blast-off of a rocket launch, there might be a cut-away of birds taking flight or a groundhog heading for his hole.

Cut-aways show important simultaneous or parallel action, such as shots of the lug nuts coming off of a wheel as the family drives down the thruway or a medium shot of the rapist taking his position in a dark doorway as the heroine loads her Mace gun.

Whether or not you choose to consider these various buildup shots as a part of the main action, their usefulness in every kind of motion picture should not be overlooked.

Motion picture transitions

Many films, particularly storyline films that deal with real time, must use pictorial transitions to signal the viewer that a shift in time or place is ocurring. In early films the "iris shot" was popular; a black circle gradually enclosed the scene until it vanished and the iris subsequently reopened to reveal a new scene. Introductory titles have also been used from silent film days to the present to begin a story or establish a new location. Many transitional devices, such as dissolves, fades, freeze frames, and wipes seem to go in and out of popularity as styles change.

Since there is no end to the kinds of transitions that can be invented, they receive a great deal of attention from many filmmakers, especially those prone to visual and technical trickery. Other filmmakers overlook the use of transitions entirely, on the assumption that the truly intelligent audience will always understand where the film is going. Obviously both extremes can confuse viewers.

Here are some examples of the most commonly used transition techniques.

An ordinary *fade-in* begins with a black screen and, in a variety of readily available lengths from about one-half to five seconds, gradually reveals the image by coming to full brightness. The opposite—from bright to black—is true of *fade-outs*. An alternative is the *fade-to-white*, in which the image grows slowly brighter until a pure white screen washes out all screen images from the viewer's eyes. Fades-to-white have been used effectively to show a transition when a player has fainted, fallen asleep, or been knocked out. *Fades-to-black*, another alternative, have been used effectively to bridge hours, days, years, and to bridge places new and distant.

Fades usully come in pairs—fade out on one scene and fade in on another. But it is not always necessary to follow the fade-out with a fade-in; the new scene may be allowed to "pop on" instead and thus startle and refresh the viewer.

Since their transitional power is very strong, fades are often used only at the beginning and end of short films. They are useful, inexpensive to have printed by the laboratory, and require no special editing.

Dissolves are simply superimposed fades. One scene fades out at the same time a new scene is fading in. Since the screen is always alive with brightness and action, the transitional power of the dissolve is not as strong as that of fades. The strength of the transition is determined to a great extent by the duration of the dissolve. As with fades, labs commonly print dissolves in lengths as short as about 6 frames to as long as 128 frames. This can make a great difference in the impact of the transition. The shortest dissolve can be used as a soft cut that minimizes the effect of what would otherwise be a jump cut or a small lapse in continuity. The long dissolves can, as with fades, span significant amounts of time or space.

There are innumerable variations on the dissolve, such as concurrent focus shifts or trick opticals that add special visual meaning to suit the needs of a given story. Motion picture optical effects houses have huge charts of standard transitional wipes, flips, and other effects for the filmmaker to choose from. An unlimited number of new effects and transitions can be created on sophisticated new optical printers.

Wipes, often associated with news and sporting events, replace one image with another by the use of a defined pattern. The pattern may be a simple vertical or horizontal line or pronounced forms such as diagonal boxes, stars, circles, and so forth. They have traditionally been used to allow brief lapses of time or quick changes of place, such as highlights from all the games of a sports season. Their rather flashy technical quality has, at least in the past, limited their use in dramatic or story films. They are usually produced by creating duplicate masters of the scenes to be combined, which are then put together by an optical effects company.

Shock cuts are the fastest moving of all popular transitional devices. Instead of allowing the viewer to recede from a scene with a slow fade or dissolve, the shock cut instantly transposes the viewer to a new time or place. An important character or story element is shown in one time and place and then, with a simultaneous sound cut, is shown in a new time or place. The jump must be so strong that no viewer can be left wondering if a transition has expired or not. This technique is used several times very successfully in Stanley Kubrick's classic film, *2001: A Space Odyssey.* Shock cuts require no optical work and add no cost. Could that be why they are so popular in today's films?

Multiple images can be used to show the completion of a process or the passage of time. With montages, many related shots appear one right after the other on the screen. A series of moving vehicles can depict an entire long trip: flipping calendar pages can show the passage of time; shots from a president's many speeches can cover a term in office. Several images combined on the screen at the same time can show several things happening at once; several angles of one event shown simultaneously can suggest an entire process transpiring.

A series of shots for montage can be assembled and joined by dissolves with ordinary editing and lab procedures, but multiple images on the screen simultaneously must be combined on a duplicate master by an optical effects company.

Sound cuts can trigger a transition effectively, the most obvious being a simple verbal title from the narrator, such as "Paris, 1913" followed by a shot of horses and wagons on the Champs-Elysées. Dissolves or *segues* from one sound effect to another, one voice to another, or one piece of music to another can also indicate a transition. Even an emphatic or significant statement by one of the actors, such as "I think I'll kill myself," can lead directly to a shot of some definite action— the actor jumping off a bridge. Sound can carry across a cut as well, such as showing a music group playing a piece in rehearsal and cutting straight to the performance with no break in the song.

The key to using transitions effectively lies in the selection of techniques that keep the audience aware of what is happening without calling attention to the techniques themselves. The audience should be neither confused nor insulted by the devices used. As with all techniques, those that smack of pure flashiness usually have only limited effectiveness.

This has been a very cursory look at directing the medium of film. As the sculptor conceives his subject in terms of form, mass, line, shape, and texture, so the filmmaker conceives his subject in terms of shots, angles, cuts, and transitions. In order actually to capture these bits and pieces, he will have to use the chief tool of his art—the camera. The next chapter goes inside for a closer look.

chapter 2

Photography for the filmmaker

In the near future, advances in metallurgy, optics, servo systems, radar, computers, and electronics will be reflected in the latest motion picture camera designs, and the filmmaker of say, 1999, will merely drop a preloaded cartridge of a multisensitive film disc or, more likely, an integrated circuit chip into a lightweight self-stabilizing box. After sighting an object, person, or scene, the cameraman will press a button and record permanently, in perfect focus, a properly exposed and virtually grainless image. When this "camera" stops, the cameraman will be able to unload and project his almost indestructible "film" without futher delay.

But until that time, there remain problems that must be acted upon before, during, and after "pressing the button." Today, a wide range of cameras are available, each with unique features, special capabilities, and assorted shortcomings.

Types of cameras

Sixteen millimeter motion picture cameras fall roughly into four categories. The most common is the *location camera*. It is used in any interior or exterior situation where the cameraman must be mobile and able to work with little or no assistance. It is often light enough to be hand held, may keep the film within its body, and usually is operable on batteries or remote power supplies.

Some location cameras are even self-blimped, operating in silence to allow simultaneous sound recording. Self-blimped cameras are among the newer entries in the camera field and, to control camera noise, have been designed with such refinements as belt drives instead of gears and specially isolated moving parts. These "hand cameras" can weigh as little as a few pounds and hold only 50 feet of 16mm film, or weigh as much as 30 to 40 pounds, require a body brace, and be magazine loaded with 400 or 1,200 feet of film.

The *studio camera* is too cumbersome and heavy to be held by hand or on a body brace. If it is not intended to function in a separate

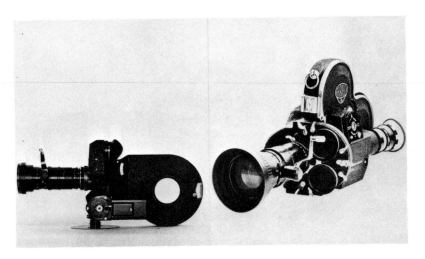

2-1. *Two location cameras: left, Eclair ACL; right, Arriflex 16ST. (Eclair International, Arnold & Richter)*

blimp (soundproof box), it will be self-blimped, contained in its own padded housing with silent running parts. This prevents studio microphones from picking up camera noise. Studio cameras use separate film magazines that hold 400 to 1,200 feet of film.

Since lightness and portability are often crucial to 16mm filmmaking, many of the blimped cameras will come out of their blimps to go on location, and the self-blimped models are light enough for many types of free-moving documentary work. Some cameras can be used both in the studio and on location, depending on how they are set up.

The *process camera* is mounted on an animation stand or optical printer and used for creating special effects in film reproduction. Some process cameras have interchangeable film-advance mechanisms so that they can be operated with either 16mm or 35mm film.

The process camera has unusual lens mountings and movements, designed to permit extremely accurate film registration. This is done

2-2. *Studio camera: the Cinema Products CP16R with "studio rig." (Cinema Products Corporation)*

2-3. *Two studio or location cameras: left, Arriflex 16BL; right, Arriflex 16SR. (Arnold & Richter)*

2-4. *Oxberry Process Camera on optical printer. (Videart Opticals, Inc.)*

so that when the film has to be run through the camera and re-exposed several times during complex animation or optical work, it will be held in precisely the same position on each pass through the camera. This guarantees that a title, for example, will not seem to be shifting around on the background over which it has been superimposed.

A fourth type of camera, the *instrumentation camera,* comes in a wide range of designs. Perhaps the more common varieties are sports cameras, such as the Photo-Sonics Actionmaster (see Camera Dataguide), which has the capability of running at speeds of up to 500 frames per second to create fabulous slow motion shots. Some other kinds of instrumention cameras may be attached to industrial test equipment, such as the sleds used in auto crash tests that provide clues for safer car design. The cameras are often capable of filming in ultra-slow motion by taking pictures at rates of up to a few million frames per second. These cameras use a variety of film advance mechanisms that bear almost no resemblance to the conventional production models.

2-5. Photo-Sonics 16mm 1 BAC Rotary Prism Recording camera, with standard speeds up to 1,000 fps. (Instrumentation Marketing Corporation)

The production camera: parts, systems, and accessories

Three basic parts form the vital organs of every camera, the *shutter,* the *gate* (with *pressure plate*), and the *film-advance mechanism,* or *pull-down claw.*

The shutter

The shutter rotates on its axis and is often shaped like one-half of a pie. It rotates at a constant speed and allows light to pass through the gate to the film for half the time required for one complete rotation. The other half of the time, when the shutter is closed, the claw is advancing the film (which is passing through the gate) downward, one

2-6. Vital organs of a camera.

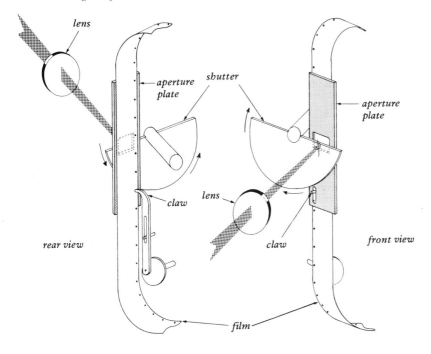

frame for each revolution of the shutter. A common variation, found in the Arriflex S, is with the shutter quartered and rotating on a shaft geared to turn at half speed. In this case, the shutter opens and closes twice per revolution and the film is advanced one frame with each opening and closing. But since most shutters are shaped like a half circle, they are often referred to as "180-degree shutters."

Shutters can also be made variable, that is, their angle of opening can be changed either when the camera is running or when it is stopped. The Mitchell 16 and the Maurer 16 are two examples of cameras with shutters that can be changed while the camera is running. They have a maximum shutter opening of 235 degrees instead of the more common 180 degrees. The shutters are constantly variable to closing. Some cameras, such as the Eclair NPR, are equipped with a variable shutter that can be adjusted only when the camera is stopped, which limits its usefulness.

The maximum width of the shutter angle is determined by the efficiency of the camera movement. Obviously the shutter must be closed during the entire time the film is being advanced: the more quickly the claw can advance the film, the more quickly the shutter can open up again for the exposure.

The shutter angle also has a direct relationship to exposure time.

Shutter angle and exposure time

The motion picture camera, at standard *sound running speed,* operates at 24 frames per second. This means that the shutter opens, closes, and the film is advanced by the claw 24 times each second. Since the classic 180-degree shutter is in position to allow light to reach the film for half of that time, the *shutter speed* or total exposure time is one half of 1/24 of a second or 1/48 second. This shutter speed of 1/48 second is not to be confused with running speed, which refers to the number of frames per second the camera is running.

The shutter speed of 1/48 second applies only to a camera running at 24 frames per second, with shutter angle of 180 degrees. This is usually rounded off to 1/50 second for easy multiplication and reference. Many light meters and other pieces of motion picture equipment are calibrated with this number in mind. But if either the shutter angle or running speed is changed, the shutter speed is also different. Since knowledge of the shutter speed is necessary to calculate exposure, it is important to know how to figure out the shutter speed under all conditions. The mathematics are very simple.

Calculating shutter speed

At 24 frames per second the shutter speed (with a constant 180-degree shutter) is 1/48 second. If the camera running speed is increased to 36 frames per second, the 180-degree shutter allows light to reach each frame for one half of the 1/36 second, leaving a shutter speed of 1/72 second. If the camera speed is increased to 48 frames per second, the shutter speed becomes 1/96 second. If the running speed is "cranked

2-7. Various shutters: (1) a regular 180-degree shutter as found in Auricon, Bell & Howell, Bolex, and other cameras; (2) a split 180-degree shutter that rotates at half speed, found primarily in Arriflex cameras; (3) shape of a 235-degree shutter found in Mitchell & Maurer cameras; (4) a 180-degree variable shutter set at a 30-degree opening.

2-8. Variable shutter control on Bolex H16. (Bolex Paillard)

up" further to 64 frames per second, the shutter speed becomes 1/128 second. Now, if running speed is slowed down to below the standard 24 frames to 8 frames per second, the shutter speed becomes 1/16 second. A running speed of 4 frames per second yields a shutter speed of 1/8 second.

Such changes of running speed are the common method of obtaining either slow motion or speeded-up motion. If a scene was filmed at a camera running speed of 48 frames per second and later projected at the standard sound speed of only 24 frames, the action would be slowed to half speed. (Motion picture projectors usually run at only the standard sound speed.)

A change in the shutter angle also enters into calculating shutter speed. If the running speed is 24 frames per second but the shutter is closed from 180 degrees to only 90 degrees, the shutter now looks like three quarters of a pie and is open to the film for only one quarter of the 1/24-second camera cycle. So the shutter speed would be 1/96 second. If the shutter closed to 45 degrees, the speed increases to 1/192, and so on.

The changes in shutter angle and in camera running speed can work in combination. For example, to slow the camera to 12 frames per second but still keep a consistent 1/48-second shutter speed, close the variable shutter to 90 degrees. Or, to make an analysis film of a fast action, increase the running speed to 96 frames per second and close the variable shutter to 45 degrees. Shutter speed is then 1/768 second, which would, upon examining individual frames, render most fast movements sharply.

Exposure at various speeds and shutter openings

Shutter angle	Frames per second									
	2	4	6	8	10	12	14	16	18	20
280°	2/5	1/5	1/7	1/10	1/13	1/15	1/18	1/21	1/23	1/26
235°	1/3	1/6	1/9	1/12	1/15	1/18	1/21	1/25	1/27	1/31
200°	2/7	1/7	1/11	1/14	1/18	1/22	1/25	1/29	1/32	1/36
180°	1/4	1/8	1/12	1/16	1/20	1/24	1/28	1/32	1/36	1/40
175°	1/4	1/8	1/12	1/16	1/20	1/25	1/29	1/33	1/37	1/41
170°	2/9	1/9	1/13	1/17	1/21	1/26	1/30	1/34	1/38	1/42
160°	2/9	1/9	1/13	1/18	1/22	1/27	1/32	1/36	1/40	1/45
150°	1/5	1/10	1/14	1/19	1/24	1/29	1/33	1/38	1/42	1/48
140°	1/5	1/11	1/15	1/21	1/25	1/31	1/36	1/41	1/45	1/51
135°	1/5	1/11	1/16	1/21	1/26	1/32	1/37	1/43	1/47	1/53
120°	1/6	1/12	1/18	1/24	1/30	1/36	1/42	1/48	1/54	1/60
100°	1/7	1/15	1/21	1/29	1/36	1/43	1/51	1/58	1/65	1/72
90°	1/8	1/16	1/24	1/32	1/40	1/48	1/56	1/64	1/72	1/80
80°	1/9	1/18	1/27	1/36	1/45	1/54	1/63	1/72	1/81	1/90
75°	1/10	1/19	1/28	1/38	1/48	1/57	1/66	1/77	1/84	1/96
60°	1/12	1/24	1/36	1/48	1/60	1/72	1/84	1/96	1/111	1/120
45°	1/16	1/32	1/48	1/64	1/80	1/96	1/112	1/128	1/144	1/160
22½°	1/32	1/64	1/96	1/128	1/160	1/192	1/224	1/256	1/288	1/320
10°	1/72	1/144	1/216	1/288	1/360	1/432	1/504	1/576	1/648	1/720
5°	1/144	1/288	1/432	1/576	1/720	1/864	1/1008	1/1152	1/1296	1/1440

So it begins to be obvious that the variable shutter is valuable for several reasons. First, it allows very sensitive or fast films to be used under bright light conditions without using neutral density filters to cut down the light. (Neutral density filters, neutral gray in color, are used to reduce the amount of light allowed to pass through the lens. They are described in Chapter 6.)

Second, the variable shutter on some cameras permits changing exposures while the camera is running. This is preferred because the lens aperture, which controls the amount of light passing through the lens to the film, has an effect on the depth of field (a lens phenomenon that dictates how much or how little of a scene is photographed in sharp focus, described in detail in Chapter 4). It is often undesirable to change the aperture while filming because that changes the sharpness in the scene. To make exposure adjustments when, for example, the sun moves in and out of clouds, a cameraman's assistant can monitor the light with a light meter and change the variable shutter accordingly.

Third, the variable shutter can create fade-outs or fade-ins at the time of shooting, although this is more commonly left for the laboratory to do in printing.

Shutter angle	Frames per second									
	22	24	32	40	48	64	72	96	120	128
280°	1/28	1/31	1/41	1/52	1/62	1/82	1/93	1/123	1/154	1/165
235°	1/34	1/37	1/49	1/62	1/77	1/98	1/110	1/147	1/184	1/196
200°	1/38	1/43	1/58	1/72	1/86	1/115	1/130	1/173	1/216	1/230
180°	1/44	1/48	1/64	1/80	1/96	1/128	1/144	1/192	1/240	1/256
175°	1/45	1/49	1/66	1/82	1/99	1/132	1/148	1/197	1/247	1/263
170°	1/47	1/51	1/68	1/84	1/102	1/136	1/152	1/204	1/254	1/271
160°	1/50	1/54	1/72	1/90	1/108	1/144	1/162	1/216	1/270	1/288
150°	1/53	1/58	1/77	1/96	1/115	1/154	1/173	1/230	1/288	1/307
140°	1/56	1/62	1/82	1/102	1/123	1/164	1/185	1/247	1/309	1/329
135°	1/58	1/64	1/85	1/106	1/128	1/171	1/192	1/260	1/320	1/341
120°	1/66	1/72	1/96	1/120	1/144	1/192	1/216	1/288	1/360	1/384
100°	1/76	1/86	1/115	1/144	1/173	1/230	1/259	1/346	1/432	1/461
90°	1/88	1/96	1/128	1/160	1/192	1/256	1/288	1/384	1/480	1/512
80°	1/99	1/108	1/144	1/180	1/216	1/288	1/324	1/432	1/540	1/576
75°	1/106	1/115	1/154	1/192	1/230	1/307	1/346	1/461	1/576	1/614
60°	1/132	1/144	1/192	1/240	1/288	1/384	1/432	1/576	1/720	1/768
45°	1/176	1/192	1/256	1/320	1/384	1/512	1/576	1/768	1/960	1/1024
22½°	1/352	1/384	1/512	1/640	1/768	1/1024	1/1152	1/1536	1/1920	1/2048
10°	1/792	1/864	1/1152	1/1440	1/1728	1/2304	1/2592	1/3456	1/4320	1/4608
5°	1/1584	1/1728	1/2304	1/2880	1/3456	1/4608	1/5184	1/6912	1/8640	1/9216

2-9. *Exposure times at various shutter speeds and openings.*

Finally, as mentioned in an earlier example, the variable shutter may also be useful for many kinds of instrumentation and scientific purposes.

The gate and pressure plate

The *gate* consists of at least two parts, a guideway that contains the rectangular opening known as the *camera aperture,* and a *pressure plate* that holds the film in or against the guideway. Do not confuse the camera aperture with the lens aperture, which is the light-controlling iris of the lens.

In some cameras, the guideway is fitted with a spring-loaded side rail to help control sideways film movement. The pressure plate must provide pressure against the rear of the film to eliminate any kind of "flutter" as the film travels intermittently through the gate. The pressure plate must also be designed with a hinge or release to allow for film loading in many cameras. Those with quick-release magazines, described later, actually have the pressure plate built right into the magazine while the guideway and camera aperture are contained in the camera proper.

Film advance mechanisms

In some cameras the *pull-down claw* is accompanied by a single or double *registration pin*. The claw has the tedious task of inserting itself into a film perforation and pulling the film down smoothly. It must start its downward travel slowly, pick up speed, and then slow the film to a stop at the bottom of its travel so as not to damage or tear the celluloid. The claw must bring the film to a stop at the proper place for exposure and then withdraw from the film before returning for another perforation and a repeat trip. All this usually happens 24 times each second; in cameras with variable speeds, it may be happening as often as 60 or 100 times each second. Since it is extremely important that each frame of film be positioned properly and be left absolutely motionless at the time of exposure, camera designers have experimented with many combinations of claw, pressure plate, and registration pin designs. Increased pressure from the pressure plate would minimize film drift, but consequent increased friction would make the pull-down more difficult. Less pressure from the pressure plate allows easy pull-down but may also permit film drift.

Some cameras have registration pins. The registration pin withdraws from the film perforations as the claw pulls the film downward. The pin then slips back into the perforations to hold the film steady during exposure. Cameras equipped in this way should take rock-steady pictures, and in fact, registration pins are required for optical and animation work where many exposures of the same scene are made onto a single strip of film. But regular production work, especially when the subject is a moving one, does not require the registration pin. All good cameras have film travel characteristics steady enough for most live work.

Some cameras with registration pins also have a built-in problem. Since the claw is engaged in a perforation when the registration pin is not and the registration pin is engaged in a perforation when the claw is not, the film is constantly engaged by either the claw or the registration pin. This means a feature must be incorporated in the camera so that the registration pin may be withdrawn or positioned properly

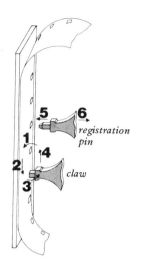

2-10. Claw and registration pin cycle: (1) claw inserts into film; (2) pull down; (3) withdraw (position shown); (4) return for next perf; (5) registration pin inserts to hold film; and (6) pin withdraws for next pull down.

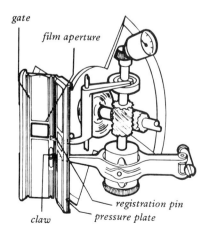

gate
film aperture
claw
registration pin
pressure plate

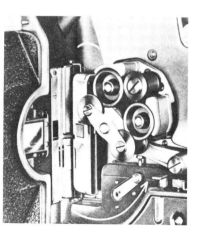

2-11. Arriflex S registration pin movement, diagram and photo. (Arnold & Richter)

during threading, allowing the film to be slipped under the registration pin at a particular place in the cycle. The pressure plate must also open and close for threading and should be removable for access to the *aperture plate*. This plate contains the precise guides for the film as well as the frame opening, determining the size and placement of the picture during exposure.

As the claw advances the film frame by frame, the *feed sprockets* are pulling the film from the supply roll and feeding it to the claw and then taking it from the claw and moving it on to the take-up roll. Here again, cameras vary widely in the design of feed sprockets and sprocket guide rollers, which must be opened and closed for threading.

The loops

Between the supply sprocket and the upper part of the gate, and between the lower part of the gate and the take-up sprocket, a free loop of film must be established in threading. These loops are necessary because the feed sprockets transport the film at a constant speed while the claw advances the film intermittently. Projectors and certain kinds of editing equipment that move the film intermittently must have these loops established in the threading as well. If the loops were not present or if the loops are lost while running because of some problem with the film or equipment, the camera will begin to make noise, and the film will tear and eventually jam.

2-12. *Eclair ACL aperture plate is readily checked and cleaned, as pressure plate is part of magazine (removed). (Harvey "T" Thompson)*

2-13. *Film loops in Beaulieu R-16 camera: left, normal loops; center, short top loop; right, short bottom loop.*

The size of these loops is very important. If the upper loop is too small, there will not be enough slack for the quick pull down by the claw. This may cause torn perforations or tension against the pressure plate, which can cause the film to go out of the proper plane of focus. If the lower loop is too small, the take-up sprocket will begin pulling the film from the gate before exposure is complete, causing a streak on the image. If either the top loop or bottom loop is too large, the film will drag across the camera interior and possibly cause scratches.

Many cameras have inscribed lines on the rear wall of the film compartment or a threading diagram on the door that shows the proper size and shape of the loops. When the camera is threaded, the cameraman should run a few short bursts of film to make certain that the loops remain stable and everything sounds smooth and quiet.

Viewfinding systems

If the shutter, the gate and pressure plate, and the claw form the vital organs of the camera, then the viewfinding system is the camera's sense organs and brain. Every prospective cameraman must carefully study the use of each different kind of viewfinding system. The identical scene can look different in each type of system. It is important to spend enough time with a new camera so that the appearance of a properly focused and framed scene in its particular viewfinder becomes familiar.

There are two categories of viewfinding systems: *reflex* and *nonreflex*. In 16mm the most frequently chosen viewfinding system is the reflex system. A reflex camera lets the viewer see exactly what the lens is seeing. Once the focus is set, what the eye sees is exactly the same as the focus on the film. The framing and composition visible through the viewfinder is also identical to that on the film. In short, the eye sees what the camera sees.

Nonreflex cameras
Few, if any, nonreflex camera systems are being manufactured today because of reflex

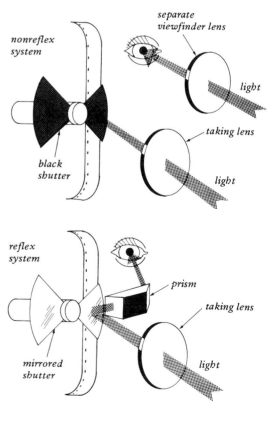

2-14. Nonreflex and reflex (mirrored shutter shown) viewing systems.

nonreflex system

separate viewfinder lens

light

taking lens

light

black shutter

reflex system

prism

taking lens

light

mirrored shutter

light

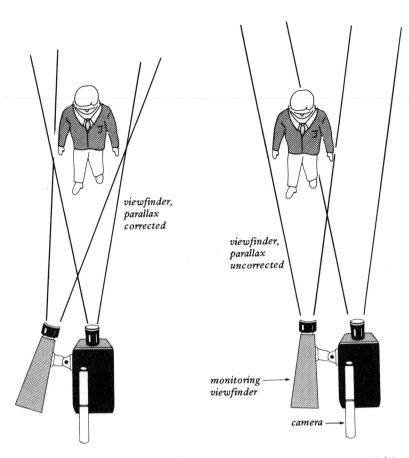

viewing's overall superiority. Much nonreflex equipment is available, however, in the used-camera marketplace, often at bargain prices, and it still provides good service in various production studios around the country.

The *monitoring viewfinder* on a nonreflex camera may be a separate optical device mounted on the side or top of the camera. The camera operator is never certain that the film is receiving exactly what is visible through this type of viewfinder. This type of viewfinder does have the advantage of providing a large, bright image that does not require the cameraman's eye to be placed on an eyepiece. This permits easier panning and tilting of the camera on tripods and dollies.

Virtually all nonreflex viewing systems must have a means to adjust for the problem of *parallax*. A comparison of the camera lens and separate viewfinder lens with the human eyes makes the problem easily understandable. The right and left eye must converge on a given object if a single image is to be seen. The angle of convergence is different for all distances, and the eyes must continually adjust to the distance of each different object.

A camera with a separate viewfinder must also adjust to the distance between the object being photographed and the camera. The separate viewfinder is usually mounted on the side or top of the camera; its lens may be three or four inches off-axis from the camera's taking lens. The viewfinder must have a facility to cause its image to converge with the camera image so that accurate framing will be possible at all distances from the camera.

But even with convergence set correctly, cameras with a separate taking lens and viewfinder have two additional problems. First, the viewfinder must be set so that its field of view corresponds to that of the taking lens. Second, the taking lens must be critically focused.

In order to set a viewfinder to frame the scene in the same way as the taking lens, at least three systems have been used. Some viewfinders have interchangeable lenses that correspond in focal length to that of the taking lens. With this system, found on the Bell and Howell Filmo, a matching viewfinder lens is required for each lens. In two cameras (the Auricon Pro-1200 and the Kodak K-100), these lenses mount right on the turret opposite the taking lens and come into correct position with each taking lens as the turret is rotated.

Some separate viewfinders have adjustable "matte lines" that can be moved by turning appropriate knobs on the top or sides of the viewfinder. This system is employed by the ancient, classic Mitchell and Maurer monitoring viewfinders.

Third, some viewfinders use replaceable "mattes," which are removeable cut-out frames that correspond to each different taking lens. Again, a different matching matte must be on hand to use with each lens. The Auricon Pro-1200 is also an example of this type.

To solve the critical focusing problem, at least four different techniques have been employed. Some nonreflex cameras (Bell and Howell,

2-16. Bell & Howell viewfinder objectives. Note geared arrangement to place objective in position with taking lens. (Harvey "T" Thompson)

2-17. Auricon monitoring viewfinder on Bell & Howell Filmo camera. (Bach Auricon, Inc.)

shutter control

inching knob

rack-over viewing tube

monitoring viewfinder

buckle trip reset

footage counter

tachometer   rack-over handle

nonreflex Bolex) have a critical focusing optical system to be used between shots with the taking lens. The focus is set by swinging the lens turret around, looking through a special peep sight, setting the critical focus, replacing the lens in position, and proceeding to take the picture.

Another approach is the *rackover* system, used by many large studio cameras, including the Mitchell 16, Mitchell 35NC, Mitchell 35BNC, and the Maurer 16. The rackover camera has a large sidemounted monitoring viewfinder to view the scene while shooting is taking place. But for critical focusing, framing, and adjusting the viewfinder between takes, the camera body shifts horizontally so that a focusing tube comes into place behind the "taking" lens. When the camera stops rolling, the cameraman racks over, views and focuses through the taking lens, and adjusts his monitoring viewfinder so that it is showing the same version of the scene as the critical finder. Then he racks back into the shooting position just before rolling. Obviously, this is not the ideal choice for the fast-moving documentary cameraman.

A variation of the rackover system, found on the Auricon Pro-1200, employs a prism that diverts the image to the viewfinder when "racked over" behind the lens between takes.

The third solution is simply to rely on the distance markings on the barrel of the lens. These markings are often accurate but not quite accurate enough; since focus is so critical at close distances, the footage markings should not be relied on unless there is great depth of field.

The advent of zoom lenses and their continuous variety of focal lengths brought about the obsolescence of separate viewfinders. It was difficult to design a nonreflex viewfinder as flexible as the zoom lens to which it was coupled. In an attempt to solve this problem, zoom lenses were designed with "built-in" viewfinders. When a nonreflex camera is properly fitted with a zoom lens containing its own viewfinder,

2-19. *Angenieux 12mm to 120mm zoom lens with 7-inch viewfinder.*

2-20. *Cinema Products CP-16 camera with Angenieux lens and finder. (Cinema Products)*

it becomes in effect a reflex camera: the lens viewfinder allows for all necessary critical focusing and framing adjustments.

There is one major drawback to this system. Although the lens itself can be accurately framed and focused, there is no guarantee that the film is receiving exactly what the cameraman sees. If the lens is not properly aligned and adjusted for the camera or if the mount is loose or dirty, it is possible to see perfectly focused and framed images through the viewfinder while the images on the film are not properly focused or framed. A nonreflex camera with a reflex lens requires that the mounting and alignment be absolutely correct. In many cameras the alignment or "lens seating" may be checked by the insertion of a prism in the film gate.

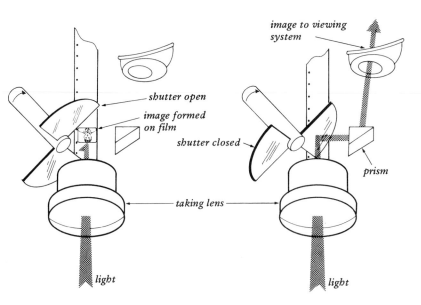

shutter open

image formed
on film

shutter closed

taking lens

light

image to viewing
system

prism

light

2-21. Left: the mir-
rored shutter is open to
the film, allowing all
the light to be used for
exposure. The viewfinder
is dark until the shutter
rotates to the closed position. Right: the shutter
is closed to the film, and
all light is reflected to
the viewing system.

Reflex cameras

Reflex cameras fall into two categories: *mirrored shutter* and *prism* or *beamsplitter.* The most common design in 16mm cameras is the mir-rored-shutter system. Motion picture camera shutters are shaped like a half of a pie (or like two quarter-pieces of pie) and revolve in front of the film. In reflex cameras the shutter is mounted at a 45-degree angle. The front surface of the shutter is mirrored, so that as light comes through the lens it is diverted onto a ground glass when the shutter is closed to the film. The image on the ground glass is magnified and viewed through an optical system. When the shutter is open to the film, the cameraman does not see anything; when the shutter rotates to the closed position, it reflects all of the light from the lens to the viewfinder.

Thus, looking through a mirrored-shutter reflex camera running at sound speed means alternately seeing and not seeing the image 24 times per second. The intermittent image is not unlike what the viewer will see when the film is projected. Due to *persistence of vision,* the marvel of the human retina that ties all these separate images together, the picture appears to be continuous instead of flickering at 24 frames per second.

Mirrored-shutter viewfinding systems have advantages and disad-vantages. One advantage is that framing and focusing can be accom-plished accurately at all times, with the camera running or not running. When the shutter is closed to the film, the ground glass is receiving all of the light coming through the lens, and the cameraman sees a bright scene in the viewfinder. Another advantage is that the taking lens itself creates the image in the finder; the cameraman sees the scene exactly the way it is recorded on film. A disadvantage is the "flicker" caused by the shutter's opening and closing. It may cause some difficulties shooting sports or other fast-moving action—during just one flicker of the shutter, the ball or a player might disappear and leave the cameraman dumbfounded. Another disadvantage common to all reflex systems is that when the taking lens is "stopped down" to a small aperture, the viewfinder receives a darker image as well. The ground glass grain becomes pronounced and the image may vignette or become even darker at the edges. Viewing under low light levels and reduced apertures is always more difficult.

A second type of reflex viewing system is known as the prism or beamsplitter. In front of the film and behind the lens is a prism with a partially reflecting surface. Most of the light from the lens passes through the prism and onto the film. A small portion of the light, about 10 percent in most cameras, is diverted by the partially reflective surface onto a ground glass and is magnified through the viewfinder. The cameraman views exactly what the film is getting.

Two obvious disadvantages to the beamsplitter are that the scene is viewed in only one-tenth of the available brightness, and that one-tenth of the light needed for exposure is being robbed by the viewfinder. If the scene is a bright one, such as a sunny exterior, the 10 percent light loss will not present any hardship. If, however, the light level is very low and it is already necessary to underexpose the film slightly, the additional 10 percent of light diverted by the beamsplitter camera is certainly not helpful, and viewing will become more difficult under these conditions as well.

The advantage of the beamsplitter is that you can view at all times while the camera is at rest or running, and there are no flicker problems.

It is possible, especially when a bright light source such as the sun is directly behind the cameraman, for light to pass back through either type of reflex viewfinder and fog the film. There is little danger when the eye is against the eyepiece, but when the eye is taken away the viewfinder must be covered. Some cameras, such as the Arriflex "S," have a manually operated door on the eyepiece for this purpose (Figure 2–23). There are also special shuttered eyepieces available which automatically open when the eye is pressed to the rubber cup. If a reflex camera is not thus

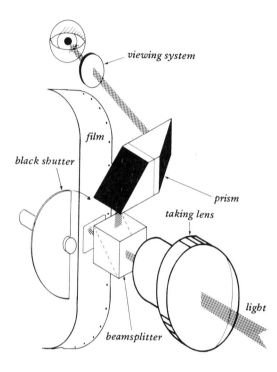

2-22. Cameras such as the Bolex H16 reflex utilize a beamsplitter that reflects about 20 percent of the light coming through the lens through the viewfinding system at all times. The remaining 80 percent of the light passes through the beamsplitter to the film. Slight exposure compensations are required.

equipped, a few layers of opaque tape placed over the eyepiece when the eye is taken away for a shot should alleviate this problem.

Ground glass and aerial image viewfinders

All viewfinders, be they nonreflex or reflex, fall into one of three categories: *ground glass, aerial image,* or *fiber optic.*

In a ground glass system the image is formed on a piece of glass that has been ground on the surface so that the glass is no longer transparent. The image comes into focus on the translucent surface just as an image comes into focus on the film in the camera. A series of lenses and eyepiece are used to magnify the image so that it can be readily seen through the viewfinder.

In an aerial image system the image is formed on a lens rather than a ground glass surface. How aerial images are formed can be demonstrated very easily. Take any camera lens and hold it out in front of you at arm's length; you will see in the lens itself an upside-down image of the scene in front of you. The image in the lens is called an aerial image.

When an image is projected onto a ground glass, the focus is just as critical as it would be on a piece of film itself. But with an aerial image, it is possible to focus back and forth without the difference being readily observed. This is because the viewer's eye compensates

2-23. Viewfinder fog shutter on Arriflex 16BL. (Harvey "T" Thompson)

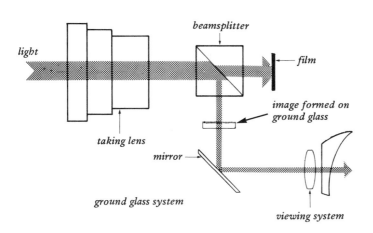

2-24. The image from the lens is reflected by the beamsplitter to a ground glass where it is magnified by the viewing system.

automatically. Thus, reflex cameras with ground glass viewfinders permit focusing with maximum accuracy, while aerial viewers may make accurate focusing deceptive and problematic. With nonreflex cameras the taking lens will have to be focused independently of the viewfinder anyway, so there is no particular value in the viewfinder having a ground glass.

Ground glass has the disadvantage of being dull and grainy because the texture of the ground glass itself is magnified in the viewfinder. The image is also darker because the ground glass reflects some of the light. With the aerial image viewfinder, the image is bright, clear, and well-defined, so details in action may be observed.

Some reflex viewfinders combine the two systems by utilizing an aerial image in the viewfinder but grinding part of the lens in which the aerial image is formed. The result is a bright, clear, sharp aerial image, except for a small circle in the center where the lens has been ground. The small ground glass image is readily utilized for critical focusing.

Several of the newest cameras have been supplied with fiber optic viewing screens. These precision-bundled and cemented screens of fine glass rods are able to provide the accuracy of ground glass with a minimum of texture approaching that of an aerial image. Relatively unaffected by low light or small

2-25. *Image as seen through ground glass viewing system.*

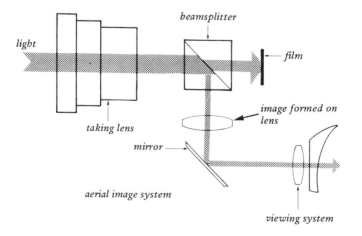

2-26. *The image from the lens is reflected by the beamsplitter to a lens where the aerial image is magnified by the viewing system.*

lens apertures, these systems are the ideal choice whenever available.

Lens mounts

Early motion picture cameras usually had one permanently mounted lens. Today, most cameras have *turrets* that hold three or four lenses at once, and alternate lenses may easily be interchanged to provide a different complement.

Unfortunately, each camera designer has had a new and different idea as to what type of lens mount is best. Considerations such as cost, ease of removal, focus, space for special optional designs, and strength have dictated numerous styles.

A list of lens mounts in common use today includes:

The "C" mount, a one-inch diameter threaded mount

The Arriflex standard mount, a 1 5/8-inch diameter threadless lens mount

The Arriflex bayonet mount, an improvement on the standard mount

The Bolex bayonet, a large diameter bayonet that adapts easily to "C" mount and others

The Eclair mount, a large, twist-lock bayonet

The Cinema Products "CP" mount, a bayonet with quick-release ring

Large mounts like the Eclair and Arriflex are strong enough to support a large lens without additional lens holders or cradles. The same large lenses in the "C" mount might require extra support to prevent wobble or lens shake. Some lenses (such as the Angenieux zoom lens) are available in many different mounts to fit almost all cameras. Conversely, some lenses, because of design or product control, are available only for specific cameras. In a few cases, adapters allow one type of lens to attach to another type of mount. A commonly used adapter is the Arriflex "C" mount, which can adapt some Arriflex-mount lenses, but not all, to "C" mount cameras.

As a general rule, adapters should be avoided. Adapters add at least one more mechanical

2-27. Image as seen through aerial image viewfinder.

2-28. Image as seen through aerial image viewer with ground glass focusing spot.

connection between camera and lens. This increases the possibility of seating, strength, and alignment problems. It is best to get lenses designed for the camera to be used. There are times when one camera will be chosen over another for a particular job simply because a special lens is designed for only that camera.

Many modern 16mm cameras have lens turrets that hold two to four lenses at one time. Their design differs as widely as lens mounts, but basically they are of two types: *flat turrets* and *divergent turrets.*

When lenses are mounted in a flat turret, they are parallel to each other. In a divergent turret, they are mounted to angle away from each other, allowing more space around the lenses and permitting the use of larger and wide-angle lenses. A wide-angle lens mounted on a flat turret next to a long or bulky lens may actually show part of the larger lens in its field of view.

Film loads

One of two types of film-loading systems is used in all 16mm cameras, and a few cameras can convert from one system to the other. The most common system uses *core-wound rolls* of raw stock loaded into camera magazines. The cores are plastic without sides. Film wound on them must be handled with extreme care: there is no protection from light, and should the roll be loosely wound there is the danger of the core and the center of the roll falling out. If this happens while the camera is being loaded, there is no way the roll can be restored without serious risk of scratching the film.

Magazines (light-tight compartments for the supply and take-up of film, attached outside the body of the camera) that use core-wound rolls must be loaded in complete darkness. Studios may have a darkroom or *loading closet* and supplies—air squeegee, brush, tape, extra cans, markers, shipping labels, and so forth—with which to load the magazines. On location, however, loading usually must be accomplished in a *changing bag,* which has two zippered chambers, one inside of the other. The magazine and can of film are put in the innermost chamber and then handled through two elastic-rimmed arm holes. The use of

2-29. One lens—many mounts. From left to right: Aaton bayonet, Arriflex standard, Arriflex bayonet, Bolex bayonet, "C" mount, Cinema Products bayonet, and Eclair CA mount.

2-30. Left: Bell & Howell Filmo with flat turret and three lenses. Notice extremely close spacing of lenses. Right: Arriflex 16S with divergent turret allowing greater physical space and wider angle of view. (Harvey "T" Thompson)

2-31. Roll center dropout.

2-32. Changing bag with Mitchell magazine and 400-foot can of film.

2-33. *Mitchell-style double compartment magazine with open take-up compartment and core.*

2-34. *Arriflex single chamber magazine with take-up core and guide rollers in position for loading. (Harvey "T" Thompson)*

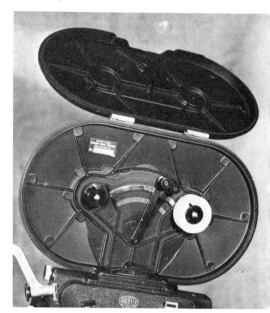

2-35. *Eclair coaxial magazine threaded with take-up side open.*

2-36. *One-hundred-foot daylight loading spool and film.*

the changing bag is described in the section on Camera Loading later in this chapter. Even if all the magazines have been loaded in a darkroom before going on location, it is important to take a changing bag along for correcting camera jams or loading problems.

Sixteen-millimeter raw stock on cores is most commonly supplied in lengths of 400 feet. Camera magazines for core-wound loads vary considerably from camera to camera. The most common configuration places the supply and take-up rolls one in front of the other, each in its own separate chamber. This design, used in the Mitchell, Maurer, Auricon, and Cinema Products magazines, affords easy loading because darkness is required only while placing the raw stock in the supply side. The rest of the threading can take place in the light, because each side of the magazine has a *light trap* where the film exits the magazine to the camera. Arriflex magazines have the same arrangement of rolls, but the magazine door is common to both sides of the magazine and therefore all the threading must be done in the dark. The Eclair magazine is coaxial—the supply and take-up chamber are side by side and the film crosses over in the threading.

2-37. *Edge flare on piece of 16mm reversal film.*

The common double-chamber magazines are the easiest to load and least expensive to buy, but they are fitted to cameras that require threading of the film through the sprockets and gate. The Arriflex M and BL magazines have built-in the film supply and take-up sprockets, and the film loop is established by properly threading the magazine. These are more expensive and harder to load, but they can be changed more rapidly since only the camera gate needs threading. Eclair NPR, ACL and Arri SR magazines (among others) also contain the film pressure plate and require no further threading when attaching them to the camera. These true quick-change magazines are the most complex to thread and expensive to buy, but they are significant time-savers during shooting.

The second major film-loading system in 16mm cameras uses *daylight loading spools.* These have opaque black sides that protect from exposure to light all but the outer layers of film on the roll. Daylight spools may be loaded in lighted rooms or outdoors in the shade. They should never be loaded in bright sunlight, because the direct light can penetrate past the edges of the film and fog major portions of the roll. Loading the spools in sunlight is the most common cause of *edge flare,* seen on the screen as fogged edges that come and go during a shot.

In most cases 100-foot daylight loading spools are used in cameras that have space for the supply and take-up rolls within the camera body. Daylight loading spools of 200 and 400 feet are also available. These must be loaded into magazines, and they are popular among crews who have no time to use the changing bag. The cameras, designed to accept 100-foot daylight spools, are highly portable, light, fast-moving instruments particularly well adapted to documentary and news-reel work. In this category fall cameras like the Beaulieu, Arriflex S, Bell and Howell Filmo, and Bolex. Some models of these cameras have removable body caps and are fitted with mounting plates to accept 200- and 400-foot magazines. These magazines add greatly to the camera's versatility, but they also mean added weight and reduced portability and ease in hand-held shooting.

Camera motors

The earliest motion picture cameras were driven with a hand crank that kept the cameraman busy cranking instead of focusing, framing, panning, and changing the f-stop. The cranking action caused unsteady pictures and fluctuations in speed. Fatigue or a change of cameramen are partly responsible for the characteristic variations in brightness of the early silent films.

The spring-wound motor soon followed, and it solved most of the big problems. The cameraman could do his cranking between takes, and while the camera was running he could concentrate on the shooting. The spring-wound motor is found on several modern cameras and is still used occasionally in 16mm location photography. A spring-wound camera is light, self-contained, runs on obscure mountaintops and in underwater housings, and never needs power or battery charging. The Bell and Howell Filmo, Kodak Cine-Special, Kodak K-100, Bolex, and Keystone cameras with spring-wound motors have been used in many areas of professional filmmaking.

The spring-wound motor is the simplest and least expensive method of running a camera, but it has two problems: it is difficult to maintain accurate speed control, and it tends to wind down during shooting. While some spring cameras have a wide variety of running speed

2-38. *Spring motor on Bell & Howell camera.* (*Harvey "T" Thompson*)

2-39. *AC motor attached to Bell & Howell camera.* (*Alan Gordon Enterprises*)

settings, they do not hold precisely at a specific speed and cannot be used for sync-sound filming. They are also a poor choice for many kinds of documentary work where long running time might be necessary to shoot never-to-be repeated action, or where there is a very little time between takes. They always seem to wind down and stop at just the most crucial moment.

A second system for operating motion picture cameras is the *alternating current* (AC) *electric motor*. AC motors used in cameras employ alternating current to maintain accurately a preset speed. They are often called "sync" motors because they are commonly used for shooting sync sound. In America AC motors in 16mm cameras use 110 volts AC and 60 Hertz. When shooting in Europe, motors must use the 50Hz AC, which is prevalent outside of the United States. There are 220-volt motors as well, in both 50 and 60 Hertz, but in this country 110-volt, 60Hz motors are usually supplied for 16mm production.

Companion audio tape recorders use the same 60-cycle current as a sync reference to provide double system sync shooting capability. Quarter-inch recorders (the type most frequently used) utilize a transformer to reduce the AC current to about one volt so that the 60Hz can be inaudibly recorded directly onto the tape to be used as a speed control track.

Power for the 110-volt AC motor comes from one of three sources. The mains (wall sockets, plug sockets) are the most common. A portable battery-operated power supply is another possibility. They use rechargeable cells and a converter to make 60-cycle, 110-volt AC. Their portability allows the sync motor to be used on locations where mains are inaccessible. The sound recorder must be plugged into the same power supply as the camera so that fluctuations in the current will be reflected in both recorder and camera, and slight variations will not affect the sync. Portable motor generators or generator trucks also can provide current in larger amounts not only for the cameras but also for the lights. Generators are expensive, bulky, and require additional personnel to operate them, however. They are also noisy and must be kept at great distances from the shooting area so as not to interfere with the sound recording. Again, audio recorders must use the same source to provide sync reference.

Another type of drive system commonly used is the low voltage *direct current* (DC) *electric motor*. Cameras with DC motors use various battery packs as power supplies. DC camera motors are of four types. First is the *variable* or *wild motor*, which can run at a variety of speeds and can be adjusted to compensate for weak batteries. It is a good motor for shooting where accurate camera speed for sync is not essential.

The second type of DC motor drive is the *crystal-controlled motor,* which uses an oscillating quartz crystal to maintain speed with extreme accuracy. When it is used with a crystal-controlled recorder, the result is totally portable independent sync sound filming. With a typical crystal motor camera, sync accuracy to within one frame of a 400-foot roll can be achieved.

The third type is the *governor-controlled* or *constant-speed motor*. Gov-

2-40. *Two "interchangeable" Arriflex motors for models S and M. Left: a crystal sync motor; right: the variable-speed, forward/reverse motor. (Harvey "T" Thompson)*

2-41. *The governor-controlled constant-speed "sync" motor on Arriflex BL camera. (Harvey "T" Thompson)*

ernor-controlled DC motors hold speed precisely enough for sync sound and can be used for that purpose if they have been fitted with a 60-Hertz sync generator to provide a reference signal for the sound recorder. With this set-up, the battery-operated DC camera can be used for shooting sync sound, but it requires a cable connecting camera and recorder at all times.

A fourth type of DC motor provides the ultimate combination. This is the *crystal-controlled variable speed motor.* With the flick of a switch, it will not only provide synchronous sound speed but also slow or speeded-up motion as well.

The battery packs for DC motors come in many forms, including batteries contained in the camera's handle or body, cigarette-pack-sized units, and shoulder and belt packs. Unfortunately, the battery packs are seldom interchangeable from one make of camera to another. They differ in the amount of voltage, the type of connectors, and kinds of electronic circuitry.

If a special shape or size battery is required, it is possible to make one for many DC-powered cameras. For example, there are no commercially available "pocket" batteries for the popular Arriflex S camera. Once the voltage is determined, the proper number of 1.5-volt dry or rechargeable cells can be combined to meet the requirement. Short lengths of hookup wire may be soldered to the positive and negative battery poles to complete the circuit. A short battery extension cable with the proper plug completes the battery. Several cells can be held together or attached to the camera or camera housing with heavy-duty tape.

There are special-purpose motors available for cameras that have removable motor units. These cameras can be fitted with stop-motion motors for shooting single frame (animation), with time-lapse equipment for compressing time, and with variable- and high-speed motors for filming slow and speeded-up motion. There are auxiliary AC motors made for many cameras that ordinarily use DC motors and vice versa. Some spring-wound cameras, such as the Bolex, can be fitted with accessory DC motors to increase their versatility.

Camera supports and accessories

Some cameras need supports because of their weight or bulk, but most modern 16mm cameras may be carried about quite readily. The decision to use a support is more often for aesthetic, rather than practical, reasons. In order to duplicate on screen the amazing ability of the eye to view objects with complete stability under all but the most violently shaky conditions, cameras must often be held rock-steady during shoot-

2-42 and 2-43. Top left: homemade battery belt, using army surplus belt and plastic battery holders. Top right: three common battery styles: left, the Arriflex 12v pack for model 16BL cameras; center, 20v pack for Cinema Products cameras; right, typical battery belt. Bottom left and right: typical nonbelt uses of the battery belt. (Top left, Harvey "T" Thompson; bottom right and left, American Cinematographer, *October, 1979, reprinted by permission)*

ing. This is particularly true when filming naturally stable, nonmoving objects such as landscapes, buildings, and trees. The photography of artwork, models, miniatures, titles, and the like also requires all the steadiness a solid camera support can provide. The choice of lens is also an important factor, however. Wide-angle lenses can be hand-held successfully with most live subject matter, but lenses of 50mm or greater focal length will quickly reveal the slightest unsteadiness.

Tripods

There are many styles and types of tripods available. The lightweight aluminum folding tripods are almost useless since they cannot support the weight of professional equipment without wobbling. In fact, an inadequate tripod can create a false sense of security and introduce factors of vibration that might have been avoided if the camera had been simply hand-held.

At the other end of the scale from the lightweight tripods are heavy monsters that can be lifted only by two people and will handle cameras weighing over one hundred pounds. Somewhere in between these extremes is a tripod that is best suited for a particular 16mm camera at a particular time.

Most professional tripods are supplied in two parts: *legs* and *heads*. Legs of various sizes are attached to standard *top castings*. Various types of heads can then be attached to the selected legs to provide tremendous versatility.

A *friction head*, like most other professional heads, has separate locking controls for the tilt and pan movements. When the head is locked tight, the camera is rigidly stable; the controls can be loosened slightly to provide for smooth frictional panning or released completely to allow for very fast pans and tilts. Large models are sometimes available with a *spring counterbalance* to help prevent a large camera from falling over when the tilt control is released. Friction heads are technologically simple, relatively inexpensive, and suited for many kinds of shooting.

The *gear head,* also frequently called the

2-44. Various tripod heads: left to right, Akeley Gyro Head, O'Connor Model 50 Fluid Head, Miller Fluid Head. (Harvey "T" Thompson)

Worrall head or Raby head, which are manufacturer's trade names, is used to carry the
heaviest studio camera. Unlike most heads,
which have a center pivot point, the gear head
employs a rolling cradle with a set of curved
rails. The cradle will tend to "self-center"
when a heavy camera is attached, unlike the
usual tripod head, which can allow the camera
to fall off center to the front or back when
it is tilted. The gear head is operated with
handle-wheels that are cranked to pan or tilt.
The side handle turns counterclockwise to pan
right and clockwise to pan left; the rear handle
turns counterclockwise to tilt down and clockwise to tilt up. The gear head is particularly
useful when very slow, smooth movements are
desired.

Perhaps the most popular head currently
is the *fluid head*. It allows panning at any
speed, slow or fast. Adjustments are provided
to increase or decrease overall "friction," but
in general, slow movements can be accomplished with little effort, while fast pans or
tilts require additional force. This provides an
amazing motion-cushioning effect that makes
it a superior all-purpose head, especially when
long lenses are employed, as well as for critical
close-up photography.

The legs on a standard tripod are four feet
long when closed and six feet long when extended. Professional tripods are also available
with "sawed-off" legs that are extendable from
three to five feet, and "baby" or "low" legs
that are extendable from two to three feet. To
attach a camera to the floor, to a mounting
board, or to a ladder, a device known as the
hi-hat is available. It is a metal casting with
three short legs and holes at the bottom for
screws or bolts. The top of the hi-hat, as with
the various professional legs, is machined to
accept professional tripod heads.

There are other features to look for in a
tripod. One is a *leveling* device. Many professional tripods are constructed with three legs
that are independently adjustable. The legs
are extended, and then the camera is leveled
by readjusting them. This can be a time-con-
suming job, but the system is satisfactory
otherwise. Other tripods have a ball-swivel

2-45. Various tripod legs. (Harvey "T" Thompson)

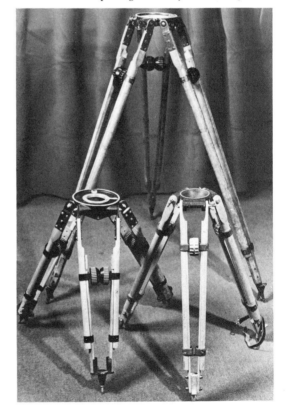

arrangement; after the legs are raised a locking knob is loosened, the ball swivel is swung around until the camera is level, and the knob is locked up again. Set-ups can be accomplished much more rapidly with the ball swivel than with the three independently adjustable legs.

The *triangle* is a tripod accessory also known as *spreaders*. This three-legged device unfolds, lies on the floor, and utilizes clamps to keep the feet of the tripod from slipping around on a smooth floor. If the tripod and triangle are to be mounted on a moving platform, on top of a truck, atop a press box high above the grandstands, or on any other precarious position, the *tie down* is helpful. These short lengths of chain are hooked to the underside of the tripod (sometimes rings are provided between the legs) and to a screw eye attached to the floor. After the tie down is in place, the legs are raised to provide tension on the chain. A strong gust of wind will now remove only the cameraman. Spreaders with wheels attached are called, in the precise jargon of film terminology, "wheelies." Generally, wheelies are not acceptable for dolly shots because their small wheels wobble slightly and tend to rock the camera back and forth.

The combination of tripod and wheelies became so popular for studio and TV-style shooting that several three-wheeled hydraulic

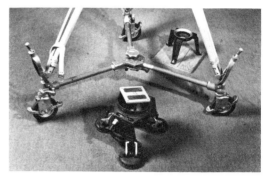

2-46. *Center: tripod on set of wheelies; front: auto suction mount; rear: hi-hat. (Harvey "T" Thompson)*

2-47. *Body brace.*
(Harvey "T" Thompson)

2-48. *Left: Steadicam with CP16R camera; right: Colortran mini-crab dolly with Arriflex 16BL camera. (Harvey "T" Thompson)*

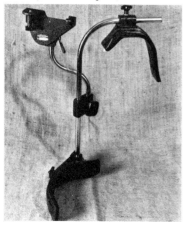

camera dolly designs have been developed. These glorified camera stands are sturdy, completely steerable, and will handle very heavy camera-blimp combinations on their hydraulic support post.

Body brace

The body brace generally rests on one or both of the cameraman's shoulders, as well as on his hips and stomach. Some braces strap completely around the body. The camera is firmly mounted on a system of adjustable support struts.

The body brace is a good support for mobility with relatively heavy cameras. It allows the cameraman to move about quickly, walk, climb, and sit down. But the body brace does not usually make the shot significantly steadier than a hand-held camera, and it is certainly not recommended for shooting fixed objects. In fact, the body brace has a movement all its own. An experienced cameraman can tell the difference between footage shot with the same camera both hand-held and on a body brace. With a body brace the shots tend to weave from side to side; with a hand-held camera they tend to dip up and down. These movements become noticeable on footage that really should have been shot with the camera on a tripod. This is another reason why it is important for the novice cameraman to view his uncut footage and learn to criticize his own application of different camera accessories.

Steadicam

A popular new camera support system is the Cinema Products Steadicam. It consists of a body harness and stabilized camera support arm. A most important feature of this system is the closed-circuit video viewfinder mounted on the camera's reflex viewing system. The TV monitor is mounted on the "sled" portion of the device and is visible to the cameraman at all times. By eliminating the need for the camera to be held to the cameraman's eye, great flexibility, freedom, and steadiness may be obtained, particularly by camera operators experienced in its use.

Dollies and cranes

A camera *dolly* is a rolling platform that utilizes an extension arm or "boom" to carry the camera. This arm can be raised and lowererd and the camera remains level at all times. The camera dolly may or may not be a *crab dolly*—a term often applied inaccurately to all dollys.

A crab dolly has a special platform so that when the steering control (a T-handle or wheel) is moved all four wheels will turn together in the same direction at the same time, turning the platform without turning the camera. This means that the dolly can move into a scene and turn left or right, but the camera continues facing in the same direction. Some dollies can be used like small cranes, moving up and down, back and forth, thereby adding a wide variety of camera movements.

Camera *cranes* offer the utmost versatility in heavy-camera placement and movement, but they are large, cumbersome devices and can be the most dangerous piece of equipment in the studio. They are designed so that the camera, cameraman, and assistant all perch together on a single platform mounted at the end of a large boom. The platform can revolve so that, during a pan or crane movement, the crew stays in position with the camera. The camera itself is also mounted on a large gear head and can be panned or tilted independently of the revolving platform. The ten-foot, fifteen-foot, or larger boom can be moved up and down, back and forth, with very little effort, while the camera platform remains level.

But a crane must be counterbalanced. When a 75-pound camera, a 175-pound cameraman, and a 175-pound assistant are all sitting at the end of the camera boom, the opposite end of the boom, which is usually shorter, must be counterbalanced with an even greater amount of weight. If a crew member should step off when the boom is unlocked, the camera and remaining crew will rise wildly. The camera can fly off and be destroyed and a crew member working by the rear of the crane can be crushed. Similarly, if the boom lock is released when the crane is unbalanced, disaster quickly follows.

Magnificent shots can be created with the help of a crane or dolly. By pulling up or back with a crane, vertical or horizontal action can easily be followed, new characters or props appear in the scene, and a wonderful effect of movement is created.

Some cranes are motor driven and can travel at speeds of up to 60mph. It is possible to drive alongside moving horses or vehicles at many different heights and angles, resulting in smooth-traveling photography.

Image stabilizers

There are two types of *image stabilizers* that solve many camera shake problems. They are either mechanical or optical.

2-49. *Scene from* Dr. Zhivago *filmed from crane. (Memory House)*

2-50. Arriflex Image Stabilizer. (Harvey "T" Thompson)

The mechanical devices use gyroscopic wheels in various ways to minimize camera dip and wobble. The units commercially available (the Kenyon stabilizers) come in three sizes (KS-3, KS-4, KS-6) to be used with cameras of various weights. They have self-contained motors, bolt onto the camera in its regular tripod socket, and require a battery pack for operation. They are nearly silent. Although they add weight to any hand-held camera, they will definitely reduce the effect of quick movements unless stresses and vibrations overcome the inertia of the flywheels. How effective they are depends on particular camera and shooting situations.

There are also optical image stabilizers, such as the Arri image stabilizer and the Dynalens. The Dynalens is a device consisting of two basic parts: a lens attachment and an amplifier/power supply. Two optical-glass plates are attached and sealed to the ends of a bellows that contains a liquid with proper refraction properties. The front glass plate is mounted to move on a horizontal axis and the rear plate is mounted to move on a vertical axis. When either plate moves, the light path is altered accordingly. The glass plates and bellows are in a housing that contains gyroscopic sensors and servo motors. The motors are attached to the glass plates. When the housing is attached to the front of a camera lens, the sensors produce electrical fluctuations that correspond to the camera movements. The fluctuating current is fed to the power supply. There it is amplified and fed back to the servos, which move the glass plates in a direction opposite to the camera movement. The system is self-centering and aligned to respond to fast vibrations. Optical vibration compensators, though expensive, are the best solution to date for many kinds of moving camera situations.

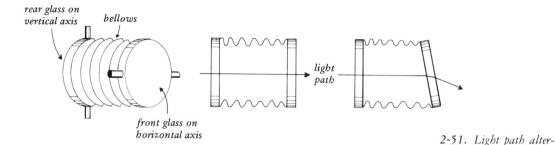

rear glass on vertical axis

bellows

front glass on horizontal axis

light path

2-51. *Light path alteration through the moving glass plates of the Dynalens.*

Camera blimps

Sound *blimps* are manufactured for many studio cameras that are not self-blimped. The blimp is basically a box into which the camera is placed so that the camera noise will not be picked up by sound recorders. But the blimp must have facilities for focusing the camera and for viewing during shooting. It must also open wide enough to allow easy access for changing magazines and lenses.

The Arriflex blimp, perhaps the most common in 16mm, has doors on the side for access to the camera and lenses, and a top lid that opens to remove the magazine for loading. But while all this sounds impressive, this blimp, like most, becomes very clumsy under any but the most leisurely shooting conditions.

Within the past ten years there has been a major industrywide shift to the new self-blimped cameras that, when in good condition and kept more than four feet from the microphone, can be used satisfactorily in the quietest studio. The once-common Arri and Mitchell blimped rigs that characterized studios a few years ago have all but disappeared today.

Matte boxes

The *matte box* is a combination sunshade and filter holder that attaches to the camera in front of the lens or turret. It is designed with bellows so that the sunshade can be compressed or extended to suit the angle

2-52. *Arriflex 16mm sound blimp for Arri 16S camera. Note focusing tube, which couples to camera eyepiece to permit reflex viewing. (Arnold & Richter)*

2-53. Arriflex 16BL
matte box and matte box
with "keyhole" matte.
(Harvey "T" Thompson)

of view of telephoto or wide-angle lenses. Slots in the top or side are
for glass-mounted filters, allowing the same filter to be used for all
the lenses in the turret. One important caution: the matte box usually
must be readjusted for each change of lens; otherwise it might be
"cropped" in the view of wide lenses and ruin the shot.

The matte box was originally so named because it provided a mounting place for the "mattes" used to create the popular "vignettes" of
earlier films. It can still be used for the same purpose today. For

2-54. Cut mattes and
matte box.

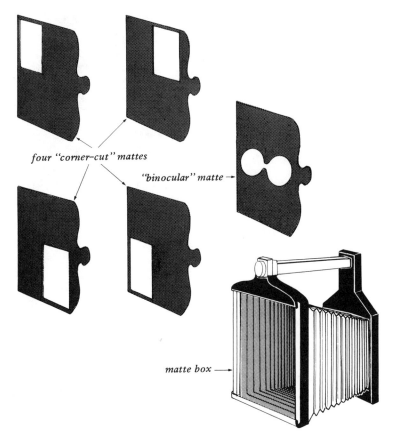

four "corner-cut" mattes

"binocular" matte →

matte box →

example, four different corner-cut mattes can be used in succession, with the film wound back between shots, to produce a four-screen composite shot. Or a cutout "binocular" matte can be used to create the point of view shot for a person using binoculars. Only imagination and the availability of black paper limits the number of different mattes that can be cut and used.

Barneys

Barneys are fitted camera-enclosing covers. They are commonly used for two purposes. *Heater barneys* are insulated cloth bags that fit closely around the camera and contain a resistance-wire heating circuit, much like an electric blanket. Plugged into available power sources, they keep the camera warm in extremely cold shooting locations.

Sound barneys are padded cloth bags that also fit particular cameras and are used to help absorb camera noises. Some supposedly self-blimped cameras and film magazines make soft noises that can be sufficiently muffled with a barney.

In order to work properly, both sound and heater barneys must fit the camera snugly. They are available as accessories from some cameramakers, as specialty items from various equipment houses, or may be homemade by crafty cameramen.

Electronic Viewfinders

Eager to take advantage of the latest technology, directors have adapted video equipment to motion picture cameras and motion picture equipment to video cameras. To date, most video-motion picture systems are in 35mm and 65mm. They are used to some advantage in large-scale production numbers where multiple cameras, numerous actors, and complicated music and dance sequences are checked with immediate videotape playback. These systems consist essentially of a blimped production camera fitted with a beamsplitter to divert some of the light from the lens to a video camera mounted alongside. The video

2-55. *Cinematographer Jess Yound using sound barney of his own design on a Bolex SEM camera.* (American Cinematographer, *October, 1979, reprinted by permission*)

2-56 and 2-57. Top left: *Aaton 7LTR camera with video pickup (light gray) for remote video viewing and recording. Bottom left: LOUMA crane with Arriflex 35BL camera; center: with Panaflex camera; right: on a Moonraker set. (Top left, Aaton Cameras; all others,* American Cinematographer, December, 1979, *reprinted by permission)*

camera is linked to a video tape monitor and recorder that can be played back instantly so that the director can check action, angles, and lip movements before proceeding to the next sequences. In some setups the cameramen are guided by a director watching all the action on TV monitors in a control room—the cameras functioning as if in a regular television studio. The 35mm Mole-Richardson "Molec" electronic camera system provides for four cameras and a van that contains the necessary control room and video tape components for location work.

Where cameras are to be applied to remote or dangerous shooting situations, TV viewfinders allow photography without a cameraman on the scene. Combined with remote focus, zoom, aperture, on-off controls, and a motor-driven pan and tilt head, the camera may perform functions in small places, on tiny dolly tracks, boom cranes, overhead suspension cables, and in locations where cameramen simply cannot go. Equipment of this kind is usually designed for a particular assignment; the engineer-cameraman will have to be supplied with ample development time and money if success is to be achieved.

An especially good example of the latest camera crane technology is the LOUMA crane, available through the Samuelson Company of Hollywood. The camera is hung from a balanced yoke at the end of an aluminum tube which extends to 20 feet. All camera functions are controlled remotely. Of special interest is the control station on which video viewfinders are mounted. By turning standard gear-head control wheels, the comparable camera movements are instantly accomplished via gyro-assisted servos.

2-58. *Loading double compartment magazine. (1) In dark, remove film from can and bag. (2,3) Remove tape and place inside can. (4) Crimp end of film. (5) Insert and pass through light trap. (6) Pull film out. (7) Drop film into magazine. (8) Align spindle into core. (9) Replace cover on supply side. (10) In light, insert film into supply side. (11) Crimp film. (12) Place in core slot. (13) Take up approximately two turns on core. (14) Replace cover. (15) Label magazine.*

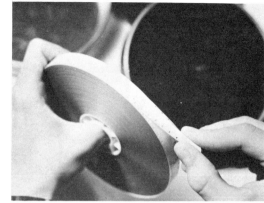

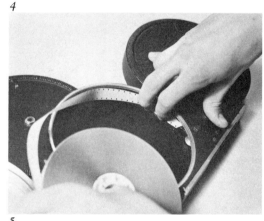

4

1

5

2

6

3

7

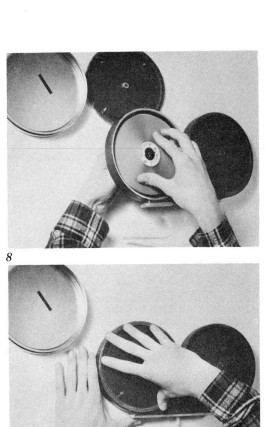

8

12

9

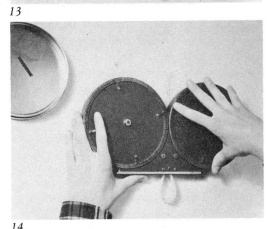

13

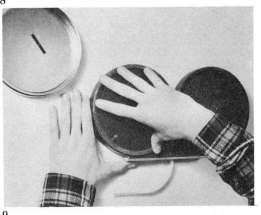

10

14

11

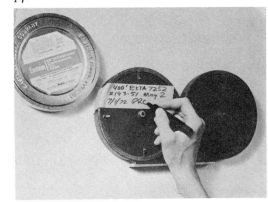

15

Camera loading

Threading and loading procedures sound complex, but they soon become a matter of routine when you gain familiarity with your equipment. Eventually, you will be able to thread your camera in the dark, under any conditions, in any position.

It is extremely important to have each part of the camera and magazine clean of particles and dust, particularly during loading. Here are some hints.

Use a rubber air squeegee or compressed air to blow out thoroughly all small pieces of dust, emulsion chips, lint, and hair. Never use your breath, which might splatter moisture and is itself moist.

Almost all magazines have light traps, soft felt rollers or pads that keep light out of the magazine. These light traps are also dirt traps, and they must be cleaned regularly. The best way is with compressed air. Guide and light-trap rollers must also be checked to be certain they are turning freely. If a light-trap roller fails to turn, the film will drag and may get scratched.

A small brush will move stubborn pieces of dirt. A penlight or small flashlight is useful for checking dark corners.

A pocket magnifier is the best way to look for hairs and dirt buildup in the gate.

Magazine loading as well as camera threading should be carried out in clean surroundings. This sometimes requires a clean-up operation or removing the camera to a loading room or other clean area.

If the camera uses magazines, they must be cleaned as well. Check to be sure each magazine is equipped with the proper core spindles and take-up core. Before loading a particular magazine for the first time, practice a few times with a full-length roll of clean leader film before going into the dark. Some general magazine loading procedures follow.

Open the supply side of the magazine and place the cover in a clean spot where you can find it easily in the dark. After turning out the light and checking for complete darkness, unwrap the raw stock and remove the adhesive tape that the manufacturer may use to keep the roll from unraveling. Stick the adhesive tape to the inside of the film can so that it cannot inadvertently end up in the magazine. Crimp the film lengthwise for a few inches to stiffen it for threading through light traps and the like. When it is threaded, carefully place the roll on the magazine core spindle. *Watch out for roll-center dropout.*

On standard double-compartment magazines the roll must be held with one hand while the other hand reaches under the magazine and rotates the shaft until the core notch drops fully onto the spindle pin. If this is not properly done, the film will be bound by the magazine cover and will not feed. With magazines that have a separate supply chamber, now replace the cover and turn on the light. Open the take-up side of the magazine and thread the film through the light trap, take-up sprockets, and so on, into the take-up side. Some magazines are inscribed with the proper direction for winding, but others are not;

be certain they are threaded correctly.

With a two-inch core in place, fold the film back over itself about two to three inches from the end and push the crease into the core slot. Then turn the core in the take-up direction several revolutions and crease the film so that it will roll tightly. Replace the take-up cover and, using white camera tape, label the magazine. Place the tape on the supply side with the end lapping over the magazine cover edge to prevent accidental removal. Label the magazine with the following information:

quantity

film type and emulsion number

magazine or roll number

date loaded

loader's initials

Loading in a changing bag

Unpack the changing bag and unzip the two compartments. Shake it out vigorously to remove dust and dirt. Inspect it inside and out for any holes, rips, or torn seams. Out of direct sunlight, place it on a flat surface, arm holes toward yourself, and put the cleaned and inspected magazine inside the inner chamber. The magazine covers should be loose but attached to keep out dirt, and the light traps should be toward you.

Untape the can of raw stock and place it in the inner compartment to the left of the magazine. Zip up both chambers and fold the zippers under the bag and away from the light. Roll up shirt sleeves. Arms go inside the bag, up past the elbows. If possible, pull sleeves back down over the bag elastics. Remove the supply side magazine cover and place it under the magazine to save space. Open the film can, remove the film from the bag, and untape the end of the roll. Stick the adhesive tape inside the film can so that it cannot inadvertently end up in the magazine. Load according to the regular procedures for the particular magazine. Do not be rushed. Remember that if anything seems out of order, stop and start over.

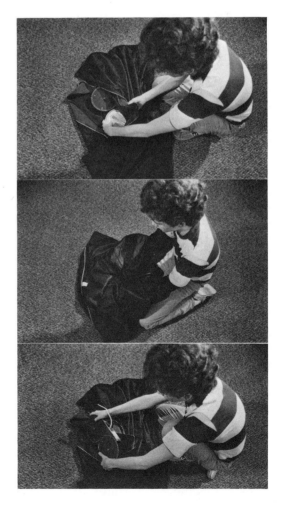

2-59. Top: placing film and magazine inside bag; center: loading with zippered bag; bottom: removing magazine with supply side loaded.

Cleaning the camera body

Open the camera completely and remove lenses, door, magazines. Dust and blow out thoroughly. Remove the pressure plate and check that it is clean and lubricated with a little bit of nose grease. Clean the gate and check for accumulated dirt around the claw, registration pin, and tiny crevices. Blow out the camera body.

If the camera has a built-in filter slot, check it. Is there a filter there already? If it is not to be used, remove it now. If it is to be used, check it for dust and scratches.

Threading

Load the roll of film or attach the magazine. Do not forget to attach the magazine take-up belt on cameras so equipped. Thread the camera very carefully. Check all guide rollers to make sure they are turning freely, and of course, check the threading pattern and be sure the loops are correct.

Loop Check: Switch the camera on and off and run a few short bursts of film while watching the gate to be certain the loops are being properly maintained. At the same time, make certain the take-up is working correctly.

Spool Check: If the camera has a daylight loading spool, be certain that the spool has not been flattened. These spools are just as wide as the film itself, and if the spool is bent even slightly, the film will not wind. It is a common cause of camera jamming. Prior to loading, many cameramen place a finger between the spool flanges and rotate the spool to feel for bends or crimps.

Gate Check: With the lens removed, look in the front of the camera while rotating the shutter to see the aperture plate. Examine the edges of the gate carefully to see if any foreign matter has been trapped there since threading. This procedure should be repeated between takes whenever time permits; nothing is more disappointing than to develop an otherwise perfect roll of film only to find a hair sticking up into the shot. With some lens, the gate check can be accomplished by opening the lens up to its maximum aperture and looking

2-60. Using finger to check daylight loading spool for crimp.

2-61. Removing lens for gate check; view of film through lens port.

through. The shutter must be open, of course, and a small flashlight is needed to accomplish this trick.

Scratch Test: Run off two or three feet so that film from the supply side goes all the way through the camera at normal speed and is taken up on the spool or core. Then stop the camera and remove the take-up core or spool with the film attached. Look at the emulsion and base sides of the film, carefully checking for any tiny scratches. Use a magnifier. If there is a scratch, do not shoot anything (except the rental agent) until you have found the reason for it. Check the gate, pressure plate rollers, and light traps, looking for burrs or nicks as well as dirt or emulsion chips. Check the threading, in case the film was passed under instead of over a roller, and so on. The scratch test is usually not performed on every roll, but certainly it should be done once or twice every shooting day.

Run Off: Before shooting, close the camera, set the footage counter to "0," clean the lenses, mount them back in the turret in the desired order, check to be sure that there are no extraneous filters on the lenses themselves, and attach the desired ones. Run off the first five feet or so since the manufacturer has punched holes in the film at about five feet from the head for identification.

Warmup

Cameras should be switched on and allowed to run free of film for a minute or two at the beginning of every working day. The lubricating oils in the camera tend to become stiff and the warmup period gives the bearings, motor, and precision parts a chance to loosen up for smooth operation. Also, if any unlubricated parts are about to cause problems, this is when they can best be heard. It is important to know what the "normal" sound level and tone of a running camera are so that service can be performed before a freeze-up or other disaster occurs.

Practical notes on camera use

This book does not deal with directing and shooting style. Elements of style and cinematic approach are the creative essence of each film-maker and are better learned from first-hand experience rather than books. But the techniques of camera handling used to produce desired visual effects must be tried and learned by all who wish to communicate in the film medium. Cameras are becoming more versatile, and creative cameramen are looking for new ways to use the new tools.

Shooting pans and zooms

Pans and zooms are visual devices used in virtually all films. Many times the difference between jerky and smooth pans and zooms means the difference between the amateur home-movie look and the quality feel of the professional.

Pans

There are at least three factors to be considered when panning: direction of the pan, speed of the pan, and focal length of the lens being used.

The direction of a pan is more of a problem when shooting with the use of a tripod than when hand-holding the camera. This is because tripods of all varieties have separate locks or friction brakes for vertical pans, properly called "tilts," and horizontal pans. When either a tilt or a pan is required separately, the brake for the direction not being used can be left partially engaged to minimize the danger of wobbles in the wrong direction. But when the camera must pan and tilt at the same time or follow a diagonal screen direction, very careful balancing of the vertical and the horizontal brake tensions is necessary. This is not easily accomplished and, as a result, diagonal moves made with conventional tripods often come out looking like the cameraman was following the treads and risers of an open staircase. Gear heads will prevent this problem, but they require a great deal of practice to learn in which way the vertical and horizontal wheels must be turned to produce the proper move. For this reason, a good fluid head is an excellent choice for many shooting jobs. It allows for the smoothest pans in all directions without the practice needed to work the gear-head wheels competently.

The speed of the pan is quite another problem. Following a fast-moving object, the pan will often render the background in a stroboscopic blur. This effect is usually quite acceptable as long as the foreground action is followed smoothly. But the strobe effect is usually unacceptable with static scenes. It is caused by panning too fast, and the result is too great a displacement between successive images photographed and projected. This "skipping" effect is exaggerated by five factors:

1. Bright objects on a dark background
2. Very high screen luminescence during projection of the footage
3. Long focal-length lenses

4. Slow camera running speeds

5. Narrow shutter openings

Subject contrast and screen brightness are very subtle variables and are not usually considered by the cameraman. Camera running speed is an important variable, but it is not often controllable—either because sound is being recorded or because the scene must appear to be in real time. A change in the shutter angle, however, is a variable that can lead to strobing pans rather easily, and that is the cameraman's province. Cameramen will sometimes close the shutter angle to compensate for over-exposure and find that a normally acceptable panning speed produces the strobing effect. On the other hand, cameras such as the Mitchell and Maurer with their 235-degree shutters (as opposed to the more common 180 degrees) can reproduce fast pans and actions more smoothly. The reason shutter angle has such a pronounced effect is that fast shutter speeds produce sharper images on each frame, and this allows for distinct recognition of any exaggerated image displacement by the retina. The wide shutter angle renders the images produced by a fast pan as a blur, and the retina is able to combine these blurred images more readily.

The magnification of the image through telephoto lenses is the most common cause of unpleasant panning strobe. With long focal lengths, even the seemingly slowest panning speeds can produce strobe effects. Some cameras, such as the Eclair, Arriflex, and Beaulieu, will produce a skipping effect in the viewfinder that is similar to what is seen when the film is projected. Viewfinder brightness is seldom great enough, however, for the problem to be recognized in time.

Timing a pan with complete accuracy is difficult, but in certain cases it is necessary, and so a stopwatch should be included in the camera tool bag. Whenever a scene contains numerous vertical lines, such as skylines, buildings with vertical rows of windows, fences, rows of poles, and the like, careful timing of the pan with the recommended speed should be tried in at least a few takes.

If the problem seems to be especially critical, it is a good idea to shoot the pan at several speeds and pick the best take later. This will benefit the editing as well, allowing the editor to choose the pan that works best with the sequence.

Tables of recommended panning speeds for 35mm cameras were published in *The American Cinematographer Manual* prior to 1980. Conversion of these tables to 16mm would be a useful, though admittedly somewhat tedious, project.

Zooms

There are numerous variations on the zoom. They go in and out, move slow and fast, start slow and speed up, start fast and slow down, change direction, and are combined with pans of all directions and speeds. Depending on the make and model of the lens and the way it is equipped, zooms are accomplished by moving a lever forward and backward, rotating a barrel or ring, turning a crank, or pressing a button. Many cameramen work with one hand on the zoom control at all times, ready to zoom at the slightest provocation. Beginners are often so zoom happy that their rushes show zooms in every shot. But regardless of their overuse, they are here to stay. The cameraman should learn how to make zooms of all kinds smoothly and steadily.

A smooth zoom while holding the camera by hand is a difficult feat, except when an electric zoom motor is used. Electric zoom motors are either an integral part of the camera and lens or are a separate attachment to be bolted-on. Used correctly, they will produce smooth zooms at a variety of speeds. They free the cameraman from the usual forward, backward, or rotational forces that also affect camera steadiness while creating the zoom. Electric zooms operate from a control unit that contains a speed rheostat and "in" and "out" buttons. They are usually battery powered. The control box is often attached to the camera or tripod handle with tape in easy reach of the fingertips.

While the advantages of zoom motors are quite obvious, there are at least two possible disadvantages. First, some models, especially when operated at high speeds for quick zooms, make enough noise to be picked up by nearby microphones. Second, unless the motor is equipped with a simple mechanical override, the cameraman must wait for the motor to zoom in to the longest focal length for focusing and then wait for the motor to zoom back out to the starting shot position. This can be a problem on fast documentary subjects, and sacrifices in zoom steadiness are often made as a result.

But with a tripod, there is really no excuse for unsteady zooms and camera wobble, even when a zoom motor is not used. The cameraman's fingers memorize starting and stopping positions with practice, and he remembers to start the zoom slowly, pick up speed, and then slow to a stop.

Changes in zoom speed during the shot have a distinct effect on the feeling or mood of the shot as well, and when a filmmaker decides to zoom, he should always make this aspect of shot psychology work to

2-63. Cinema Products zoom motor and control. (Harvey "T" Thompson)

his advantage. For example, there is the "discovery zoom" that works like this: a child has been lost in the woods and the script calls for a shot that pans slowly across the edge of the forest and then zooms in on the child's white form as it becomes recognizable in the shot. The purpose of the shot is twofold: to show the audience how difficult it might be to see the child in such a setting, and to show the audience the child's location and condition. The cameraman's job is to plan his zoom and pan so that when the white spot in the long shot is discovered, the zoom moves to a close-up with increasing speed. The cameraman must simulate the way people normally focus in on an object of interest. The zoom should start at the proper moment of discovery and end quickly enough in order to prevent an unnecessary lag in communication time.

Used and photographed with care, each zoom and pan will not only add a feeling of movement but will also support the inherent message of every scene. Shot analysis sometimes leads to the realization that the particular pan or zoom is not needed at all; other times, it becomes clear that the movement is so important that the shot should be made at several speeds so that the audience cannot miss its meaning.

Changes in camera speed

Through cinematography, time can be expanded or compressed to a fantastic degree. Assuming that the projection speed is fixed at a constant rate, changes in the time of the projected film are accomplished by changes in camera running speed.

Slow motion

Camera speeds higher than projection speed create slow motion. Speeds of up to about 400 frames per second (fps) can be attained with slightly modified standard cameras. Speeds of up to about 6,000 frames per second can be attained with instrumentation cameras that are readily available for rent or sale. Special cameras that bear almost no resemblance to ordinary cameras have exposed about 3,000,000 fps. When a scene is shot at 3,000,000 fps and projected at standard sound speed of 24 fps, the motion is slowed by a ratio of about 125,000 to 1, which means that a piece of action only 1/2,000-second long will be projected for a full minute.

But in conventional motion picture production, slow motion effects used with people in action are created with speeds rarely exceeding 150 fps. Most standard production cameras are capable of speeds in that range if certain precautions are taken and the necessary motor is provided.

Many spring-wound and battery-operated cameras can shoot up to about 64 fps with nothing more than the turning of a speed-control knob. But when commercial cameras are used for slow motion photography, they should be lubricated more often than usual—as often as once per roll is recommended for some models; the manufacturer's instructions should be consulted. The camera should be run without film at normal speeds and then at high speed to "warm up" all bearings, moving parts, and the motor.

Cameras without registration pins are particularly susceptible to all sorts of film drift, weave, and flutter when used for slow motion photography. The only preliminary insurance possible is the usual careful threading and cleaned gate. If the photography is of subjects where at least a portion of the shot contains stationary objects or if title superimpositions are planned, image steadiness considerations will be paramount; a registration pin camera such as the Arriflex or Mitchell should be procured for the occasion. But whether or not a particular camera will give acceptable results can be revealed solely by testing.

Speeded-up motion

Speeded-up motion is produced with camera speeds lower than the fixed projection speed. At a standard of 24 fps, this includes everything from 23 fps down to one frame every six months or longer. The term "speeded-up motion" is usually reserved for speeds down to a few frames per second. Lower speeds such as one frame every minute are called *time-lapse photography,* which is discussed in the next section. As with slow motion, the low running speeds needed to produce speeded-up motion can be performed by many battery-powered and spring-wound cameras. Cameras that use AC motors will have to be fitted with a variable-speed motor and a tachometer so that the slow or fast speeds can be produced.

The slightly speeded-up effect of old movies is produced by shooting at 16 fps and projecting at 24 fps. Sixteen fps is called "silent speed" on many projectors, and today is reserved for old silent films or home movies. It seems that 16 fps is about the slowest projection speed that will not produce excessive flutter; slower speeds do not meet the persistence of vision needs of the retina. So films were shot and projected at 16 fps until the advent of sound. Sound reproduction was so poor at 16 fps that 24 fps was adopted for sound motion picture shooting and projection.

Car chase scenes and bits of action that gain excitement with slightly exaggerated speed are often shot at around 18 to 20 fps. With cars the effect is quite convincing, and an even greater difference between shooting and projecting speed can be used. The audience is hardly aware of the speeded-up effect. When such action is being filmed, extra care must be taken with scenes where people's movements are clearly evident, for these will reveal the speeded-up effect as phony. For commedy and the like, which can use more extreme speeded-up effects, 10, 12, or 14 fps may be the answer. A few tests will reveal which speeds best suit the particular action.

With slow running speeds, new exposure calculations will have to be made. Applying the principles stated previously, the adjusted shutter speed can be found quite readily. Slow running speeds mean longer shutter speeds; this can be an advantage with poorly illuminated stationary objects. Shooting at, say, 4 frames per second, a shutter speed of 1/8 second would result. This is equivalent to more than two stops of extra exposure, compared to running at 24 fps, and could be useful for such subjects as evening scenery or building interiors. As long as

Shutter angle	Frames per second									
	2	4	6	8	10	12	14	16	18	20
235°	1/3	1/6	1/9	1/12	1/15	1/18	1/21	1/25	1/27	1/31
180°	1/4	1/8	1/12	1/16	1/20	1/24	1/28	1/32	1/36	1/40
90°	1/8	1/16	1/24	1/32	1/40	1/48	1/56	1/64	1/72	1/80

2-64. Shutter speeds, in seconds, of camera at lower than normal running speeds and with three different shutter angles. Slower than normal running speeds produce speeded-up motion.

there are no moving objects to reveal the changed running speed, successful exposures can be made in what would otherwise be an impossible situation.

The length of the shots must be timed by a multiple equal to the difference in speed, or else by watching the footage counter on the camera. Otherwise the takes will be much shorter than intended. For example, shooting at 8 fps is one-third the normal projection speed of 24 fps; for a 5-second take, the camera must be run for three times that amount, or 15 seconds. Or by watching the footage counter, simply wait for 3 feet (equal to 5 seconds) to run through. While pans and zooms are very difficult to execute at slow running speeds, they may be done successfully if the speeds of the movements are also scaled down proportionately.

Time-lapse photography

Time-lapse photography is responsible for such spectacular footage as a flower budding, blooming, and withering within 45 seconds of screen time, the changing cloud patterns of an entire day compressed into a single minute, the sun setting like a falling basketball, the two-year construction of a high-rise building presented in a few minutes, and a month's tidal flows as ocean waves.

Time-lapse photography is accomplished with stop-motion motors or single-frame camera settings. Stop-motion motors use a special switching system; with the press of a button, only one frame is exposed. These motors are used for animation photography as well as for time lapse. Cameras with a single-frame release will also expose one frame at a time. With either approach time-lapse photography may be accomplished manually by watching a clock and exposing a frame at the intended interval. There are, however, rather elaborate control systems available. They will turn on the lights, expose a frame, and turn off the lights, all in sequence and within a wide range of time cycles. These switching systems are called *intervalometers,* and they can perform a wide variety of scientific work.

The shutter speed needed for exposure with animation or time-lapse photography is not a function of running speed, but depends on the cranking speed of the stop-motion motor or single-frame system. Stop-motion motors have their own running speed, which applies to each frame exposed. They will turn the camera shutter and advance the film at a certain speed regardless of how many frames per hour, minute, or second are exposed. The running speed of the motor being used is usually marked clearly on the case or in the accompanying literature; this speed is divided in the usual way, depending on the camera shutter angle, to arrive at the shutter speed.

With spring-wound and battery-operated cameras that have single-frame releases, the shutter speed is usually the same as it would be when running normally at the running speed at which the camera is set. If a camera is set at a running speed of 24 fps, but the single-frame release is exposing, say, one frame every minute, the camera would still theoretically rotate the shutter and advance the film at 24 fps each time. The shutter speed in this case would be 1/48 second. It is difficult, however, for these cameras to achieve full speed in a one-frame interval; the resulting shutter speed may be slower than that indicated by the camera speed setting. The problem of overcoming inertia in the moving parts is responsible for this discrepancy. Some manufacturer's guide books give a table of measured shutter speeds that can be used for exposure calculations.

There is, however, another solution to the problem. The camera speed may be turned to a low setting, such as 4 or 6 fps. These speeds are well below the camera's inertia difficulties; with single-frame release, a shutter speed accurately corresponding to the running speed setting can be relied upon. For example, if the running speed dial is set at 6 fps and the camera has a 180-degree shutter, the shutter speed would be 1/12 second for each single-frame exposure.

2-65. Intervalometer for controlling camera and lights to produce time-lapse cinematography.

Photography on the move

When dollies are used on exterior locations, either steel tracks or wooden beds must usually be laid to assure a smooth ride. Large cranes, while able to perform trucking shots and sweeping moves with superior stability, are, to say the least, bulky. All this means extra setup time and crew costs. With the inflated prices of large pieces of studio equipment such as dollies and cranes and the ever-rising costs for their operation, filmmakers are constantly devising ways to move the camera with less expense. The camera is moving in more ways and in more places than ever before. With servo motors on the focus, zoom, and on-off controls, cameras are being placed where humans cannot go at all. Video viewfinders allow for remote viewing. Even animals and birds are used as cameramen. The cinematographer functions as engineer, builder, designer, installer, and tester of camera mounts of all descriptions.

Walking the camera

The most economical camera dolly is the cameraman himself. For sheer setup time and crew costs he cannot be beat. Whether a "walking shot" or a "running shot" will be acceptable or not is *usually* determined by the style of the film—in newsgathering or documentary work they are usually perfectly acceptable, but in a slick commercial or theatrical film, the inherent wobble may be very objectionable.

The body brace is useful for walking larger cameras. If the knees are kept slightly bent and the top of the magazine is held to prevent excess wobble, surprisingly good results may ensue. In general, the cameras that rest on your shoulder without a brace give the best results. Walking with the camera is a technique that, like all the other physical feats, requires a certain amount of practice. Hand-holding a front-heavy camera like the Arriflex BL while keeping an eye on the viewfinder leads to excessive bounce and should not be attempted. Increased camera running speed (in nonsync sequences) will help to smooth the bumps

2-66. *Cameraman with Arriflex 16BL on body brace. (Harvey "T" Thompson)*

2-67. *Cameraman running with Beaulieu R-16 camera. (Harvey "T" Thompson)*

and should be used whenever the action will allow for it. Wide-angle lenses are the only possible choice. With longer than normal focal lengths, even keeping the action within the viewfinder becomes a problem.

When it becomes necessary to run with the camera (as happens occasionally in very fast-moving action sequences), the lightest camera available should be selected. The Beaulieu is a good example because the grip is somewhat centered under the balance point. Then try the following approach.

Take the widest lens possible and preset the focus for a given shot. Hold the camera at the subject's eye level and center the subject through the viewfinder. Then, without moving the camera, stand up and examine the position of the camera in relation to the subject. See how the camera must be pointed to keep the subject in the proper place within the frame. Tape the eyepiece to prevent light from fogging the film. With arms as shock absorbers, run while holding the top and bottom of the camera. The camera may bob up and down as a unit, but it must not dip or rotate on any axis. While running, maintain the distance and aim that will keep the subject properly focused and framed. Shooting this way can lead to some very exciting photography, especially when slow motion is also employed.

To lower the camera further, build a simple cradle that has a carrying handle on the top. The Eclair is already thus equipped. With rigs like this, the cameraman merely prefocuses the lens at the working distance, tries his best to aim at the subject, and holds the camera so he does not film his own legs while walking. With wide lenses to minimize camera shake, interesting footage can be obtained.

Photography from wheelchairs, cars, and boats

When floors are smooth, the wheelchair may be one of the most useful pieces of nonstudio equipment available. Its large wheels smooth out small bumps, and the comfortably seated cameraman has every possibility for steady hand-held work. When devices other than dollies are used for dolly shots, the largest wheels are the best. Tripods mounted on mover's dollies do not work too well, for example, because the tiny casters cause too many small shakes.

The automobile is readily available and useful for shooting passing scenery or subjects on the streets or sidewalks. The properly rehearsed cameraman, lightweight camera in his hands, will often produce acceptably steady results from a car. A platform fastened with bolts or straps on the outside of the car eliminates problems with windows and lowers the point of view. The hand-held camera, with the cameraman seated comfortably and bracing the camera with his elbows against his sides, usually gives the best results. Cars or pickup trucks on smooth road surfaces are stable enough for the use of a tripod. A lightweight balanced camera like the Canon Scoopic, is best on bumpy roads; with the viewfinder taped, use your arms to cushion the bumps. As always, increased camera running speed will help smooth out the inevitable camera shake.

2-68. *Cameraman using wheelchair as dolly.* (*Memory House*)

Shooting subjects inside the car from within the car is done with the camera on a plate fitted with suction cups and straps. Mounted on a sturdy hood or door, these grip mounts permit enough stability so that the subjects inside the car can be photographed with satisfactory steadiness. (The mounts can be bought, rented, or fabricated with roof-rack cups. They are frequently used to shoot commercials for tires and other car parts.) A few large strips of tape running across the top of the magazine and attached to the car will reduce camera wobble even further. Mounts of this sort work well because the camera and the subject move and bounce together. They do not work well when the subject is not attached to or riding in the vehicle.

Similar rules apply to photographing on boats. Larger boats are better than smaller boats, and calm weather is worth waiting for, especially when photography is from the boat to a separate subject. A tripod works well for photography of subjects on the same boat, but it is impossible to shoot steady footage of even moderately distant objects from a small boat on a rough day.

Aerial photography

Weather conditions and time of day play a more important role in aerial photography than in any other kind. The slightest haze on the ground looks like a forest fire from the air. Gusty winds have strongly adverse effects on helicopters and fixed-wing aircraft. In most localities there is a great deal more time spent waiting for ideal weather and light conditions than there is in shooting.

The angle of the sun is important. In general, try to plan all air-to-ground photography for mornings and evenings so that the angle of the sun will reveal the textures of the land or buildings. Shots made directly toward earth at midday, particularly during the summer in the northern hemisphere, will be lighted from such a flat angle that the photography will be very flat and disappointing. This problem is minimized when shooting toward the horizon from low altitudes, such as a helicopter-to-car-on-bridge shot where the midday sun is near 90 degrees overhead. Air-to-air shots should be planned so that the sun models the subject in the desired fashion and may work out well at any daylight hour, depending on the desired effect.

The choice of aircraft and camera mount is dependent, more than anything else, on money. The more costly helicopters are capable of maneuvers not possible with fixed-wing aircraft. When people on the ground are involved as subjects, the helicopter is the usual choice, but air-to-air photography of a fast jet plane has to be made from a similar craft. Specially counterbalanced, gyroscopically stabilized and fluid-dampened vibrationless supports, such as the Tyler mount, are the ideal choice for helicopter photography. They reduce the shakes and wobbles—but they are also rendered quite useless on a gusty day. Helicopter mounts require a bit of practice; when budgets permit, it is best to leave specialized photography of this sort to people experienced in the business. There are a few famous pilot and cameraman teams who can be hired when the money is available. Fixed-wing aircraft can, of course, be fitted with stabilized camera mounts for successful aerial photography. The main problems with these setups are their limited maneuverability and the relatively high stall speed, which prevents going slowly for shooting near the ground.

On an ideal windless day even a hand-held camera with wide or normal lenses can give acceptable results. Increased camera speed will reduce the bumpiness; use it whenever possible. When it is time to shoot, select a position in the aircraft where the wind is minimal even if the door has been removed. Sit in a balanced manner; leaning to one side or the other is not steady. The best position is often on the floor, feet hanging out the door. Use safety straps for both personnel and equipment.

In black-and-white photography, yellow, orange, or even red filters

2-69. *Helicopter camera stabilizer provides smooth results even when helicopter rests on railroad dolly as in this shot from* This Property Is Condemned. *(Memory House)*

will help cut through haze and darken the bright sky. For color photography, use a 1A ultraviolet haze filter and be sure to attach the biggest sun shade possible to the lens. Exposures are best calculated with reflected-light meters on air-to-ground work and with incident meters on air-to-air work. Cameras with properly adjusted through-the-lens meters are probably ideal for air-to-ground photography, but they should not be used with fully automatic servo-controlled apertures; if the camera pans up to include some sky, the automatic aperture will overcompensate and the ground exposure will be ruined. Use reflected-light measurement instead, and make the usual allowances for the sky, white sand, water reflections, or dark trees.

The pilot of the plane serves as a key member of the film crew, performing all maneuvers in accordance with the camera's needs. Work out a complete system of hand signals for the cameraman and pilot; cabin noise may make verbal communication impossible. Radios are essential for air-to-air and air-to-ground communications.

Underwater photography

The first prerequisite for underwater work is to be an experienced diver. This means full training and great experience in the use of scuba equipment.

Unlike aerial photography, which takes advantage of angled rays from the sun, underwater photography is best accomplished in midday and as near the equator as possible. When the sun is perpendicular to the water, the greatest illumination reaches the greatest depths. Clear water is preferred because haze caused by suspended particulate matter not only reduces light but also drastically reduces the working distances between photographer and subject. Calm water is also preferred, particularly for surface operations. Warm water temperature is best because it means longer shooting hours. All of these factors are of go—no-go importance.

The camera must be placed inside an underwater blimp or housing. There are several varieties available; they are either pressurized

2-70. Bolex underwater housing with external focus and aperture controls, and stabilizer fins. (Bolex Paillard)

to withstand the underwater pressure or are strong enough to be pressure-resistant. A good blimp has room inside for at least a 400-foot magazine (so the diver-cameraman does not have to go back and forth to the surface to reload) and for camera batteries as well. The housing is fitted with controls that operate through waterproof glands to move the focus, aperture, and on-off switch. There may be lamps to illuminate various camera dials, and there must be windows for viewing all settings and the footage counter. The lens shoots through a glass or plexiglass porthole that must be kept clean, free of scratches, and clear of condensation. Viewfinding is accomplished through reflex systems using special eyepieces or through exterior sports-type viewfinders.

Exposure readings are usually made from reflected light because of the ever present haze factor. The reflected-light meter used from camera position will automatically take the haze into account, whereas an incident-light meter will not. Through-the-lens metering systems are ideal for this kind of shooting, and the fully automatic servo-diaphragm solves virtually all exposure problems. External meters will need to be placed in their own plexiglass housings; these will need to contain visible tables or external controls for the computation dials.

Auxiliary underwater lights are available from the largest equipment sources. There are several quartz models that use battery power as well as high voltage supplied from the surface. But underwater light falls off very quickly. Artificial illumination will provide satisfactory light on a close foreground subject, but the background will usually be much too dark. The sun provides the best overall lighting, but auxiliary lights do provide two important benefits. For one, they restore some of the red color that has been filtered out by the water (discussed further shortly). This can make a difference in the quality of many shots, particularly nature close-ups. These lights also permit shooting in caves and at greater depths where sunlight is unavailable.

The visibility problem affects the choice of lenses in a major way. Objects several yards from the camera become lost in haze, so wide-angle lenses are used to allow the aqua-cameraman to move in close to his subject. Lenses of 9mm or 10mm are the usual choices for 16mm cameras. Since the turrets are usually not operable through the housing, the lens is selected before the dive. Zoom lenses are not often used because of their modest maximum apertures and relatively long focal lengths.

Because water has a different refractive index than air, objects underwater appear to be closer than they actually are. If a straight piece of wood is held so that part extends underwater at an angle, there appears to be a "bend" in the stick; the portion in the water appears to be closer to the surface than it actually is. Underwater cameras must be focused not on the real distance but on the *apparent* distance. Setting the focus scale to the actual distance from lens to subject is wrong! Focus must be either through a reflex finder—which is very hard because of the lack of illumination and the difficulty of getting the eye close enough to the eyepiece in the underwater housing—or with the use of a specially scaled measuring tape. Also, visual approximation works

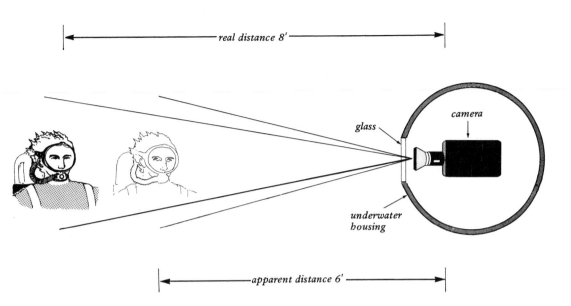

real distance 8'

glass

camera

underwater
housing

apparent distance 6'

2-71. Underwater fo-
cus. An object 8 feet
from the camera appears,
both to the eye and the
camera, to be 6 feet
away. The camera lens
must be set for the ap-
parent distance, which is
three-quarters of the real
distance.

well underwater because the eyes are affected by the different refractive index of the water and also see in terms of apparent rather than real distance. The apparent distance is actually three-quarters of the real distance. Scales may be worked out accordingly, or the real distance may be measured and divided by three-quarters to give the correct focus setting.

Most sea water appears blue or cyan because it has the ability to absorb red light. Ten feet of water can almost eliminate all red from an underwater scene, including the normal flesh tone of actors. Even people with suntans are rendered a sickly green unless at least some of the red is restored through color correction filters. As a rule, about four wratten CC red or magenta filter units are required to completely correct each foot of sea water. But with this heavy amount of filtration, all of the light needed for exposure at 20 or 30 feet begins to filter away, so full color compensation generally is not attempted. CC 30, CC 40, and CC 50 red or magenta filters are recommended for shooting in 15 to 30 feet of water when enough light is available. These filters will not fully correct the scene, but they do help restore flesh tones.

Most underwater equipment is hand held, and most divers prefer housings that are very nearly weightless in water when loaded, although there are strong differences of opinion about matters of one or two pounds in either direction. Strong currents and special locations, however, may require a very heavy tripod to steady the camera. In dangerous locations (e.g., high shark population) weighted housings with television viewfinders and surface-operated on-off switches may be lowered from the support vessel. Peter Gimbel, in his film Blue Water, White Death, used metal cages to protect himself and his cameramen from sharks.

Extreme cold and heat

The arctics and the tropics affect both cameras and film (not to mention cameramen) severely.

In extreme cold, camera bushings and ball bearings lubricated with ordinary oil become stiff and cease to operate. Prior to an arctic or mountain expedition, the cameras must be disassembled and degreased. Oil is replaced with graphite, Molycote, or other dry lubricants that are unaffected by extreme cold. In general, the less precisely made cameras are more likely to operate in extreme cold because of the lower machine tolerances used in their manufacture. Test cameras by leaving them overnight in a freezer (0° to 10° F is valid for testing) and then observing how they operate. They should come up to normal speed almost as quickly as in normal temperatures and should not make any strange noises. Remember that moist fingertips and eyelids will freeze and stick to extremely cold metal, so use gloves and a rubber eye cup.

In extreme cold conditions the film becomes brittle and may break with the bending necessary for threading. Therefore, cameras and magazines with simple threading paths are preferable. Cameras with large-diameter drive sprockets are less likely to snap film than those with tiny rollers. Try to find warm places in which to load and thread because most breaking occurs during this operation. Keep the film warm prior to threading and try to keep some magazines warm as well. During shooting, protect the camera from wind by using insulated covers or barneys; an electric heater barney is the best investment of all. Allow the camera and magazines time to warm up and free themselves from any possible condensation before unloading. Equipment can be placed in airtight plastic bags before being brought in from the cold to prevent excess moisture buildup.

Extreme heat may be accompanied by either very dry or very humid conditions, depending on the locality and time of the year.

Dry conditions mean dust problems. Make certain either compressed air or a large air squeegee is available for blowing out all cameras, magazines, interiors, and parts. A soft camel's hair brush will loosen persistent material on gates and lenses. Lens and body caps should be used at all times when shooting stops. In hot, dry conditions, the sun's heat usually keeps equipment dry enough to eliminate corrosion and mildew, and relubrication may be more of a problem.

Humid conditions mean mold, mildew, and corrosion problems, particularly inside cases and on absorbent materials. During transporting and shipping, empty cameras should be stored in sealed containers with liberal amounts of moisture-absorbing desiccants, such as silica gel. Remember that once silica gel has become saturated with moisture, it is quite useless unless it can be dried out for reuse. During use, cameras should be stored in closed rooms with dehumidifiers, in hot boxes (which are cabinets with a few light bulbs to raise the temperature 10° higher and eliminate most moisture) or aired in the sun regularly.

In warm and especially in humid conditions, the film will be susceptible to emulsion softening, condensation, and water marks. If sufficient moisture is absorbed by the gelatin in the emulsion, it may even peel off or stick to the back of adjacent layers on the roll. To prevent these problems, take the following steps:

Double-tape all film cans before leaving for location with a moisture-proof tape.

Open cans only immediately prior to shooting. It is a bad idea under these weather conditions to have several extra magazines loaded and ready, because the longer film is exposed to the damp atmosphere, the greater the chances of moisture problems.

Unload the film immediately after shooting and double-tape the can again. Ship to the lab as soon as possible.

Shipping containers should be insulated, sealed and contain moisture-absorbing desiccants.

Heat itself is not good for emulsions, but drastic changes in temperature are worse. Always keep magazines out of direct sun. Open air shade during the day is usually ample to avoid cooking the film. In desert conditions, be careful of the nightly drops in temperature.

More fill light is required on locations where few or no clouds are present because relatively little fill light is produced by the sky. Take along several reflectors when strong sunlight is expected. In tropical climates such things as haze, moisture in the air, and smoke from brush fires all diminish contrast. Be prepared with polarizing, ultra-violet, and (for black-and-white) yellow filters.

The selection and procurement of cameras

Unfortunately, the requirements of the script or shooting assignment are not the only factors affecting the decision of what kind of camera to acquire. Cameras are expensive, both to buy and to rent, and so budget restrictions are the most frequent cause of compromise in camera selection.

For example, compare renting an Arriflex S (a reliable location camera) equipped with an Angenieux 12-120 lens and battery with renting a similarly equipped Beaulieu: the Beaulieu runs $100 less per week in the same rental catalog. If the Beaulieu's only disadvantages were a slight tendency toward greater fragility, a little more difficulty in threading, and an undetectably poorer registration, which camera would be the choice? Factors such as prestige, the impression on the client, and the satisfaction of a prima-donna cameraman become important elements in making the decision.

The fact that no single 16mm camera is best for all jobs is usually a strong argument for renting the best camera for each particular job and owning nothing. On the other hand, there are pick-up, delivery, and shipping problems as well as occasional equipment malfunctions with rented equipment. Twenty or 30 weeks of rental fees equal the purchase price of many new cameras, and half that amount can buy good used equipment. As a result, most producers own a skeleton package of cameras, sound, lighting, and editing equipment so that productions of an average nature can be handled with relatively little rental.

Those who seek advice on which particular camera to choose for a given job will receive conflicting opinions from each cameraman and expert consulted. This is because of the wide variety of usual and unusual experiences that have led people to stay with particular pieces of equipment year after year. If a cameraman happened to have a bad day when using a particular new camera, he may regard it as inferior equipment even though his problems were not related to the camera at all. All cameramen have "pet" features that are particularly important to them.

The Camera Dataguide (Appendix 1) lists the approximate sale price and typical rental prices of various pieces of equipment as well as the overall purpose, advantages, and disadvantages of each item. In general, the higher-priced equipment will give the best results; however, specific camera condition, the ability and experience of the camera operator, shooting conditions, film type, and a whole list of special problems can change these advantages and disadvantages around. Some of the inexpensive cameras have been known to run under the worst possible conditions when even the most expensive and precision-made cameras have failed. But to think that a $200 camera is capable of precise optical or professional-quality animation work is foolhardy.

In the final analysis, the particular list of job requirements—portability, sound or silent shooting, power availability, camera weight, length of take, lens availability, size of magazine, time allotted for setup, money, and impressions on the client—will have to be the guides to a selection. A certain amount of trial and error is inevitable.

Cameraman's tools

All experienced cameramen carry a "ditty bag" or a small case of tools with them on every job. In fact, the size of a cameraman's tool bag is a good indication of his experience, as well as his psychological insecurity. There are times when equipment must either be fixed or the shooting session abandoned. The successful filmmaker knows what makes his camera go and what makes it stop. For cleaning, as well as repair, the following items should never be left behind:

Soft lens brush, stiff magazine brush, lens tissue, rubber air squeegee for camera and lens cleaning

Small flashlight for checking and threading purposes

A few wooden toothpicks for poking out emulsion chips, buildups from the gate, and so forth

Small scissors and tweezers for handling gelatin filters and large scissors for cutting cardboard mattes, heavy tape, and the like

At least a 50-foot steel or cloth measuring tape for checking camera-to-subject distances

Marking pens, chalk, pencils, pens, and grease pencils for marking magazines, writing on slates, making notes, filling in reports, writing lab instructions, marking positions on lenses, tripods, floors, dollies

Large, small, and jeweler's screwdrivers for disassembly, adjustment, and assembly of all equipment

Combination, pointy nose, side cutting, and channel lock pliers, and a set of allen wrenches for general assembly and maintenance of equipment

Fine sandpaper and fine steel wool for cleaning eletrical contacts and polishing rusty surfaces

A small black cloth and pieces of opaque paper for blocking light from around the lens and other light-sensitive areas

A tiny camera oil dropper, small jar or tube of petroleum jelly, equipment grease, a can of solvent for petroleum products, and, of course, nose grease (supplied by the cameraman himself)

A small volt ohm meter and a roll of electrical tape for checking available power and making connections

Rolls of camera tape, masking tape, and strong, three-inch-wide gaffer tape to hold everything together

Location camera checklist

The following checklist can be used for packing up to go on location by checking the appropriate boxes. Make photocopies of this list for each location trip and use it both coming and going.

Camera

The camera(s)	( ) 1.	Take-up spools	( ) daylight
	( ) 2.		( ) cores
	( ) 3.	Magazine take-up belts	( )
	( ) 4.	Batteries	( )
Magazines	( ) 200 foot		( ) chargers
	( ) 400 foot	Viewfinders	( )
	( ) 1200 foot		( ) eye cups
Changing bag	( )		( ) periscope
Torque motors	( )		( ) attachments
Camera motors	( ) wild		( ) offsets
	( ) sync	Power supplies	( )
	( ) stop motion		( ) power cables
	( ) crystal		( ) sync cables
	( ) high speed		( ) plug adaptors

Lenses	( ) regular
	( ) 1.
	( ) 2.
	( ) 3.
	( ) 4.
	( ) anamorphic
	( ) prisms
	( ) converters
Zoom lenses	( )
	( ) zoom lens motor
	( ) batteries
	( ) controls
	( ) support braces
Close-up lenses	( ) 1.
	( ) 2.
	( ) diopters
	( ) bellows
	( ) extension tubes
	( ) sunshades
	( )
Matte boxes	( )
Matte cutters	( )
Filters	( ) glass
	( ) gelatin
	( ) color conversion
	( ) color correction
	( ) contrast
	( ) haze
	( ) special purpose
	( ) polarizer
	( ) gauze
Time Lapse	( ) intervalometer
	( ) shutter release
Blimps	( ) sound
	( ) parallax cams
	( ) accessories
	( ) heater barney
	( ) batteries
	( ) sound barney
	( ) underwater housings

Camera supports

Pistol grips	( )
Body braces	( )
Shoulder harness	( )
Tripods	( )
	( ) tripod heads
	( ) mounting screws
	( ) pan handles
	( ) tripod legs—regular
	( ) tripod legs—short
	( ) tripod legs—baby
	( ) hi-hat
Camera adapters	( )
	( ) riser plates
	( ) tilt plates
Suction supports	( )
Triangles	( )
Rubber feet	( )
Tie downs	( )
Stabilizers	( ) gyroscopic
	( ) Dynalens
	( ) power supply
	( ) cables
	( ) Steadicam
Three-wheeled tripod dolly	( )
Crab dolly	( )
	( ) tracks
	( ) steering handles
	( ) air pump
Spider dolly	( )
Porta dolly	( )
Platform dolly	( )
Cranes	( )

Additional accessories

Light meters	( ) reflected
	( ) incident
	( ) color temperature

Director's viewfinder	( )		( ) tungsten
Depth of field tables	( )		( ) high speed
Camera manuals	( )		( ) special
Polaroid camera	( )	Extra film cans	( )
	( ) flash	Extension cords	( )
Still camera	( )	Cables	( )
	( ) film	Cube taps	( )
	( ) flash	The address and	( )
	( ) lenses	directions to the	
Cameraman's tool kit	( ) (listed separately)	location	
Motion picture film	( )	Maps	( )
	( ) daylight	Change for a phone call	( )

chapter 3

Films for motion pictures

The physical, chemical, and photographic properties of film are basics that form the foundation for understanding virtually all aspects of motion picture production.

The physical aspects of film determine the methods by which professionals handle film before, during, and after shooting; during processing and printing; and all through the editing and reproduction process. The chemical aspects determine the capabilities of each film and how the images may be developed, preserved, and reproduced. The photographic properties of film have an overwhelming effect on the decisions of what things can be photographed under what conditions, using which lighting and camera equipment, at what cost, how well the film can be reproduced, and, most important of all, what the end result will look like. The competent filmmaker not only understands the fundamental chemistry and inherent characteristics of film but also makes a point of researching, buying, using, and manipulating all of the latest products of the industry. Although a wide range of products with unprecedented quality and latitude are available to today's cameraman, his knowledge of all the different film types and how to use them can make the difference between achieving new levels of visual excitement or creating photographic disasters.

The composition of film and how it works

Two separate innovations in the 1880s made possible the motion picture process as it is known today. Gelatin, the jellylike substance made from animal bones, feet, and hides, was first tried as a suspension for coating light-sensitive silver compounds onto glass. Then, in 1889, the Eastman Dry Plate Company of Rochester, NY, managed to obtain a patent for celluloid roll film. This was two years after a New Jersey clergyman named Hannibal Goodwin had first applied for a similar patent; he did not complete the patenting process for 11 more years because of a lack of funds.

In 1892, photography was applied to reproducing motion through a series of still photo-

3-1. Edison's 1899 Strip Kinetograph developed at West Orange, New Jersey. (Edison National Historic Site, National Park Service, U.S. Department of Interior)

graphs, and not until 1899 did a strip of perforated film jerk its way through Edison's Strip Kinetograph (believed to be the first motion picture camera). Since that time, there have been no basic changes in the essential ingredients of light-sensitive photographic films.

Cross section of a modern black-and-white film

The *supercoat* on film is a tough coating applied to prevent scratching of the gelatin emulsion during photography, developing, handling, and printing. The all-important light-sensitive *emulsion* layer will be discussed in detail later in this chapter.

The present-day *base* material upon which the emulsion is coated, dried, exposed, developed, and viewed or reproduced, is *cellulose triacetate*, which replaced the highly flammable cellulose nitrate just after the Second World War. It is strong but flexible, not overly susceptible to shrinkage, optically transparent, colorless, and homogeneous. It is also chemically stable, does not melt in warm places, and is unaffected by moisture.

The *subcoat* is a mixture of gelatin and cellulose esters. It is applied to both sides of the base to help prevent curl and to form a proper surface for emulsion adherence.

3-2. Cross section of film.

scratch-resistant supercoat

gelatin emulsion

light-sensitive crystals

adhesive subcoat

cellulose triacetate base

adhesive subcoat

antihalation backing

The *antihalation backing* is a dark-colored dye coating. It prevents light, which has passed through the film, from reflecting off the rear surface of the base or off the camera pressure plate, bouncing back to the emulsion, and causing re-exposure. Some coating usually appears to be dark gray or black and is washed off during the processing of the film.

Emulsion sensitivity and the functions of gelatin

The *emulsion* layer concerns filmmakers the most. It consists of light-sensitive silver halides coated onto the film in a *gelatin* suspension. When struck by light, the silver halides are reduced chemically to grains of metallic silver, thus becoming opaque.

It is easier to understand how the emulsion layer works if the developments that led to film as it is known today are understood as well. Collodion and early gelatin emulsions would have been useless for motion pictures because of the long exposure times required to affect their extremely limited sensitivity.

Sixteen frames per second is about the slowest rate pictures can be presented without noticeable flicker, and this means that about 1/32 second is the longest exposure time possible in normal filming. In the early days of photography this was considered an extremely fast shutter speed. The production of more sensitive films was required for motion picture photography to be possible.

The process that increased a film's sensitivity was discovered in 1878 by Charles Bennett; its principles are still applied today. The light-sensitive properties of silver halides combined with gelatin were already widely known. The silver halides were mixed with gelatin, the gelatin was immediately coated on a support, and the support was dried for use as film. The all-important increase in sensitivity occurred when Bennett left his mixture of silver halides to stand or "ripen" in gelatin for five to seven days at 90 °F. It became clear that the gelatin was far more valuable in photographic emulsions than simply as a carrier of the light-sensitive silver halides.

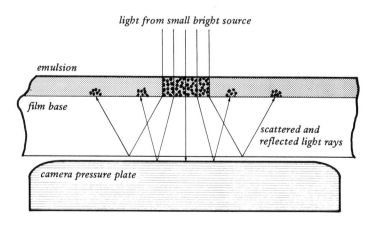

3-3. *Light strikes the emulsion, causing initial exposure (dark specks), and proceeds to scatter and reflect off the rear surface of the film base and pressure plate, causing "halation" or re-exposure.*

The word "gelatin" is derived from the French *gelatine:* a soup made from fish. It is a hard, transparent, tasteless, colloidal protein produced from bones, white connective tissue, and skin of animals. It is soluble in hot water and cools to a jelly but is insoluble in alcohol or chloroform. Edible gelatin, used for food and drugs, is a highly refined product of yellowish tint. Technical gelatin is used in photography, lithography, and in the manufacture of sizing and plastics, among many other things.

In about 1925 it was discovered that minute quantities of sulfur in the gelatin were responsible for the speed (sensitivity) increase that occurred during ripening. The explanation of the exact mechanism of gelatin's ripening effect is still hypothetical, but films of higher speed can be produced with gelatin than with any other coating agent.

Summing up, gelatin is vitally important in the manufacture of today's photographic emulsions for several reasons, some of which are:

Gelatin provides for the increase of speed created by chemical ripening.

It keeps the silver halides in perfect stable suspension during preparation and coating.

It protects the unexposed silver halides from reduction by the reducing agents or developers. (When the halides are exposed and reduced to silver, a negative is made.)

The gelatin, wet or dry, is transparent, allowing the embedded images to be retained on the film, viewed, and projected.

Gelatin can be dissolved in hot water for coating, softened in tepid water for development, and hardened or softened as needed by the addition of chemical agents.

Gelatin allows control of excess ripening through built-in restrainers that prevent oversensitivity and fog. (*Fog* is a detectable opacity— "density"—in the developed film usually caused by age, accidental exposure to light, or exposure to X rays. Gelatin's built-in restrainers prevent fog caused by age.)

Emulsion, grain, and the light-sensitive silver halides

There are three basic silver halides used in photographic emulsions— bromide, chloride, and iodide. Bromide is the most sensitive and used the most. Chloride and iodide are almost always used with bromide. By combining these ingredients in varying amounts, the consequent light and color sensitivity and the grain size of the film can be modified for specific purposes.

Under a high-powered microscope, the small crystals of these silver halides appear in various shapes and sizes. The shape and size of the crystals are responsible for the presence or absence of "grain" in a projected motion picture. Their size is determined during manufacturing by several conditions, including the temperature, concentration, time, and the addition of silver halide solvents. During the mixing and ripening of gelatin and silver halides, a reaction takes place that produces small amounts of silver sulfide and silver. They show up as extremely tiny specks on the surface of the crystals. These "sensitivity specks" are in part responsible for triggering the reduction to silver during development—if they have been struck by light.

The exact effect of light upon these specks and crystals is very elusive—no change in the crystals can be seen after exposure even under the most powerful electron microscope. Scientists claim that as little as two photons of light (one million-billionth of a flashlight bulb for one second) are enough to do the trick. The extra electron is released from a bromide ion, which is then collected by the impurity, or sensitivity speck. The presence of these silver atoms at the speck cause the formation of the invisible "latent image" of the exposed, but undeveloped, negative.

It is very clear that larger crystals with larger specks are much more sensitive to light than small ones. Herein lies one of the fundamental paradoxes that the cameraman faces on every shooting job. The sensitive, or faster, films will render a grainier and often less desirable image, whereas slow films will have very fine grain patterns.

In general, fine-grain low-sensitivity films are made with dilute halides, concentrated gelatin solutions, and low temperatures with slow ripening. The large-grain faster films are made with concentrated halides, less concentrated gelatin, and higher temperature, with longer ripening time.

If ripening continues for too long, the emulsion would eventually be developable into silver without any exposure at all. This is the fog mentioned earlier. Careful dating and storage of film is therefore very important. In general the faster films also have shorter shelf life.

Emulsion, contrast, and relative grain sizes

The *grain size* within a given batch of film is not precisely consistent. There are relatively larger and smaller grains dispersed throughout the surface of the light-sensitive emulsion. If a

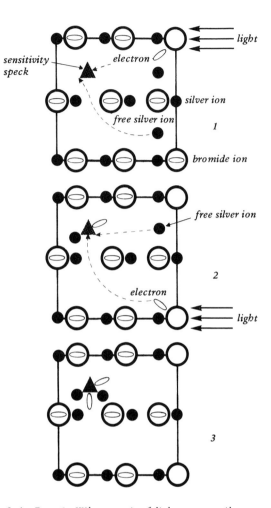

3-4. *Part 1: When a unit of light energy strikes a silver bromide crystal, the light provides energy to the electron, which causes it to roam free. When it reaches a sensitivity speck (impurity), it produces a negative electrical attraction, which pulls a positively charged free silver ion to the speck as well. Part 2: Additional light causes additional electrons to be released and to join with silver ions at the sensitivity speck. These are now atoms of pure silver. Part 3: The presence of silver atoms in the crystal constitute a latent image. The developer will convert the entire crystal to metallic silver, thus, with the help of millions of other crystals, producing density in the developed negative.*

given film receives a given small amount of light, only the larger crystals respond. If the film receives more light, medium-sized crystals respond. With more light still, the smallest crystals respond and become developable. This sequence of action explains the *contrast factor* of various emulsions. If all of the crystals were exactly the same size, a given amount of light would cause the exposure of all the crystals, creating a film with an extremely narrow exposure latitude. If the sizes of the crystals vary widely within an emulsion, the film will respond to a wide variety of amounts of light, thereby having a wide exposure latitude or low contrast.

To summarize, the three major characteristics of any given film are:

Sensitivity or speed

Size of the grain

Contrast

Sensitivity to color

Silver halides have one additional characteristic: sensitivity to various parts of the visible spectrum, or color, of light. If a pure silver bromide emulsion is exposed to different parts of the spectrum, only the blue and the short-wavelength portions of the spectrum will cause exposure. Silver chloride is sensitive to the violet. Silver iodide is sensitive to the blue-green. Given these alternatives, it is obvious that films would be sensitive only to scenes illuminated with light containing blue and to blue objects in a scene. While this would certainly allow photography under daylight conditions (daylight contains a great deal of blue), the rendering of any scene would strongly favor (cause to be light in the gray tones of the photograph) objects containing blue colors.

Suppose an object that is, say, red, and a blue object of about equal tonal value and with equal illumination are photographed. The blue-sensitive film responds with great ease to the blue-colored light from

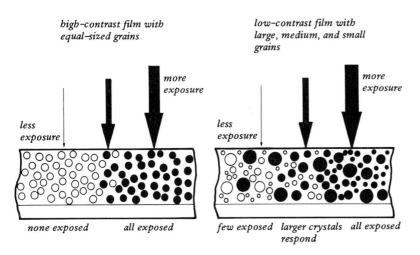

high-contrast film with equal-sized grains

more exposure

less exposure

none exposed   all exposed

low-contrast film with large, medium, and small grains

more exposure

less exposure

few exposed   larger crystals   all exposed
              respond

3-5. Left: where grains are relatively uniform in size, a slight additional exposure causes a sudden response on the part of all crystals. Right: where grain sizes are mixed, large grains respond to small amounts of light, and gradually smaller grains respond to increasing exposure, thus producing a lower-contrast negative.

the blue object and produces a heavy density in the developed negative. Red light, from the red object, has little or no effect on the blue-sensitive emulsion; thus there is little density in the developed negative. When the negative is printed, the light density produces a dark tone, the heavy density produces a light tone. The result: the finished photograph favors the blue colors.

Films that are blue-sensitive (not sensitive to orange and red) are called *orthochromatic*. Photographic paper that can be used in a darkroom with a red safelight—because it is not sensitive to red—is coated with an orthochromatic emulsion. Black-and-white 16mm print films are also orthochromatic.

In 1873, H. W. Vogel discovered that certain dyes mixed into the emulsion would extend its sensitivity to yellow and green. In 1919, further discoveries pushed the color sensitivity into orange and red with cyanine dyes. Today, color sensitivity has been extended all the way into the infrared zone. Films that are sensitive to all colors of the spectrum are called *panchromatic*. Although films with sensitivity to particular areas of the spectrum are available for special purposes today, those made for general photography (both black-and-white and color) are panchromatic.

Development

Developing agents or *reducers* convert the exposed silver halide to metallic silver. To do this properly, the agent must be able to distinguish between exposed and unexposed grains. With different combinations of ingredients, developers are capable of greatly affecting the outcome of the exposed negative. For example, highly active agents will reduce grains that have had relatively little exposure to light. These are sometimes called high-speed developers because they increase the film's effective sensitivity.

Developing agents can also be called low or high contrast because they are, relative to other developers, more or less selective about the size grains they reduce.

The amount of time the film is left in the developer, the amount of agitation the film receives, and the temperature of the solution all affect the outcome of the negative. An increase in any of these three factors causes increased film speed and increased contrast. More action by the developer means more developed grains. If the fog level, which is the minimum background density found in all films (see "sensitometry," later in this chapter), remains constant and the most heavily exposed areas continue to be developed, the contrast will rise. There is a peak level of contrast and speed beyond which the fog level begins to rise and overall density is produced in the negative.

Sometimes the motion picture laboratory will offer "forced development" or "pushing" of the film if required by the cameraman. This is a useful option when light conditions require underexposure. Usually such pushing is restricted to one or two stops of additional speed. The consequently increased contrast and grain result in slight losses of image quality.

There are four commonly used developing agents:

Metol, comparatively low contrast and high speed

Phenidone, low contrast and high speed with a tendency to fog

Hydroquinone, low energy (not as powerful by volume), high contrast, low speed

Paraphenylene and *iamine,* common color-developing agents; low energy, low speed, high contrast

Combinations of these agents can produce greatly successful developers with more than the best characteristic of any agent alone. But the developing solution contains at least three other important ingredients:

The *preservative,* which helps keep the developing agent from becoming exhausted by oxidation.

The *alkali,* which softens the gelatin and acts as an activator for the developing agent. In fact, many developing agents will not work without an alkali. The alkali causes oxidation of the developing agent and therefore is usually stored separately.

The *restrainer,* which retards the overactivity of the developing agent, prevents indiscriminate development of exposed and unexposed grains, and prevents premature exhaustion of the developing agent.

Reversal development

As anyone with experience in still photography knows, the developed negative is of little value for viewing purposes. The brightest areas of the scene are rendered as darkest density on the negative and vice versa. The negatives must be printed (reproduced by re-exposure) on another piece of film or on photographic paper before proper viewing can take place.

Reversal development is an alternative to the basic negative-positive system of photography. It allows for the original camera film to be developed in such a way as to produce a positive image for viewing. The film emulsions designed for reversal processing do not differ greatly from those for negative processing. The difference lies in the processing techniques themselves. Negative film is developed once, while the reversal process has about four stages:

1. *First development:* similar to negative development except that the density is kept low.

2. *Bleaching:* removal of the developed negative image, leaving the unexposed, undeveloped halide on the film.

3. *Reversal exposure:* uniformly and completely exposing the film to light, unless the second developer is equipped with a fogging agent.

4. *Second development:* developing the remaining exposed halide.

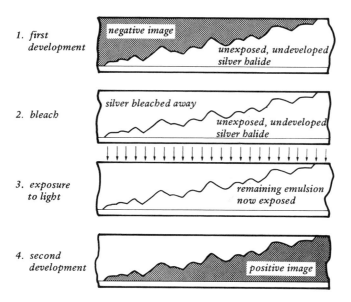

1. first
development

negative image

unexposed, undeveloped
silver halide

2. bleach

silver bleached away

unexposed, undeveloped
silver halide

3. exposure
to light

remaining emulsion
now exposed

4. second
development

positive image

3-6. Reversal process.

The finished reversal film can then be duplicated by printing onto
another piece of reversal film.

Sensitometry—Measuring film's characteristics

Sensitometry is the scientific measurement of the effect of light on photographic materials. It is possible to determine the effect of light and
development on a given emulsion. Considering all the variables in the
chemical makeup and manufacture of emulsions, the range of possible
exposures, including colors and the actions of different combinations
of developing agents, it becomes clear why scientific methods of measurement, evaluation, and data recording are important.

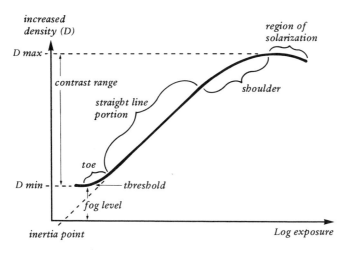

increased
density (D)

region of
solarization

$D\ max$

contrast range

straight line
portion

shoulder

toe

$D\ min$

threshold

fog level

inertia point

Log exposure

3-7. Parts of the char-
acteristic curve.

The sensitivity of the particular emulsion on the film being used is measured through testing, and assigned and maintained at a consistent level by the manufacturers. Development to the proper density is left to the (hopefully) competent laboratory. But the methods used for plotting exposure values and densities of films are of great interest to the cameraman: they can help him predict his results.

In order to show the characteristics of a film emulsion, scientists plot values of density corresponding to values of exposure on a graph. This graph is called the *characteristic curve* because all films plot a somewhat similar curved line on the graph. It is also called the D Log E (Density Logarithm Exposure) or the H and D curve (named after two pioneer researchers, Hurter and Driffield).

Characteristic curves

In figure 3-7 the values of density increase up the scale at the left and the values of exposure increase from left to right (across the bottom). Beginning at the lower left corner of figure 3-7, the features of the curve are as follows:

The fog level: the straight-line portion at the bottom of the density scale where exposure has been insufficient to cause density on the negative. It is essentially the density of the film base and unexposed emulsion.

The threshold: minimum amount of exposure needed to cause a measurable increase in density.

Toe: a curved portion where the film begins to react increasingly to more exposure.

A straight-line portion: where increases in exposure cause directly proportional increases in density.

Shoulder: another curved portion, where increases in exposure have progressively less effect on density.

Region of solarization: where increases in exposure actually prevent development, resulting in a downward curve.

Rating the film's speed
The position of the characteristic curve on the graph in relation to the exposure scale indicates the speed of the film. The problem has always been to provide a simple system of sensitivity values so that photographers can adjust exposure without studying the curves. Over the years at least six different systems have been tried and scrapped. The present system is called ASA/BSI/DIN and is usually referred to simply as the *ASA System* (for American Standards Association). The International Standards Organization (ISO) is currently in the process of consolidating the various systems into one index that will replace, but equal in

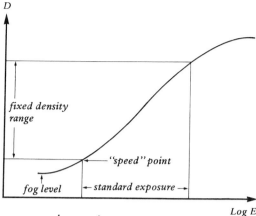

3-8. *The ASA rating system "speed" point is positioned above the fog level when the film is developed to a specified contrast value.*

numeric value, the ASA exposure index. Since the change is in transition and most current guides and equipment (not to mention cinematographers) use the ASA prefix, this book will use that term as well.

Most characteristic curves have a rather sharp curve at the toe (representing the shadow portion of the scene where minimum exposures are beginning to cause measurable densities), but have a rather slow tapering curve at the shoulder. Early speed rating systems gave all their attention to the toe because it seemed to be the most critical area of exposure. But these early systems ignored the contrast range of the film (shown by the steepness of the straight-line portion). It became obvious that the best exposure for a given situation would be one that most closely fit the various bright and dark objects in the scene within the contrast range of the film. Later speed rating systems incorporated the contrast range and were calculated by dividing an increase in density by an equivalent increase in exposure. The mathematical product, the contrast value, was called *gamma*.

The new system uses measurements made when all tested films are developed to the same gamma. An exposure index is then assigned to a fixed amount above the fog level. So, the new system takes into account the contrast range of the film emulsion and the toe (most critical) portion of the curve as well. The section of this book on exposure (chapter 6) examines how the assigned exposure value is used in determining the proper exposure. This chapter compares the characteristic curves of slow and fast films, flat and contrasty (or low- and high-contrast) films, and films with normal and forced development, both negative and reversal.

The curves of slow and fast films in figure 3-9 developed to the same gamma or contrast value. The fast film gives consistently greater density to equivalent amounts of exposure.

Notice that the low-contrast film in figure 3-10 gives small increases in density range to the increases in exposure. The high-contrast emulsion provides little density until exposure reaches a certain point. Then it suddenly gives much greater density to a small increase in exposure, and remains at a high level of density.

Notice that the overall density increases in figure 3-11 and that the upper curves are also steeper, indicating increases in contrast as well.

In figure 3-12, minimal or threshold exposure causes little density on the negative, maximum density on the reversal. Increases in exposure cause increased density in the negative and decreased density in reversal.

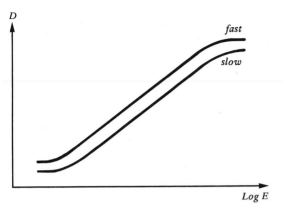

3-9. *Curves of slower and faster film emulsions.*

3-10. *Curves of low and high contrast films.*

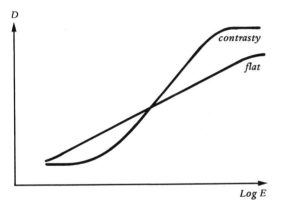

3-11. *Effect of increased development.*

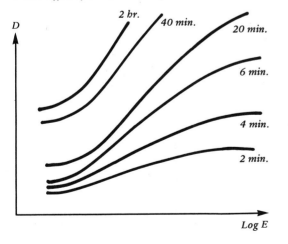

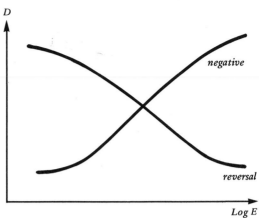

3-12. *Difference of curves for negative and reversal films.*

3-13. *Two different-contrast films with same exposure range.*

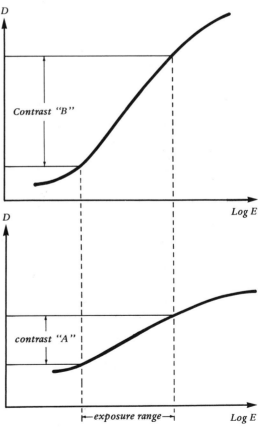

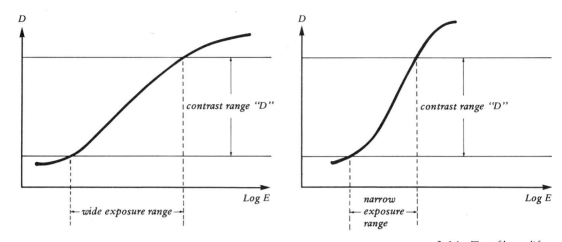

3-14. *Two films, different exposure range but same contrast range.*

Figure 3-13 shows that A, the low-contrast film, renders a narrow density range, while B renders a wide or contrasty density range.

Figure 3-14 shows how two different emulsions, or the same emulsion developed to a higher contrast, will render the same contrast range for two different exposure ranges (or scene contrast). The low-contrast film is on the left and the contrasty film is on the right. The steep curve of the contrasty negative allows for the same tone rendering of a flat scene as the flat negative provides for the contrasty scene.

By examining the curves in figures 3-9, 3-10, 3-11, 3-12, 3-13, and 3-14, it is possible to draw several general conclusions about the way films respond to light and development.

Each film has a different but specifically limited exposure range.

Each film has a different but specifically limited contrast or density range.

Different developing agents, as well as different amounts of development by a given agent, will alter the density reproduced from a given range of exposures.

Films with inherently greater or lesser contrast, as well as the use of different amounts of exposure and development time, can be used to "adjust" the contrast to suit a particular scene.

A particular scene may need to be adjusted to be appropriate to the contrast, speed, and development of a given film.

These conclusions and relationships can all be experienced directly by the still photographer who does his own developing; they are a fundamental part of every day's work. In motion picture production, however, that is not so. The reason is simple. In the majority of productions, there is a need for consistency in the footage shot from day to day, week to week, place to place. Because of this, manufacturers are always finding ways to make their products more uniform. The laboratories also maintain uniform development from day to day and week to week. Considering the frequent need to reshoot a portion of a given scene or to match carefully the color balance, contrast, and exposure of shots that will be cut together in the finished film, it is easy to see why the common ideal is rigid consistency from fresh film to finished print. Since filmmakers do not have the option of manipulating contrast and exposure in manufacture or during development, the characteristics of given curves must be understood and scenes and exposures adjusted accordingly.

Forced development and flashing

Many film labs offer two techniques for modifying the normal film speed and film contrast. The first and most common is called *forced development* or *pushing*. Almost all color, black-and-white, reversal, and negative films respond well to one or two stops of forced development. As may be observed in figure 3-9, increased development gives a boost to overall density, resulting in an increase in film speed.

Under many circumstances, particularly documentary and news cinematography, the available light is simply not adequate; "pushing" is a helpful option. It is accomplished in the lab by either raising the temperature of the developer, increasing development time, or both. Pushing increases contrast, however, and the graininess becomes obvious when films are pushed much more than one stop. It is a good idea to try a one- and two-stop pushing test with the raw stock and intercut the pushed material with normally developed material. The real benefits of pushing can be judged this way, taking into consideration the many other factors affecting its suitability for a given project.

Flashing is another technique that results in a slight gain in film speed but has the major benefit of reducing contrast. Film can be flashed either before or after exposure. It is usually accomplished by running the raw stock through a printing machine and exposing the film to a very small quantity of white light. This produces a certain amount of fog, which helps give much-needed tone to the shadow areas of the image. Flashing is particularly useful with faster reversal color emulsions such as the Ektachrome news films and EF films when they are to be intercut with commercial Ektachrome. When the High Speed Ektachromes are flashed, the resulting fog and reduced contrast produces an original that is more compatible with the notably low-contrast commercial Ektachrome (see Appendix 2, Film Dataguide).

Certain labs offer chemical fogging, which may be combined with forced development to produce images under extraordinarily difficult circumstances. For best results, check with lab managers in your area to get advice on latest techniques and possible results.

Color film

The radiant energy called light occupies only a very narrow band in the electromagnetic spectrum of waves. Within this visible portion are relatively longer and shorter waves that are perceived as different colors—ranging from the deep blue (short wavelength) through the green to the red (long wavelength) end of the color spectrum. When

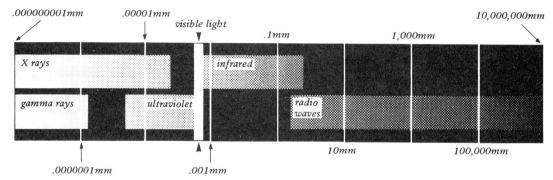

all wavelengths are mixed in nearly equal proportions, the waves are perceived as white light. And if equal portions of red, blue, and green light are superimposed on a white background, the combination will be perceived as white light by the retina.

The retina has nearly 7 million light sensitive elements, divided into rods and cones. The rods are very sensitive to light but cannot distinguish color. The cones are less sensitive to light but can distinguish color. Objects seen in a darkened room will be distinguishable, if barely—but color will not be at all distinguishable. When more light is added, the color begins mysteriously to appear.

There is evidence that the cones are of three types: those with pigment able to receive blue; those able to receive green, and those able to receive red. This three-color theory presumes that vision operates in the same fundamental way that color films work; the films use three different emulsions to distinguish and register these three colors separately.

3-15. The electromagnetic spectrum of waves. While the eye is stimulated by only the very narrow band of wavelengths known as visible light, films can be made to respond to a range of waves that begins with the shortest X rays and extends all the way into the infrared region. It is hard to imagine that light and radio waves are the same, yet the only physical difference is their length.

Additive and subtractive primaries

Since eyes and color films perceive color as combinations of blue, green, and red, and since mixtures of light in these colors can be combined to produce all the colors of the spectrum, they have been named the *additive primaries*.

Paint, ink, dye, and the "colored" pigments of all objects reflect the specific wavelengths that comprise their color. They absorb all other wavelengths. When the eyes (or camera) see colored objects they are seeing light from which wavelengths have been selectively reflected by the object. White surfaces reflect all visible wavelengths; black surfaces reflect none (at least theoretically).

The three-color primary theory can be tested by using colored filters in projectors and showing the combined colored light on a screen, or by putting colored patches on a wheel and spinning the wheel to combine the colored reflected light. When the red and green lights are combined the color yellow is produced, when red and blue are combined magenta is produced, and when blue and green light are combined the color cyan is produced. Cyan, magenta, and yellow are known in photography as the *subtractive primaries*.

When the additive primaries (red, blue, green) are viewed through cyan, magenta, and yellow filters the following can be observed. The cyan filter passes the blue and green, but the red appears as black. Therefore cyan is referred to as minus-red, because it subtracts red from the three additive primaries. The magenta filter will pass red and blue, but this time the green appears black; magenta is therefore minus-green. And the yellow filter passes red and green but blocks the blue; yellow is thus minus-blue.

If the three subtractive primary-colored filters are overlapped on a white light source, the additive primary color common to any two subtractive colors will be transmitted. In other words, where the cyan and yellow filters overlap, their common color of green is transmitted, where yellow and magenta overlap, their common color of red is transmitted, and where magenta and cyan are combined, their common color of blue is transmitted. A similar experiment with the additive primaries produces an entirely different result. Overlapping red, blue and green filters demonstrates that where any two overlap no light is transmitted. The additive primaries transmit only their own color and absorb all others.

The behavior of additive and subtractive primaries shows how these colors will perform when used as dyes or filters on a color film. By understanding the special abilities of these primaries, modern color films can also be understood, because they contain dyes in layers of gelatin. These layers act as filters.

Although the additive primaries were used in several early color film processes, the process using the subtractive primaries was found to offer strong advantages. The reason is obvious. The additive primaries pass only their own wavelengths and absorb all others: any two in combination result in no light transmission. If the film used red, blue, and green as the colored dyes, each pure primary passed only about one-third of the projection light; where the additive primaries overlapped on the film image, little or no light at all was passed. Successful systems required either the use of three projectors—one each for red, blue, and green—that combined colored light on the screen, or mosaic patterns on the film that carefully separated the primaries into tiny dots—resulting in substantially poorer image definition. In the subtractive process two colors may combine as filters, passing their common additive color. Three subtractive colors combine to reproduce black. None are needed to reproduce white.

Composition, development, and printing of color film

Color film, whether developed as a negative or as a positive transparency (through reversal development), has three separate emulsion layers. The only exception is the three-strip Technicolor camera, where a beam-splitter behind the camera lens allows for three separate rolls of film

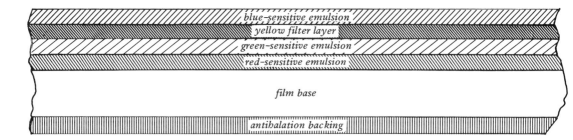

blue-sensitive emulsion

yellow filter layer

green-sensitive emulsion

red-sensitive emulsion

film base

antihalation backing

3-16. The major components of an integral tripack color film.

to be exposed at the same time. But in 16mm and in virtually all other original photographic methods, the three-layer film is used. It is called the *integral tripack.*

The top emulsion layer is sensitive only to blue light. Under this layer is a yellow filter that screens out any remaining blue light (yellow subtracts blue but passes red and green). This is followed by a second emulsion layer that is sensitized to register green light but not red. Since the yellow filter has absorbed all blue light and since the second emulsion is not red-sensitive, this layer provides the green record. The remaining light passes to the third layer, which is panchromatic and red-sensitive but designed to have a low sensitivity to green. This third layer provides the red record.

With these three layers of individually sensitive film functioning correctly, only one problem remains to complete the reproduction cycle. These layers must be converted during development to colored dyes. In the negative (or in the negative stage of the reversal process) this means that the top layer (blue record) must be converted to a yellow dye image, the middle layer (green record) must produce a magenta dye image, and the bottom (red record) must produce a cyan dye image. The yellow filter between the blue and red and green layers must be bleached away.

This process is accomplished by some very elaborate chemistry called *dye coupler development.* There are two ways of doing it. In the first, dyes in special form are incorporated in the color developer. They react as the developing agent oxidizes in converting the silver halide to silver. Dye globules are released from the developer to surround the exposed silver grains with the proper color. An example of this system is the Kodachrome process.

In the second process, the dye couplers are built into the emulsion during manufacture and are already in position to react to the color developer. Then, as in the first process, they surround the exposed silver halide crystal with a globule of properly colored dye. This is the Ektachrome process.

Figure 3-17 shows how the integral tripack reproduces all colors, from exposure through projection, in both the reversal development and the negative/positive system. Colors in the original scene are reproduced by the dyes remaining on the developed and printed integral tripack. The only major alternative to the tripack system is the one used by Technicolor to produce 35mm release prints. It is known as *relief image, dye transfer,* or *dye inhibition.* The process is partially photographic and partially mechanical.

In the Technicolor process the tripack negative is printed onto three strips of black-and-white panchromatic film, each separate printing being done through one of the three additive primary color filters. These three resulting full-length black-and-white prints are developed in a special "tanning" or hardening developer that has the ability to harden the gelatin surrounding the exposed silver halides. After the exposed areas are developed and hardened in this way, the film is washed in hot water, which removes the gelatin from the unexposed areas. This leaves a positive image in relief on the emulsion side of the film. These three black-and-white relief prints, which correspond to the three additive primaries, are called *color matrices.* Each *color matrix* is soaked in the subtractive color dye opposite of the additive primary color through which it was exposed. It is then contact printed to transfer the dye physically to a triacetate film base, which has a gelatin surface to hold the dye. The three matrices are each printed in careful register onto the single release print, producing a three-dye positive transparency for projection.

The advantages of this sytem lie in the fact that the color of each dye used in printing can be controlled to reproduce scenes as faithfully as possible. Since development of the prints is unnecessary, the sytem may be less expensive with large print orders, but it can be used only with 35mm printing.

Color sensitivity and color balance

Human vision has three distinct advantages that the cameraman exposing color film would surely wish that the film had as well. First, the eye has the ability to alter its own sensitivity to light, which allows viewing under extremely wide light variations. To date, color and black-and-white films do not have this ability; the cameraman has a rather limited choice of sensitivities.

Secondly, the retina is capable of reproducing an extremely wide range of brightness or contrast within a given scene. Films, and particularly color films, are not very flexible in this area either, which is why careful contrast control is necessary in cinematography. The ways the cameraman deals with this problem are discussed further in chapters 5 and 6.

The third special advantage of human vision is the ability to compensate for alterations in the color of light. When the eyes have just a moment to adjust, scenes containing white, black, and an assortment of colors appear to be the same indoors or out. People who are more aware of light and color than most will have observed how complexions seem red at sunset and how some colors seem to be enhanced by special

Overleaf

3-17. The reproduction of colors through the use of integral tripack negative and reversal films. Follow the process from top to bottom—negative/positive on left, reversal on right. Notice that light passing through the developed films may be filtered by none, one, two, or all three layers to produce the final results.

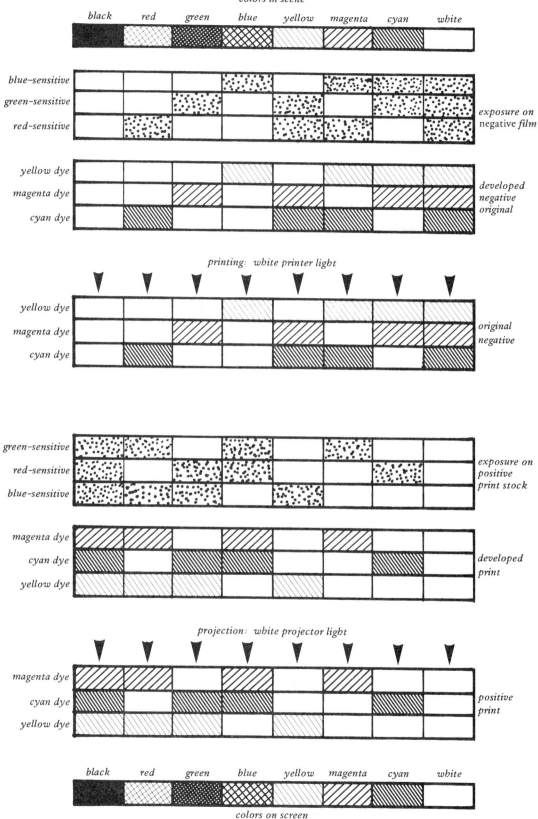

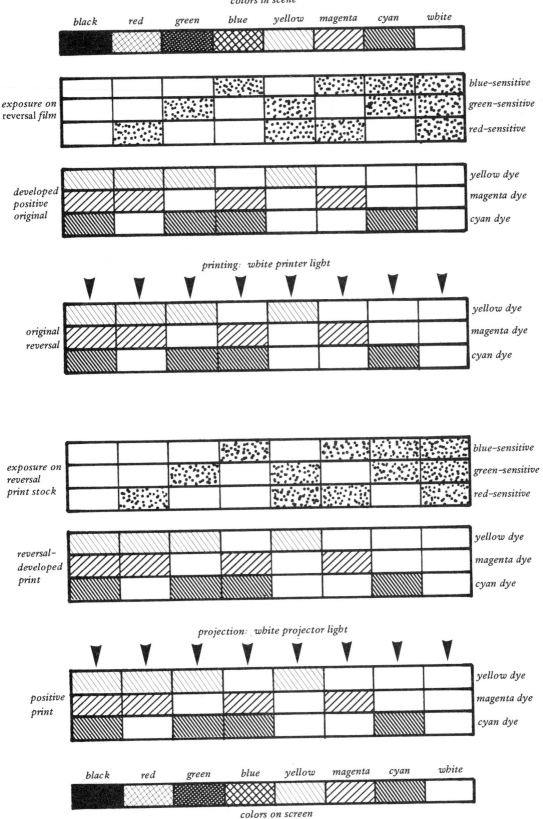

colors in scene

| black | red | green | blue | yellow | magenta | cyan | white |

exposure on reversal film — blue-sensitive, green-sensitive, red-sensitive

developed positive original — yellow dye, magenta dye, cyan dye

printing: white printer light

original reversal — yellow dye, magenta dye, cyan dye

exposure on reversal print stock — blue-sensitive, green-sensitive, red-sensitive

reversal-developed print — yellow dye, magenta dye, cyan dye

projection: white projector light

positive print — yellow dye, magenta dye, cyan dye

| black | red | green | blue | yellow | magenta | cyan | white |

colors on screen

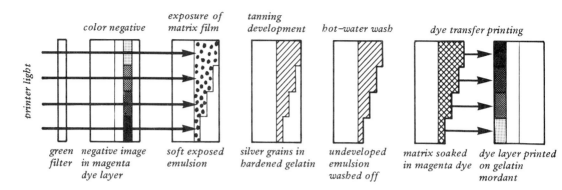

3-18. The basic stages
in the dye inhibition
printing process. The
cyan and yellow layers
are produced in the same
way.

lighting situations. Artists who paint in studios illuminated with tungsten lamps are often surprised by the apparent color shift when the paintings are hung in a gallery illuminated with fluorescent lights or viewed outdoors.

The retina adapts to each situation so well that, in daily life, few people are conscious of the changes in the color of environmental light. Color films, however, do not adapt to changes of light at all. They are absolutely inflexible and reproduce each scene in accordance with the kind of illumination available.

The problem for the cameraman is how to get an accurate or at least pleasing color rendition of a scene on film, and how to maintain consistency of rendition from scene to scene, studio shot to exterior shot, and so on.

Color temperature

The problem of rendering color accurately is solved by measuring the color quality or, as it is properly called, the *color temperature* of the light and then using a film that is balanced for that temperature.

If a color film balanced for the color temperature of daylight is exposed with standard household lamps, it will turn out looking very red-orange. If one balanced for tungsten studio lamps is exposed with daylight, the results will be very bluish. Unfortunately, once the scene is rendered off-color on film, the eyes refuse to adjust and it simply remains off-color to the viewer.

The color temperature of light sources is measured on the Kelvin scale. If a piece of matter, called for measuring purposes a "black body," is heated to increasingly higher temperatures, it will eventually begin to glow; it is emitting radiation in the visible spectrum (e.g., the heating of metal during welding until it glows red). As the temperature of the black body is raised higher and higher it gives off light that is less red and more blue. With the Kelvin system its temperature is calibrated in centigrade, starting with $-273°$ or absolute zero. Its color at various temperatures can be matched to the color of various light sources. Figure 3-19 is a table showing some common light sources and their color temperatures in degrees Kelvin.

Color films for general photography are manufactured to match three different color temperatures of light sources.

Daylight film: color-balanced to 5,400°K for use in daylight where sun and skylight are present.

Type A tungsten: color-balanced to 3,400°K for use with photoflood bulbs. They are generally employed in amateur movie lights. Most amateur films—those produced for original projection and not for duplication—are type A. Kodak Ektachrome SM film Type A is the only common example in 16mm.

Type B tungsten: color-balanced to 3,200°K for use with studio lamps. Most professional films are of this type.

Color conversion filters

With the use of *color conversion filters,* theoretically all films can be used with all types of light. And in fact, conversion filtering is a very common procedure because most production films are balanced at 3,200°K for use with studio lamps. In order to use these emulsions in daylight, a number 85 color conversion filter is required. Specifics about color balance and filtration for each film are given in Appendix 2, Film Dataguide.

Source	°K
Candle, approx.	2,000
Dawn sunlight, approx.	2,000
Domestic tungsten lamps (40–60w)	2,800
Domestic tungsten lamps (100–120w)	2,900
Floodlighting tungsten lamps (500 and 1,000w)	3,000
Warm white fluorescent lamps	3,000
Studio tungsten lamps	3,200
Projector tungsten lamps (500w)	3,200
Tungsten-halogen lamps	3,300
Photoflood tungsten lamps	3,400
White fluorescent lamps	3,500
Carbon arc	4,000–6,000
Cool white fluorescent ("Daylight") lamps	4,300
Carbon arc (projector)	5,000
Midday sunlight, approx.	5,400
Xenon arc (projector)	5,600
Typical average daylight	6,500
Northlight fluorescent ("Artificial Daylight") lamps	6,500
Overcast sky, approx.	6,800
Hazy sky, approx.	8,000
Clear blue sky, approx.	10,000–25,000

3-19. Color temperatures of various light sources.

Color conversion filters are fine, except—like any filter—they reduce the amount of light reaching the film. Most professionals express this reduction as a lower sensitivity rating (exposure index or film speed) when the filter is in place. The exposure reduction is not usually a problem with films balanced for tungsten (3,200°K) and used with a filter in daylight, because there is usually plenty of light available from the sun. However, when a film balanced for daylight is used with tungsten light, the needed filter makes obtaining sufficient exposure all the more difficult. Since all films have extra inherent sensitivity to the blue end of the spectrum, conversion of daylight films to tungsten requires an extra measure of exposure index. For example, Ektachrome Commercial Type 7252, which is balanced for tungsten, is rated at an ASA exposure index of 25. When used in daylight with a #85 conversion filter, the ASA is 16. This is a reduction of almost one stop. But when Ektachrome M.S. film type 7256, which is balanced for daylight, is used in tungsten light with a #80A conversion filter, the daylight ASA of 64 is reduced to 16—two full stops of light are lost. In general, converting tungsten films to daylight is a practical technique, but converting daylight films to tungsten is not.

With a color temperature meter, it is possible to measure a given lighting situation, calculate the difference between the Kelvin temperature shown on the meter and that of the closest manufactured film type, and use a color balancing filter that adds the proper amount of red or blue. But fortunately it is not usually necessary to do this, because the color temperature of most light sources is known and the necessary correction can be made without the need of a color temperature meter.

Filters can also be used directly on light sources and on windows to balance light. These filtering techniques are discussed in chapter 5.

Minor corrections in the color rendition of scenes can also be made by the laboratory. It is important to note that the negative-positive process allows for sufficient correction to accomplish a full conversion from daylight to tungsten, and it is not uncommon for Eastman Color Negative Type 7247 to be exposed in daylight without a filter and then corrected in printing. This practice is not recommended, however, and certainly should not be attempted with reversal films, which have a much smaller margin of correctability.

Choosing the right film

Before buying the film for a production or shooting job, the filmmaker must make several decisions. The first, whether black-and-white or color, or both, would probably be made before many other production questions are answered.

Negative vs. reversal

Another basic question is: negative or reversal? This choice is surprisingly complex because it is partially aesthetic; some people strongly prefer the results from one system or the other. Even successful film-makers with much experience may not be helpful with this problem, because people tend to stay with the first system that brought success. This is why it is important for people in the film business to set aside enough time and money for experimentation.

But to make the decision intelligently it is necessary to understand which particular types are better for reproduction in the quantity and quality needed. Appendix 2 contains a brief description of the obvious characteristics of each film and how it can be reproduced, with comments on the quality of the reproduction.

The choice of negative and reversal stocks in 16mm black-and-white is quite wide, with DuPont, Eastman Kodak, GAF, and Ilford offering about 17 different negative stocks and 10 different reversal emulsions.

In negative, the ASA ratings are as low as 20 and as high as 500 without forcing. In reversal, they range from ASA 40 to 400. If these numbers alone indicate anything, it is that negative films are slightly more versatile.

In terms of image quality, it is only logical that negative films, requiring just one step of development, have an easier role in the reproduction chain. With careful exposure and development control, negative films will generally produce images with lower contrast.

Whenever films are duplicated or printed, there is always an increase of contrast in the print. A camera original of finer grain and lower contrast will yield better-looking results; negative emulsions generally stand the best chance of rendering this. Reversal films, however, are ready for projection on development, and therefore are used widely in the television and industrial film business. There is one other important consideration—that of dirt. When a speck of dust on a negative is printed onto a positive print, it shows up as a white speck, whereas dirt on a reversal original shows up as a black speck. It is impossible to eliminate all dust and dirt, but reversal materials often appear cleaner because black spots are less obtrusive than white ones.

The introduction of two improved color negative films in 16mm, namely Eastman color negative Type 7247 and high-speed negative Type 7293, have caused a major shift away from the widespread use of reversal films. The capabilities of 7247 and 7293 are often compared with Ektachrome Type 7252, the most widely used professional reversal color film. When a producer is trying to make a negative-reversal decision, these are the emulsions that dominate the discussions because of their availability, lab acceptance, and obtainable results. Here is how they compare.

ECO (the manufacturer's code letters for 7252) is balanced for tungsten and has an ASA of only 25. ECN is rated at 100, two full stops faster. ECH has an exposure index of 250. Thus the negative films offer the greater speed. As to contrast, when prints from the original are compared, the two types have about equal tone renditions in the shadow areas but the negative films have possibly two stops or more of printable latitude in the highlight areas. The graininess of the negative and reversal films is about equal. When it comes to possible color correction at the lab, which reduces the need for color balancing filters in scenes with known color shifts, the negative films have the advantage by a wide margin. Overall exposure error is also considerably more correctable with negative.

ECO originally had a major advantage as a production medium because of the very good internegative system of obtaining multiple release prints. The internegatives are relatively inexpensive, and the color rendition and contrast on prints made from them easily rivals prints directly from the original. But as labs gain more experience with the color reversal internegative, or CRI, color negatives will produce release prints of equal or even superior quality to the reversal/internegative system. The CRI, however, is expensive and difficult to produce both in terms of color development and cleanliness. But it should be mentioned that these problems are on the decline as more labs accept and gain experience with these materials.

ECO, ECN, and ECH can be pushed or force-developed for as much as a two- or three-stop increase in speed. Some labs, by using light or chemical flashing techniques and forced development, have produced even greater speed increases with 7247 and 7293, however, and some truly incredible available light cinematography has resulted.

Speed vs. grain

Film speed and its accompanying graininess are also topics of much discussion. Some professionals will insist that any noticeable grain is a fault and therefore the slowest and finest grain films must always be used—even when it means extremely cumbersome lighting equipment and heavy power requirements. Others will argue that the only essential thing is to capture the images, and proceed with fast film and as little auxiliary lighting as possible. In any case, the most important ability to know is how to get the results you desire. Faster films, all things being equal, will render images with more obvious grain patterns than slower films, and faster films are characteristically higher in contrast as well.

Factors contributing to graininess
In addition to the grain characteristics of particular emulsions, other factors have a considerable effect on the print's visible graininess.

The more the original is developed or forced in processing, the greater the graininess.

The greater the overall density of the print, whether from negative or reversal original, the greater the grain. It is important to avoid underexposing negatives and overexposing reversal originals.

The graininess seems more apparent when there are large areas of uniform density in the picture. This is especially true when these values are darkish middle tones (gray, tan, light orange, light blue). Pictures of bright, small, bold shapes and colors are the least likely to show graininess.

The amount of enlargement during projection is an important consideration. There is a great deal of difference between the size of a television screen and a movie screen. Whereas a relatively grainy image will look perfectly acceptable on television, it may appear very grainy on a large screen. Visible graininess increases in almost direct proportion to the amount of magnification used.

Intercutting fine- and coarse-grain films in a single production adds to the awareness of the presence of grain. Again the eye tends to be forgiving—until a sharper image suddenly appears. Cutting from a fine-grained image to a coarse one almost invariably brings a groan and a "What happened there?" response from someone in the screening room.

All of these factors must be considered when the choice of a film emulsion for a production and the various sequences within it is being made. The film can determine lighting costs, lens and personnel requirements, and other factors that strongly affect production feasibility.

After considering all of the possibilities, the filmmaker will probably use the finest grain film he can afford, considering the cost of lights, power, and extra crew, and use the coarsest grain film he can get away with, considering the size of projection, fears of the client, and his ability to control quality all along the line.

Raw stock formats and packaging

Single or double perforation

Single or *double perforation* (or *perf*) will be decided by the type of camera being used and whether single-system sound is being recorded. Cameras with double pull-down claws or double registration pins must be loaded with double perf film, or serious problems will occur as the camera creates new perforations. Double perf film can be run through all 16mm cameras and is always safe to order, except when magnetic or optical single-system sound is being recorded (see chapter 1). Single perf film has room for the single-system sound track on the nonperforated edge. Most film types are available from the manufacturer in a magnetic striped version.

Laboratories often express some preference for double perf original film, even though all of the printing and processing equipment handles single perf film as well. The reason for this is twofold. First, if a row or section of perforations becomes damaged along one edge, the film can be rerolled and printed in the other direction. Thus, the double set of perfs give extra protection. Second, producers are sometimes careless about intercutting short portions of single perf film into rolls with double perf leaders at the ends. When unwitting lab personnel thread the roll on a piece of machinery and the single perf section comes along, strange noises and small film chips emerge from the machine. *When single perf film is used anywhere within a given roll, single perf head and tail leaders must also be used.*

"A" wind and "B" wind

Single perf films are supplied in *"A"* and *"B" wind* depending on their use. All camera films in single perf are supplied in winding "B," certain

3-20. Rolls of film are wound emulsion-in. Left roll is "B" wind, right roll is "A" wind.

print and duplication films are supplied in winding "A," and double perf camera films are either "A" or "B" wind.

Notice that the "B" wind roll is wound emulsion side in (correct for cameras) and that the perforations are along the rear or far edge. In the cameras, the sprocket teeth and the claw are also on the rear or far side of the gate and sprocket. The "A" wind roll has the perfs along the front or near edge and obviously would not "thread up" properly. After double perf camera film is exposed and developed, it becomes "B" wind, because the image itself must be printed correctly in terms of right to left. Beginners are always confused by this little problem, with good reason. For example, if a piece of unexposed single perf "B" wind film was rewound once, it would appear to be "A" wind, and vice versa. To avoid confusion, just remember that camera films and exposed original film are always winding "B."

3-21. Daylight loading spools for 100, 200, and 400 feet.

Perforation and pitch

Films are manufactured in *long pitch* and *short pitch,* depending on whether they are intended for direct projection or for duplication. When a piece of film is printed in most laboratory printing machines, the original and the print stock pass over a curved drum for exposure while being sandwiched together emulsion to emulsion. Because of the thickness of the films themselves, the print stock (which is on the outside of the two as they pass over the drum) must be slightly longer between perforations to prevent slippage between the two as it travels ever so slightly further. Choosing between available pitch options is not a problem for everyday production, but cinematographers involved with exacting optical matte photography (as in *Star Wars*) must be very concerned with the proper choice of pitch throughout the original photography and all the many duplication stages.

3-22. Two-inch type "T" core and three-inch type "Z" core.

Spools and cores

Depending on the camera or magazine being used, film will be purchased on *daylight loading spools* or *cores*. The spools, which hold 100, 200, and 400 feet, are made of flat-black finished aluminum. They are designed to fit the width of the film rather closely, so that they

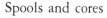

can be removed from their cans and loaded into cameras in subdued light without exposing more than the outer few wraps on the roll. The 100-foot size is most common because it fits within the body of many 16mm cameras and allows the cameraman to load and unload (when another daylight spool is used for take-up) without the use of a darkroom or changing bag. Care must be taken to prevent any direct bright light from falling on the edges of the spools, as it will cause edge flare.

Rolls of 400 feet and longer loads for most magazines are commonly supplied on cores. The smaller core has an outside diameter of two inches and is called a type "T" core. It is supplied with rolls of 400 feet or less. The larger core has an outside diameter of three inches and is called a type "Z" core. It is supplied with rolls of more than 400 feet. These plastic centers on which the film is wound are useful, but a few cautions must be mentioned.

Unlike daylight loading spools, cores offer no protection to the film from light; therefore film supplied on cores must be handled in complete darkness. This means taking a changing bag (chapter 2) along on location or loading and unloading magazines in a darkroom ("loading room," "hot box"). Since the film is wound on itself, there is always the danger of the center falling out of the roll. When this happens in the dark it is nearly impossible to remedy the situation without damaging the roll in some way. Many cameras do not have very powerful torque motors to take up the film in the magazine, and the exposed roll may be particularly "loose." The entire roll must be supported evenly with the hand during unloading, so that the core coming away from the hub of the magazine will be felt immediately. Again, be careful!

Magnetic striped film

Striped films are those on which a strip of iron oxide for magnetic recording is applied to the nonperforated edge of the film, on the base side. There is also a narrower "balance" stripe applied at the perforation edge so that even thickness will be maintained. Striped films can

3-23. *Roll center dropout.*

3-24. *Emulsion (left) and base (right) sides of magnetic striped film. Stripe is applied to base side.*

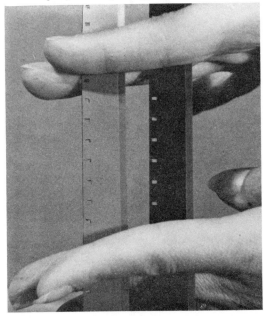

be used in any camera with single pulldown claw and single registration pin, but are intended for use with cameras equipped with a magnetic recording head used in single-system sound recording.

Buying and storing film

Buying professional motion picture film is not simply a matter of running down to the local drugstore and grabbing a few rolls. In fact, in all but the largest cities in the United States and the world at large, purchasing a roll of professional 16mm film may be completely impossible, even at the best-stocked camera stores. And just try to get a roll in New York or Hollywood on a Sunday afternoon!

The professional camera supply houses that do sell film usually have only limited stock, and that of only the most common emulsions. They add a considerable markup on price too, so they are generally relied upon for supplying the few extra rolls needed on very short notice, as when overshooting has exhausted the supply on hand.

There are at least five reasons why most professional cameramen, production companies, optical houses, animation studios, laboratories, TV stations, and other major film users buy their film directly from the supplier or manufacturer.

First is freshness. Film, and particularly color film, must be stored carefully and used quickly if color rendition is to be consistent and exposure indices relied upon. This is not only a problem for the cinematographer but also for the labs and optical studios.

Ordering all of the film required for a production and then storing it in the same manner throughout the production eliminates this variable. Most manufacturers recommend storing black-and-white film at a temperature of 55°F for no longer than six months and storing color film at a temperature of 50°F for no longer than six months. For long-term storage (six months to a few years) temperatures as low as 0° to −10°F (−18° to −23°C) are recommended. When removed from cold storage, the film must be left in its sealed containers until it reaches the temperature of the room in which it is to be opened. It is best to spread the box or cans out on a table and leave them for several hours until they reach room temperature. If the film is loaded cold, moisture may condense on the film and all kinds of trouble can begin. Old, improperly stored, or outdated film is still useful for tests, experiments, and might even be useful for an isolated shooting job when it has been checked by testing and approved.

Exposed film should be removed from the magazine or camera, be put back in its bag and can, and the can retaped as soon as possible after shooting. It should be processed as soon as possible after exposure, particularly when the humidity is high. Care should be taken to keep all packages, magazines, and film cartons out of direct sunlight, away from heaters and radiators, out of closed cars and trunks. Exposed or unexposed film can be adversely affected by temperatures above 75°F (24°C) and more than 60 percent humidity after several days.

A second reason for ordering film directly from the manufacturer is so that all the film used in a production will come from the same emulsion batch. Only certain quantities of emulsion can be mixed at any given time. Each batch is then tested before it is approved for sale. All of the film produced from a given batch is assigned what is called the *emulsion number,* which is stamped on the label and package. It is a very good idea to use film of the same emulsion number throughout a production. When ordering from the manufacturer, specify that all rolls be from the identical emulsion batch. Slight variations in color rendition due to different emulsion batches can be corrected by the laboratory, but it is just one more variable best eliminated when possible.

A third reason for buying direct is that it is the only way some types of film can be obtained in the needed volume. This is more of a potential problem for labs and busy studios than for independent filmmakers, however.

A fourth reason is that only by buying direct can many less frequently ordered types of film be obtained. In 16mm, there are many differences in the way even the most common emulsions are supplied, making certain combinations difficult to obtain anywhere. All of the duplicating and sound track emulsions are bought directly from the manufacturer by the labs and other users.

Finally, buying direct eliminates the price markup added by retail houses, and some manufacturers even give a small discount for payment in cash. Ordering by mail requires an account with the manufacturer or cash payment.

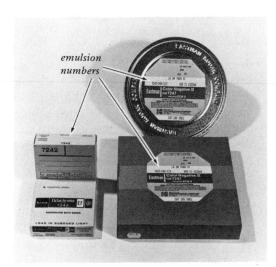

3-25. *Location of emulsion numbers on Kodak cans and boxes.*

Ordering raw stock

When ordering raw stock by mail or over the phone, supply the following information:

The number of rolls

The width of the film (16mm, 35mm)

Length of the roll (standard lengths for 16mm camera films are 100, 200, 400, and 1,200 feet)

Name of the film

Type number

Perforation and pitch: single or double perforation; short pitch will be assumed unless you are ordering for high speed cameras or direct projection, in which case 2R-3000 would be specified. This number means double perf and .3000 inches between perfs. For special orders of this type, check the manufacturer's specification sheets for the stock number

"A" wind or "B" wind. If single perf for camera use, "B" wind will be assumed

Core or spool type (1,200-foot loads are available only on the type Z, three-inch od cores)

Specify magnetic stripe, when needed.

A typical order would be: 12 rolls, 16mm, 400 feet, Ektachrome Commercial, Type 7252, single perf, short pitch, "B" wind, on type T cores. Suppliers other than Eastman Kodak supply similar-length rolls on similar spools and cores, but call their spools and cores by a variety of names, so again it is always best to check the manufacturer's specification sheet before ordering. Of course, terms like "daylight loading spools" and "two-inch cores" are universally understood. When ordering Eastman films, catalogue numbers are available for all combinations of type, size, length, pitch, and so forth, and this useful piece of information can be obtained from Appendix 2.

The hazards of travel

With the use of x-ray equipment and metal detectors at airports and because of the various shipments of radioactive materials for medical use, there is always the danger of films getting fogged in transit. These problems seem to be greatest in international shipping. For this reason, cameramen often carry their exposed but undeveloped footage with them personally when traveling.

When getting on and off airplanes and going through customs, tell the various agents that you are carrying film, show them the case, and tell them not to x-ray it. When shipping, always attach a large label that says "Photographic film—Keep away from radioactive materials—Do not x-ray." Use the most reliable shipping agency you can find. Always leave instructions about who should be notified of the package's arrival as well as his phone number.

Characterístics

Today, almost everyone has seen, if not handled, a typical modern photographic lens. The lens is made of coated glass elements set in a metal barrel, with iris diaphragm and focusing controls provided. The rear of the barrel is designed to attach to particular cameras, and the front is threaded to receive filters, sunshades, and so on. This chapter concentrates on the optical principles that apply to everyday filmmaking.

There are two primary optical characteristics of a photographic lens: *focal length* and *aperture*.

Focal length

Focal length is defined as the distance between the optical center of the lens and the film, or focal plane, when the lens is focused at infinity. In order to understand this definition, *optical center* first needs to be defined.

Every lens used for photographic purposes is a *positive* combination of elements. *Elements* are made up of the single lenses, or cemented groups of single lenses, that make up a total "lens." The combination of these elements has an overall positive optical effect. An image, represented by light rays approaching the front of the lens in parallel lines, will pass through the lens and converge at a point somewhere behind it. This is where the image comes into *focus,* and it is called the *focal plane.* (In a "negative" lens the light rays do not converge on a point but spread out, never coming together into focus. A positive lens always brings an image into focus. Negative lens elements are used in combination with positive lens elements to produce the complete photographic lens; the overall effect, however, must be positive for the lens to function.) The theoretical point within the lens at which the parallel rays of light begin to converge is known as the *optical center* of the lens. The distance between the optical center and the focal plane when that lens is focused at infinity (i.e., when the rays of light approaching the lens are parallel) is the *focal length.*

chapter 4

Lenses

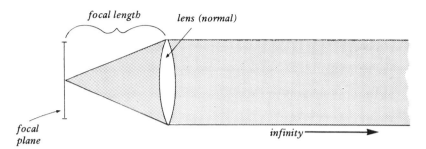

4-1. *Focal length— normal lens.*

A strongly positive lens will make the rays of light converge at a wide angle very close to the lens itself; such a lens is called a *short-focal-length* or *wide-angle lens*. A lens of a lower positive value makes the light rays converge at a very narrow angle or at a great distance behind it is a *long-focal-length lens* or *telephoto lens*.

The characteristic of focal length is built into the lens and is very much part of the way the lens is designed, ground, and put together. The important concept is what focal length means to the magnification of the image. The object in view is magnified to a relatively large image size with a long-focal-length lens and is proportionately reduced with a short-focal-length lens.

Normal lenses
The eye has a focal length of about one inch. That means the distance between the optical center of the eye's lens and the retina is about one inch. The focal length of the human eye is directly related to the diameter of the eye itself. The same is essentially true of a camera. All cameras have a "normal" lens that seems to represent a scene on the

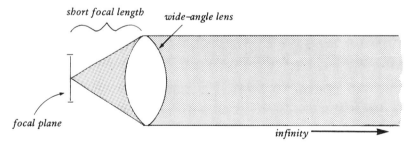

4-2. *Focal length— wide-angle lens.*

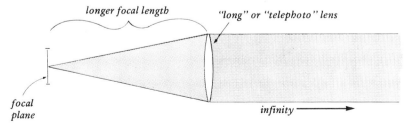

4-3. *Focal length—long lens.*

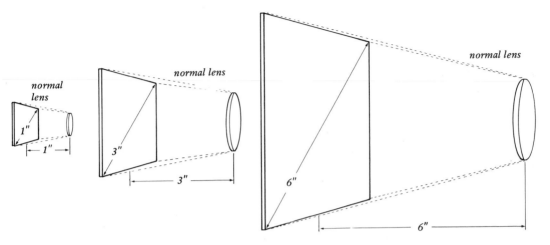

4-4. *Normal focal length for a given format.*

film as it would appear to the eye. The normal lens for a film format is determined by this rule: the *focal length is equal to the diagonal of the film plane.* In other words, given the size of the camera's focal plane or film aperture plate, the distance from one corner to the other will be approximately equal to the focal length of the normal lens for that camera.

In still photography this rule is closely adhered to; the normal lens on, say, a 4 × 5 view camera will give about the same field of view as the normal lens on a 35mm still camera. (*Field of view* properly refers to the width and/or height of a scene covered by a given lens at a specified distance, and with a particular camera aperture. *Angle of view* refers to the angle of acceptance of the lens.)

In motion picture photography, it has become the standard to call slightly "long" lenses "normal." The reason for this difference has to do with the perspective in the still photograph as compared with a projected motion picture. If a still photograph is enlarged to, say, an 8 × 10 print, the usual viewing distance is arm's length, or about 25 inches. To view a 14 × 20 inch print, four feet is supposedly the comfortable distance. If the full negative was printed, the perspective in the print at these distances would indeed appear to be the same as the perspective in the original scene. If the print is viewed from a greater distance, however, the perspective seems slightly exaggerated. This is the effect usually obtained with a wide-angle lens (see "Extension and Compression," later in this chapter.) Conversely, if the print is viewed from very close to its surface, the perspective seems slightly reduced, the effect usually obtained with a long-focal-length lens. Because of screen size in the typical movie theater, most of the audience views the image from a greater than normal viewing distance for the size of the picture. To compensate, the moviemaker uses as his lens one that is slightly longer than the diagonal of the film plane. In this way he maintains a basis for projecting with "normal" perspective. Theoretically, a normal lens for a 16mm camera would be about 12

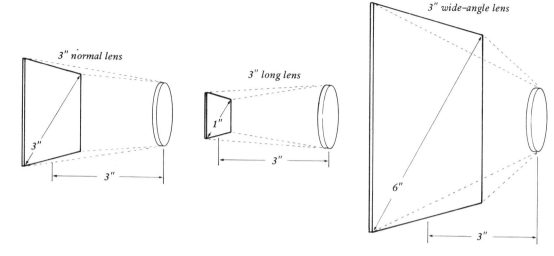

4-5. *Same focal length, different formats.*

to 15mm. But the working normal lens is 20 to 25mm. A 35mm motion picture camera's normal lens is theoretically about 25 to 30mm, but in practice the normal lens is 40 to 50mm.

It is important to understand that a normal lens for one camera might be a wide-angle lens for another, if the second camera had a larger film format than the camera for which the lens was considered normal. The converse is also true.

Although positive photographic lenses are theoretically interchangeable, in practice it often does not work out that way. If the 25mm normal lens from a 16mm camera were put on, say, a 35mm still camera, it would obviously be an extremely wide-angle lens for that camera. However, the image would appear on the film plane as only a small circle. The 25mm cine lens of usual design cannot begin to cover such a large format. Conversely, a six-inch lens that is normal for the 4 × 5 view camera would be, if placed on a 16mm camera, a very long-focal-length lens for that format. In this case, because the six-inch lens was designed to cover the entire surface of the 4 × 5 negative, it certainly would be able to cover the 16mm film format. This change of lenses might work satisfactorily if the necessary adapters to accomplish the switch physically could be found. The important fact to understand is that what is a normal lens for one format will be a wide-angle lens for a larger format and a long-focal-length or telephoto lens for a smaller format.

Long-focal-length lenses

The term "telephoto lens" is often used incorrectly. Not all long-focal-length lenses are telephoto lenses. However, telephoto lenses and long-focal-length lenses can be of the same focal length and give the same image magnification. A "long lens" is a simple lens of long focal length—a combination of relatively few optical elements that causes convergence of the light rays at a great distance behind the lens' optical

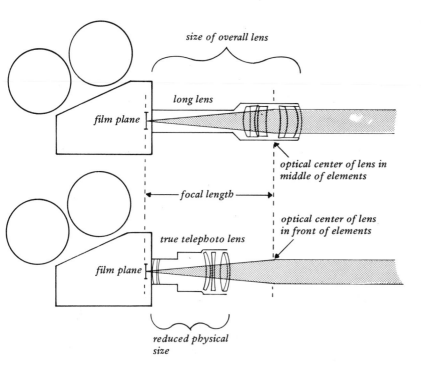

size of overall lens

long lens

film plane

optical center of lens in
middle of elements

focal length

optical center of lens
in front of elements

true telephoto lens

film plane

reduced physical
size

4-6. *The difference be-
tween long focal length
and true telephoto lenses.*

center. But the true telephoto lens is a special combination of elements
that works together to play optical tricks.

These lenses are usually an arrangement of a very strong negative
combination of elements placed behind a relatively strong positive
combination of elements. The optical center of the true telephoto lens
is actually out in front of the lens itself. For example, in a seven-inch
long-focal-length lens, the lens elements will have to be located physically seven inches away from the film. The optical elements of a true
telephoto lens with a seven-inch focal length may have to be placed
only three inches from the film because its optical center is four inches
in front of the lens itself. The benefit of a true telephoto over the
"long" lens is that the comparable telephoto is smaller, shorter, lighter
in weight, and easier to handle.

Short-focal-length lenses

The "inverted telephoto" lens is the opposite of the telephoto. The
strong negative element is at the front of the lens, which moves the
optical center of the lens to a point behind the lens itself. This allows
for extreme wide-angle lens designs that still allow space behind the
lens for the shutter, the reflex mirror, and other parts.

In fact, if it were not for the many components between the lens
and the film gate in modern cameras, simple short-focal-length lenses
could be used as wide-angle lenses, as discussed earlier. In still photography, view cameras and other cameras with a simple "box" design
utilize ordinary short-focal-length lenses for wide-angle purposes.

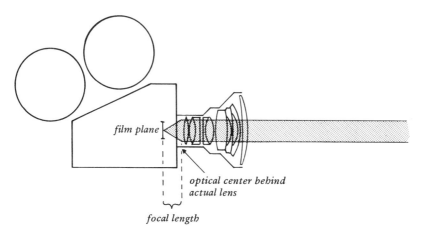

film plane

optical center behind
actual lens

focal length

4-7. The "inverted tele-
photo" type of wide-
angle lens.

Aperture

The second primary characteristic of a lens is its maximum aperture. The *aperture* in photographic lenses is actually a set of leaves, often called the *diaphragm* or *iris,* that enlarge or reduce the pathway of light through the lens. The aperture is the lens' light valve and is controlled from outside the lens barrel or casing by turning a dial or *aperture ring.* The widest or most open aperture of the lens is usually about equal to the diameter of the smallest element of the lens itself. At the widest aperture most lenses utilize the entire area of the lens elements. When the lens is stopped down, light passes through only the center portions of the lens.

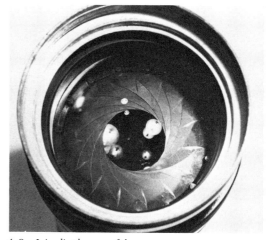

4-8. Iris diaphragm of lens.

F-stops

The aperture control ring on all photographic lenses is inscribed with a series of reference numbers called *f-numbers* or *f-stops.* The lowest f-number on the aperture ring corresponds to the largest opening of the diaphragm and is used to describe the lens' maximum speed. The other f-numbers correspond to various "stops" along the way to the lens' smallest opening.

When a lens is described, its maximum opening is used as one of its primary characteristics. Thus a lens would be called "a one-inch, f/2.5 lens." The "one inch" refers to the focal length and the "f/2.5" to its widest possible aperture setting. This combination of terms is always used when describing lenses.

Any given f-number may be derived by dividing the focal length of the lens by the diameter of the diaphragm opening. For example, if a lens has a focal length of two inches and the actual diameter of the diaphragm at a given setting is one-half inch, the f number would be 4. The most commonly used series of f-stop numbers inscribed on all photographic lenses is f/1.4, f/2, f/2.8, f/4, f/5.6, f/8, f/11, f/16, f/22, f/32. By trying a few of the division problems, it will be easy to see why the higher numbers represent small openings and the low numbers represent large openings.

A further explanation of why these particular numbers are used can be found in chapter 6. But it is very important to understand the relationship between them. The light-passing ability of a lens depends mathematically not on the diameter but on the area of the diaphragm opening. The familiar formula for determining the area of a circle is: πr^2. If the actual diameter of a lens aperture is determined and its area calculated with this formula, and then the same is done at the next f-stop setting, it will be found that the net area either halves or doubles from stop to stop. That means that every time the aperture ring is moved to the next number the amount of light is either halved or doubled, depending on which way the ring is moved. When the camera is "stopped down," changing one f-stop gives one-half the light, changing two f-stops gives one-quarter the light, changing three f-stops gives one-eighth the light, and so forth. When the lens is "opened up," changing the setting by one f-stop gives twice the light, two stops gives four times the light, three stops gives eight times the light, and so on.

It is important to remember this relationship, because changes in film sensitivity rating, filter factors, and camera running speeds are all easily calculated in terms of halves and doubles. (More on this in chapter 6.)

The standard series of numbers must be memorized by any prospective cameraman so that changes of two or four or eight times in exposure can be calculated mentally from any starting point on the aperture dial. Professional light meters of all varieties give exposure readings in terms of this standard series of f-numbers.

The widest aperture of a given lens is, as mentioned earlier, determined by the size of the lens itself, so the f-number referring to the maximum opening may not be one of the numbers in the standard series. Thus the maximum f-stop may not allow exactly double the amount of light to pass as the next adjacent f-stop. But regardless of whether the maximum f-stop is a number in the standard series or not, the next adjacent f-number and all others inscribed on the lens will provide exactly half or double the light values, as described.

T-stops

Many lenses are marked with a T-stop scale in addition to the f-stop scale. The T-numbers are usually located on the aperture ring opposite the f-numbers. The numerics are generally the same as the standard series but the iris setting will be slightly different. The "T" in "T-stop" refers to transmission; T-stops are measured rather than calculated.

4-9. Two sides of the same aperture control ring. Left: F-stop scale; right: T-stop scale.

A lens, particularly a lens with many groups of elements such as a zoom lens, may not actually pass as much light as the f-stop says it does. This is because a small amount of light is reflected by the surfaces of the glass elements rather than transmitted through them. With glass of the type used in movie camera lenses, about 5.5 percent is reflected and 94.5 percent transmitted. In a zoom lens with 18 glass-air surfaces, the loss becomes appreciable. For this reason the lens surfaces are coated with magnesium fluoride, among other substances. These lens coatings have the ability to cancel reflected rays of light as they enter the glass surface and thereby reduce light loss.

But in some lenses overall light loss still occurs to a measurable degree. If the f-stop were used, an exposure of less than the desired amount would be achieved. Therefore, the transmission of light through lenses with numerous elements is measured and calibrated with the T-stop scale. The T-numbers provide a more accurate exposure setting; they should always be used when the lens being used has a T-stop scale.

Depth of field

It is imperative that every cameraman understand the phenomenon known as *depth of field*. Its effects have to be dealt with every time a picture is taken.

Depth of field is simply the portion of a scene that is "in focus." Even those who have no familiarity with photographic lenses are aware of this phenomenon, because depth of field is a part of the eye's vision too.

Take a ruler inscribed with bold inch markings and hold it up to your face, with the end resting on your cheek. Place your finger or a pen at about the seven-inch mark and focus your eye carefully on it, while sighting down the ruler. You will notice that the six-inch mark and the eight-inch mark appear fairly sharp and clear, while the distant numbers and close numbers are completely out of focus.

The distance between six inches and eight inches (or whatever portion seems sharp) is the depth of field. All lenses under all circumstances

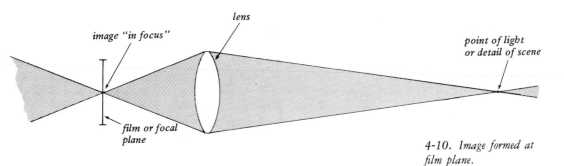

lens

image "in focus"

point of light or detail of scene

film or focal plane

4-10. *Image formed at film plane.*

have depth of field characteristics, but the depth of field differs greatly under different circumstances. The skillful photographer will control depth of field and use either "selective focus" or total sharpness to solve photographic problems and express ideas.

Depth of field exists because of the eye's willingness to accept slightly out-of-focus images as sharp. The question is how much "out of focusness" the eye will accept as sharp when looking at a photograph or a movie screen. To answer it is necessary to take a close look at the nature of focus itself.

The circle of confusion

When a sharp point of light or a single tiny area of a scene is *refracted* by a positive lens, the rays of light that make up that "point" form a similar point at the focal or film plane, as in figure 4-10. The rays of light approach the film in the shape of a cone and if the film did not block the rays, they would cross and spread out behind the focal plane. But if the film plane is moved toward or away from the lens slightly, the cone from the scene no longer forms on the film as a point but as a *circle*. This circle is an out-of-focus point. The name for it is the *circle of confusion*. Quite obviously, the size of the circle of confusion has a direct relationship to how much a given point in the scene is out of focus. Different-sized circles of confusion have been measured and standard tolerable-sized circles for photographic purposes have even been established. This *tolerable circle of confusion* is the basis for establishing the greatest deviation from perfect focus permissible that the eye will still accept as sharp. The standard circle is used to calculate numerous charts and lens tables available to the cameraman as guides to depth of field.

4-11. *Formation of the circle of confusion.*

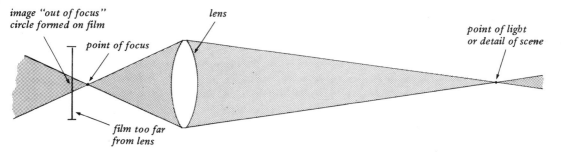

image "out of focus" circle formed on film

lens

point of focus

point of light or detail of scene

film too far from lens

In the *American Cinematographer's Manual*, for example, the section entitled "Depth of Field" includes charts for the depth of field of lenses for 35mm and 16mm photography. At the upper right of each page the allowable circle of confusion upon which the chart is based is given. For the 35mm format .002 inches (or 1/500 inch) is the established maximum. For 16mm photography .001 inches (or 1/1000 inch) is the maximum allowable circle of confusion. With this variable fixed, it is time to deal with the remaining three factors that control depth of field:

1. The *distance* from the camera to the object the lens is focused upon

2. The *focal length* of the lens being used

3. The *aperture* at which the lens is set

The distance from the lens to the object: Try sighting down the ruler again, holding your finger or pen at six inches; only the adjacent inch or two appears reasonably sharp or within your depth of field. But move the pen back to about twelve inches. You will notice that four or five adjacent inch markings appear to be within your depth of field.

The principle observed here is that when focus is on a given object very close to the camera lens, the depth of field will be much less than when focus is on an object a great distance away. The increased magnification caused by focusing closely makes the depth of field (and thus the act of focusing the lens) much more critical. Focused at an object 50 feet away, a lens may have a depth of field from 10 feet in front of the camera all the way to infinity. This is a great distance, to say the least. But when that same lens is focused on an object six inches away, the depth of field may be only from 5 3/4 inches to 6 1/2 inches, a depth of field of only 3/4 inch!

The focal length of the lens being used: This is a factor similar in its effect to the distance focused upon. Long-focal-length or telephoto lenses magnify small portions of the scene to fill the camera frame or viewfinder. They give, in effect, the field of view (and magnification) that a normal lens would give if it was moved close to the subject. Therefore a telephoto lens magnifies like a normal lens moved closer, and moving closer creates a shallower depth of field. The increased magnification of a telephoto lens gives less depth of field than a normal lens focused at the same distances. Conversely, a wide-angle lens gives more depth of field, because the magnification of the image is less, when focused at the same distance as a normal lens. Again, this is because the wide-angle lens shows the same field of view as a normal lens moved further from the scene, and it gives the increased depth of field characteristic of a normal lens at a greater distance.

It begins to be clear how these two factors are interdependent. A wide-angle lens will give more depth of field than a telephoto lens focused at the same distance. But the wide-angle lens may give less depth of field when focused very closely than a telephoto lens focused at a great distance. The combination for the least depth of field would be a telephoto lens focused upon an object near the camera, and the

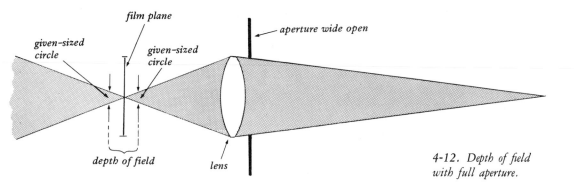

4-12. Depth of field with full aperture.

combination for the most depth of field would be a wide-angle lens focused at great distance.

The cameraman chooses the lens and distance combination that will create the appropriate feeling in the final picture. If the actress is to be sharp but the background out of focus, use a telephoto lens or move in closer. If everything in the scene needs to be very sharp from near to far, use the wide-angle lens or move back. Focal length and distance are clearly interdependent in motion picture photography.

The aperture: That the aperture or light-controlling diaphragm should have anything to do with the sharpness of the scene is the source of much confusion. But the aperture does have a very striking effect on depth of field. It works this way: in the simple diagram that shows the creation of the circle of confusion, the lines that represented the rays of light take up the entire diameter of the lens.

Figure 4-12 shows the angle of the light rays as they approach the film when the lens is set at its maximum aperture. But if the lens were to be stopped down with a smaller aperture, the angle at which the rays of light reach the film becomes considerably less.

Depth of field is partly determined by the allowable size of the circle of confusion. When a lens is stopped down, the film could be moved farther from or closer to the lens before the same sized circle of confusion would be produced as in the lens that is not stopped down. A given lens, focused at a given distance, yields greater depth of field when closed down to a small aperture than it does wide open.

4-13. Increased depth of field with lens aperture closed down.

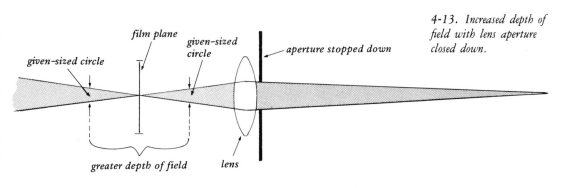

It is now plain that controlling depth of field is indeed a matter of manipulating the three factors of aperture, focal length, and the distance focused upon. There will be times when extra lights will be needed to make the scene bright enough so that the aperture can be closed down to a stop that will give sufficient depth of field. There will be other times neutral-density filters will be needed on the lens to reduce the light, thus allowing opening of the aperture for a very precise focus. The greatest depth of field possible is achieved with a wide-angle lens focused on a distant object and stopped down to a small aperture. The least depth of field is achieved with a long-focal-length or telephoto lens focused at an object near the camera, with the aperture wide open.

The cameraman often wants the greatest depth of field achievable under the given circumstances. Increased depth of field helps compensate for focus imperfections (important in fast documentary-style shooting where there is little time to focus on the subject) and makes footage look sharp and clear. Very often one factor can be used to help compensate for another. For example, with a telephoto lens, if the light level is boosted or a more sensitive film is used, the lens can be stopped down and some of the depth of field that the telephoto lens ordinarily will not allow can be retrieved.

The terms "depth of field" and "depth of focus" are used by many people interchangeably, but in truth there is an important and very simple difference. *Depth of field* is, as said earlier, the portion of the scene that will be rendered in acceptable focus. *Depth of focus* is exactly the same thing—but at the film plane instead of in the scene.

In all cases and with all lenses, whatever happens in front of the lens also happens behind the lens. The depth of field, which may be several inches or several feet into the scene, is represented by a corresponding tiny distance at the film plane. To help make this clearer, consider the example of taking ultraclose "macro" shots of a tiny insect. With the use of special attachments (such as extension tubes, explained later), the distance from the lens to the subject may be less than the distance from the lens to the film plane. With this setup, the depth of field would be a smaller distance than the depth of focus. If the lens were precisely midway between the subject and the film, the depth of field and depth of focus would be equal. To cameramen involved with ultraclose-up and other kinds of optical cinematography, the distinction between these terms is vitally important.

Hyperfocal distance

The *hyperfocal distance* is expressed as a footage to which the focus ring of a lens can be set. This distance setting is derived by determining the closest point at which the lens could be focused so that its depth of field would include infinity as the far extreme.

The hyperfocal distance number does not say what the depth of field is to the near extreme (toward the camera) but only at what point to set the lens so that infinity will be included. The figure changes with each lens of a different focal length and with each aperture setting of

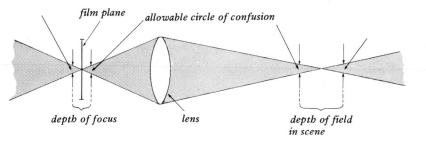

film plane   allowable circle of confusion

depth of focus   lens   depth of field
                                       in scene

the same lens. Hyperfocal distances are nearer to the camera with wide-angle lenses because their inherently greater depth of field makes them include infinity when focused closer. Hyperfocal distances are also closer with small apertures, again because of the greater depth of field.

Inexpensive, special-purpose, or wide-angle lenses mounted in non-focusing barrels are usually preset at the hyperfocal distance corresponding to the focal length and maximum aperture. A 10mm f/2 wide-angle lens has a hyperfocal distance of seven feet. With the focus set at this distance, the lens has a depth of field from five feet four inches to infinity (at f/2). At f/22, the depth of field extends all the way from six inches to infinity. A 100mm, f/2 lens has a hyperfocal distance of 665 feet. Its depth of field is from about 400 feet to infinity at f/2. At f/22, depth of field extends from 61 feet to infinity. Obviously, a fixed-focus wide-angle lens is more practical than a fixed-focus telephoto. There are, in fact, several useful fixed-focus wide-angle lenses that rely on their great depth of field and close hyperfocal distance for focusing.

Focusing lenses

The factors that control depth of field logically indicate a few techniques to be used when focusing lenses.

It should be obvious that focusing a wide-angle lens is a less critical operation, generally, than focusing a telephoto lens. If the focus is inaccurate, the greater depth of field of the wide-angle lens is more likely to disguise that fact than the shallow depth of field of the telephoto. But in practice, determining the precise focus often seems more difficult with the wide-angle lens.

It is possible to turn the focus ring of a wide-angle lens back and forth a great deal before there is any noticeable difference in focus. But with a telephoto lens, the slightest movement of the ring can throw the scene out of focus. The fundamental answer to the problem is to take the time to focus each shot carefully, making sure that the viewfinder objective on the camera is properly adjusted for the photographer's eye (if adjustable at all) and that the footage markings on the wide-angle lenses correspond to the actual distance focused upon.

16mm Camera depth of field, hyperfocal distance, & field of view

Lens focal length: 10.0mm   Circle of confusion = .001" (1/1000")

	(Field of view is based on full 16mm aperture: .402" × .292")								
Hyperfocal dist.	6'6"	4'8"	3'3"	2'4"	1'8"	1'2"	0'10"	0'7"	
	f/2	f/2.8	f/4	f/5.6	f/8	f/11	f/16	f/22	
Lens focus (feet)	Near Far	Near Far	Near Far	Near Far	Near Far	Near Far	Near Far	Near Far	Field of view
25	5'2" INF.	3'11" INF.	2'11" INF.	2'2" INF.	1'7" INF.	1'2" INF.	0'10" INF.	0'7" INF.	25'6" × 18'6"
10	3'11" INF.	3'2" INF.	2'6" INF.	1'11" INF.	1'5" INF.	1'1" INF.	0'9" INF.	0'7" INF.	10'2" × 7'5"
3	2'1" 5'6"	1'10" 8'4"	1'7" 33'2"	1'4" INF.	1'1" INF.	0'10" INF.	0'8" INF.	0'6" INF.	3'0" × 2'2"
2	1'6" 2'10"	1'5" 3'6"	1'3" 5'0"	1'1" 12'7"	0'11" INF.	0'9" INF.	0'7" INF.	0'6" INF.	2'0" × 1'6"
1½	1'3" 1'11"	1'2" 2'2"	1'0" 2'9"	0'11" 4'0"	0'10" 13'9"	0'8" INF.	0'7" INF.	0'5" INF.	1'6" × 1'1"
1	0'10" 1'2"	0'10" 1'3"	0'9" 1'5"	0'8" 1'8"	0'8" 2'5"	0'7" 5'0"	0'6" INF.	0'5" INF.	1'0" × 0'9"
10"	0'9" 0'11"	0'9" 1'0"	0'8" 1'1"	0'7" 1'3"	0'7" 1'7"	0'6" 2'5"	0'5" 16'3"	0'4" INF.	0'10" × 0'7"
9"	0'8" 0'10"	0'8" 0'11"	0'7" 1'0"	0'7" 1'1"	0'6" 1'4"	0'6" 1'10"	0'5" 5'2"	0'4" INF.	0'9" × 0'6"
8"	0'7" 0'9"	0'7" 0'9"	0'7" 0'10"	0'6" 0'11"	0'6" 1'1"	0'5" 1'5"	0'5" 2'9"	0'4" INF.	0'8" × 0'6"

Lens focal length: 12.5mm   Circle of confusion = .001″ (1/1000″)

	(Field of view is based on full 16 mm aperture: .402″ × .292″)								
Hyperfocal dist.	10'2″	7'3″	5'1″	3'8″	2'7″	1'11″	1'4″	1'0″	
	f/2	f/2.8	f/4	f/5.6	f/8	f/11	f/16	f/22	
Lens focus (feet)	Near Far	Near Far	Near Far	Near Far	Near Far	Near Far	Near Far	Near Far	Field of view
25	7'3″ INF.	5'8″ INF.	4'3″ INF.	3'2″ INF.	2'4″ INF.	1'9″ INF.	1'3″ INF.	0'11″ INF.	20'5″ × 14'10″
15	6'1″ INF.	4'11″ INF.	3'10″ INF.	2'11″ INF.	2'2″ INF.	1'8″ INF.	1'2″ INF.	0'11″ INF.	12'3″ × 8'11″
8	4'6″ 37'4″	3'10″ INF.	3'1″ INF.	2'6″ INF.	1'11″ INF.	1'6″ INF.	1'2″ INF.	0'10″ INF.	6'6″ × 4'9″
6	3'9″ 14'7″	3'4″ 33'9″	2'9″ INF.	2'3″ INF.	1'10″ INF.	1'5″ INF.	1'1″ INF.	0'10″ INF.	4'10″ × 3'6″
4	2'11″ 6'7″	2'7″ 8'10″	2'3″ 18'1″	1'11″ INF.	1'7″ INF.	1'3″ INF.	1'0″ INF.	0'9″ INF.	3'3″ × 2'4″
3	2'4″ 4'3″	2'2″ 5'1″	1'11″ 7'2″	1'8″ 15'11″	1'5″ INF.	1'2″ INF.	0'11″ INF.	0'9″ INF.	2'5″ × 1'9″
2	1'8″ 2'6″	1'7″ 2'9″	1'5″ 3'3″	1'4″ 4'4″	1'2″ 8'6″	1'0″ INF.	0'10″ INF.	0'8″ INF.	1'7″ × 1'2″
1½	1'4″ 1'9″	1'3″ 1'11″	1'2″ 2'1″	1'1″ 2'6″	0'11″ 3'6″	0'10″ 6'9″	0'8″ INF.	0'7″ INF.	1'2″ × 0'10″
1	0'11″ 1'1″	0'11″ 1'2″	0'10″ 1'3″	0'10″ 1'4″	0'9″ 1'7″	0'8″ 2'1″	0'7″ 3'10″	0'6″ INF.	0'9″ × 0'7″

4-15. Sixteen millimeter camera depths-of-field for lenses from 10mm to 100mm.

16mm Camera depth of field, hyperfocal distance, & field of view

Lens focal length: 16.0mm   Circle of confusion = .001″ (1/1000″)

	(Field of view is based on full 16mm aperture: .402″ × .292″)								
Hyperfocal dist.	16′7″	11′10″	8′4″	5′11″	4′2″	3′1″	2′1″	1′7″	
	f/2	f/2.8	f/4	f/5.6	f/8	f/11	f/16	f/22	
Lens focus (feet)	Near Far	Near Far	Near Far	Near Far	Near Far	Near Far	Near Far	Near Far	Field of view
50	12′6″ INF.	9′7″ INF.	7′2″ INF.	5′4″ INF.	3′10″ INF.	2′11″ INF.	2′0″ INF.	1′6″ INF.	31′11″ × 23′2″
25	10′0″ INF.	8′1″ INF.	6′3″ INF.	4′10″ INF.	3′7″ INF.	2′9″ INF.	1′11″ INF.	1′6″ INF.	15′11″ × 11′7″
15	7′11″ 151′10″	6′8″ INF.	5′4″ INF.	4′3″ INF.	3′3″ INF.	2′7″ INF.	1′10″ INF.	1′5″ INF.	9′6″ × 6′11″
10	6′3″ 25′0″	5′5″ 61′11″	4′7″ INF.	3′9″ INF.	3′0″ INF.	2′4″ INF.	1′9″ INF.	1′4″ INF.	6′4″ × 4′7″
8	5′5″ 15′4″	4′9″ 24′3″	4′1″ 179′1″	3′5″ INF.	2′9″ INF.	2′3″ INF.	1′8″ INF.	1′4″ INF.	5′1″ × 3′8″
6	4′5″ 9′4″	4′0″ 12′0″	3′6″ 21′1″	3′0″ 0′0″	2′6″ INF.	2′0″ INF.	1′7″ INF.	1′3″ INF.	3′10″ × 2′9″
5	3′10″ 7′2″	3′6″ 8′7″	3′2″ 12′4″	2′9″ 29′6″	2′3″ INF.	1′11″ INF.	1′6″ INF.	1′2″ INF.	3′2″ × 2′4″
4	3′3″ 5′3″	3′0″ 6′0″	2′9″ 7′7″	2′5″ 11′10″	2′1″ 70′3″	1′9″ INF.	1′5″ INF.	1′2″ INF.	2′6″ × 1′10″
3	2′7″ 3′8″	2′5″ 4′0″	2′3″ 4′8″	2′0″ 5′11″	1′9″ 10′2″	1′6″ 82′7″	1′3″ INF.	1′0″ INF.	1′11″ × 1′4″
2	1′9″ 2′3″	1′9″ 2′5″	1′7″ 2′7″	1′6″ 3′0″	1′4″ 3′9″	1′3″ 5′6″	1′1″ 24′8″	0′11″ INF.	1′3″ × 0′11″

Lens focal length: 25.0mm   Circle of confusion = .001″ (1/1000″)

	(Field of view is based on full 16mm aperture: .402″ × .292″)								
Hyperfocal dist.	40′5″	28′11″	20′3″	14′6″	10′2″	7′5″	5′2″	3′9″	
	f/2	f/2.8	f/4	f/5.6	f/8	f/11	f/16	f/22	
Lens focus (feet)	Near Far	Near Far	Near Far	Near Far	Near Far	Near Far	Near Far	Near Far	Field of view
50	22′5″ INF.	18′4″ INF.	14′5″ INF.	11′3″ INF.	8′6″ INF.	6′6″ INF.	4′8″ INF.	3′6″ INF.	20′5″ × 14′10″
25	15′6″ 65′1″	13′5″ 180′11″	11′3″ INF.	9′2″ INF.	7′3″ INF.	5′9″ INF.	4′3″ INF.	3′3″ INF.	10′2″ × 7′5″
15	10′11″ 23′9″	9′11″ 31′0″	8′8″ 56′10″	7′5″ INF.	6′1″ INF.	5′0″ INF.	3′10″ INF.	3′0″ INF.	6′1″ × 4′5″
10	8′0″ 13′3″	7′5″ 15′3″	6′9″ 19′7″	5′11″ 31′8″	5′1″ 398′7″	4′3″ INF.	3′5″ INF.	2′9″ INF.	4′1″ × 2′11″
8	6′8″ 9′11″	6′3″ 11′0″	5′9″ 13′2″	5′2″ 17′8″	4′6″ 36′1″	3′10″ INF.	3′2″ INF.	2′7″ INF.	3′3″ × 2′4″
6	5′3″ 7′0″	5′0″ 7′7″	4′8″ 8′6″	4′3″ 10′2″	3′10″ 14′4″	3′4″ 29′7″	2′9″ INF.	2′4″ INF.	2′5″ × 1′9″
5	4′5″ 5′8″	4′3″ 6′0″	4′0″ 6′7″	3′9″ 7′7″	3′4″ 9′8″	3′0″ 14′10″	2′7″ 122′4″	2′2″ INF.	2′0″ × 1′6″
4	3′8″ 4′5″	3′6″ 4′8″	3′4″ 5′0″	3′2″ 5′6″	2′11″ 6′6″	2′7″ 8′6″	2′3″ 16′11″	1′11″ INF.	1′7″ × 1′2″
3	2′10″ 3′3″	2′9″ 3′4″	2′7″ 3′6″	2′6″ 3′9″	2′4″ 4′2″	2′2″ 4′11″	1′11″ 7′0″	1′8″ 13′6″	1′2″ × 0′10″
2	1′11″ 2′1″	1′11″ 2′2″	1′10″ 2′3″	1′9″ 2′4″	1′8″ 2′6″	1′7″ 2′8″	1′5″ 3′2″	1′4″ 4′1″	0′9″ × 0′7″

4-15. (cont'd)

16mm Camera depth of field, hyperfocal distance, & field of view

Lens focal length: 35.0mm   Circle of confusion = .001″ (1/1000″)

	(Field of view is based on full 16mm aperture: .402″ × .292″)								
Hyperfocal dist.	79′3″	58′8″	39′8″	28′4″	19′11″	14′6″	10′0″	7′4″	
	f/2	f/2.8	f/4	f/5.6	f/8	f/11	f/16	f/22	
Lens focus (feet)	Near Far	Near Far	Near Far	Near Far	Near Far	Near Far	Near Far	Near Far	Field of view
50	30′8″ 135′0″	26′7″ 420′1″	22′2″ INF.	18′2″ INF.	14′3″ INF.	11′3″ INF.	8′4″ INF.	6′5″ INF.	14′7″ × 10′7″
25	19′0″ 36′5″	17′4″ 44′7″	15′4″ 67′1″	13′4″ 203′6″	11′1″ INF.	9′2″ INF.	7′2″ INF.	5′8″ INF.	7′3″ × 5′3″
15	12′8″ 18′6″	11′11″ 20′4″	10′11″ 24′0″	9′10″ 31′7″	8′7″ 59′7″	7′5″ INF.	6′0″ INF.	4′11″ INF.	4′4″ × 3′2″
10	8′11″ 11′5″	8′6″ 12′1″	8′0″ 13′4″	7′5″ 15′4″	6′8″ 19′11″	5′11″ 31′5″	5′0″ 840′8″	4′3″ INF.	2′11″ × 2′1″
8	7′3″ 8′11″	7′0″ 9′4″	6′8″ 10′0″	6′3″ 11′1″	5′9″ 13′3″	5′2″ 17′6″	4′6″ 37′9″	3′10″ INF.	2′4″ × 1′8″
7	6′5″ 7′8″	6′3″ 8′0″	6′0″ 8′6″	5′8″ 9′3″	5′2″ 10′8″	4′9″ 13′4″	4′2″ 22′5″	3′7″ 121′3″	2′0″ × 1′6″
6	5′7″ 6′6″	5′5″ 6′8″	5′3″ 7′1″	5′0″ 7′7″	4′8″ 8′6″	4′3″ 10′1″	3′9″ 14′7″	3′4″ 30′10″	1′9″ × 1′3″
5	4′9″ 5′4″	4′7″ 5′6″	4′5″ 5′8″	4′3″ 6′0″	4′0″ 6′8″	3′9″ 7′6″	3′4″ 9′9″	3′0″ 15′1″	1′5″ × 1′0″
4	3′10″ 4′2″	3′9″ 4′4″	3′8″ 4′5″	3′6″ 4′8″	3′4″ 5′0″	3′2″ 5′6″	2′11″ 6′6″	2′7″ 8′6″	1′2″ × 0′10″
3	2′11″ 3′1″	2′10″ 3′2″	2′10″ 3′3″	2′9″ 3′4″	2′7″ 3′6″	2′6″ 3′9″	2′4″ 4′3″	2′2″ 4′11″	0′10″ × 0′7″
2	1′11″ 2′1″	1′11″ 2′1″	1′11″ 2′1″	1′11″ 2′2″	1′10″ 2′3″	1′9″ 2′4″	1′8″ 2′6″	1′7″ 2′8″	0′7″ × 0′5″

Lens focal length: 50.0mm   Circle of confusion = .001" (1/1000")

		(Field of view is based on full 16mm aperture: .402" × .292")							
Hyperfocal dist.	161'7"	115'6"	80'11"	57'10"	40'6"	29'6"	20'4"	14'10"	
	f/2	f/2.8	f/4	f/5.6	f/8	f/11	f/16	f/22	
Lens focus (feet)	Near Far	Near Far	Near Far	Near Far	Near Far	Near Far	Near Far	Near Far	Field of view
50	38'3" 72'3"	34'11" 87'11"	30'11" 130'3"	26'10" 361'9"	22'5" INF.	18'7" INF.	14'6" INF.	11'6" INF.	10'2" × 7'5"
25	21'8" 29'6"	20'7" 31'10"	19'2" 36'1"	17'6" 43'10"	15'6" 64'7"	13'7" 157'7"	11'3" INF.	9'4" INF.	5'1" × 3'8"
15	13'9" 16'6"	13'4" 17'3"	12'8" 18'4"	11'11" 20'2"	11'0" 23'8"	10'0" 30'2"	8'8" 55'5"	7'6" INF.	3'0" × 2'2"
10	9'5" 10'8"	9'3" 10'11"	8'11" 11'5"	8'7" 12'1"	8'1" 13'2"	7'6" 15'0"	6'9" 19'4"	6'0" 29'8"	2'0" × 1'6"
8	7'8" 8'5"	7'6" 8'7"	7'4" 8'10"	7'1" 9'3"	6'8" 9'11"	6'4" 10'11"	5'9" 13'0"	5'3" 16'11"	1'7" × 1'2"
7	6'9" 7'4"	6'7" 7'5"	6'5" 7'8"	6'3" 7'11"	6'0" 8'5"	5'8" 9'1"	5'3" 10'7"	4'10" 13'0"	1'5" × 1'0"
6	5'9" 6'3"	5'9" 6'4"	5'7" 6'6"	5'5" 6'8"	5'3" 7'0"	5'0" 7'6"	4'8" 8'5"	4'4" 9'11"	1'2" × 0'10"
5	4'10" 5'2"	4'10" 5'3"	4'9" 5'4"	4'7" 5'5"	4'6" 5'8"	4'4" 6'0"	4'0" 6'7"	3'9" 7'5"	1'0" × 0'9"
4	3'11" 4'1"	3'10" 4'2"	3'10" 4'2"	3'9" 4'3"	3'8" 4'5"	3'6" 4'7"	3'4" 4'11"	3'2" 5'5"	0'9" × 0'7"
3	2'11" 3'1"	2'11" 3'1"	2'11" 3'1"	2'10" 3'2"	2'10" 3'3"	2'9" 3'4"	2'8" 3'6"	2'6" 3'9"	0'7" × 0'5"
2	2'0" 2'0"	2'0" 2'0"	1'11" 2'1"	1'11" 2'1"	1'11" 2'1"	1'11" 2'2"	1'10" 2'2"	1'9" 2'3"	0'4" × 0'3"

4-15. (cont'd)

16mm Camera depth of field, hyperfocal distance, & field of view

Lens focal length: 75.0mm   Circle of confusion = .001″ (1/1000″)

(Field of view is based on full 16mm aperture: .402″ × .292″)

Hyperfocal dist.	363'6″	259'9″	181'11″	130'0″	91'1″	66'4″	45'8″	33'3″	
	f/2	f/2.8	f/4	f/5.6	f/8	f/11	f/16	f/22	
Lens focus (feet)	Near Far	Near Far	Near Far	Near Far	Near Far	Near Far	Near Far	Near Far	Field of view
100	78'6″ 137'10″	72'3″ 162'4″	64'7″ 221'5″	56'7″ 429'11″	47'9″ INF.	39'11″ INF.	31'5″ INF.	25'0″ INF.	13'7″×9'10″
50	44'0″ 57'11″	42'0″ 61'10″	39'3″ 68'10″	36'2″ 81'0″	32'4″ 110'3″	28'7″ 200'4″	23'11″ INF.	20'0″ INF.	6'9″×4'11″
25	23'5″ 26'10″	22'10″ 27'8″	22'0″ 28'11″	21'0″ 30'11″	19'8″ 34'4″	18'2″ 39'11″	16'3″ 54'7″	14'4″ 97'8″	3'4″×2'5″
15	14'5″ 15'8″	14'2″ 15'11″	13'10″ 16'4″	13'6″ 16'11″	12'11″ 17'11″	12'3″ 19'4″	11'4″ 22'2″	10'5″ 26'11″	2'0″×1'6″
10	9'9″ 10'3″	9'8″ 10'5″	9'6″ 10'7″	9'4″ 10'10″	9'0″ 11'2″	8'9″ 11'9″	8'3″ 12'9″	7'9″ 14'2″	1'4″×1'0″
8	7'10″ 8'2″	7'9″ 8'3″	7'8″ 8'4″	7'7″ 8'6″	7'4″ 8'9″	7'2″ 9'1″	6'10″ 9'8″	6'6″ 10'5″	1'1″×0'9″
7	6'10″ 7'2″	6'10″ 7'2″	6'9″ 7'3″	6'8″ 7'5″	6'6″ 7'7″	6'4″ 7'10″	6'1″ 8'3″	5'10″ 8'9″	0'11″×0'8″
6	5'11″ 6'1″	5'10″ 6'2″	5'10″ 6'2″	5'9″ 6'3″	5'8″ 6'5″	5'6″ 6'7″	5'4″ 6'10″	5'1″ 7'3″	0'9″×0'7″
5	4'11″ 5'1″	4'11″ 5'1″	4'10″ 5'2″	4'10″ 5'2″	4'9″ 5'3″	4'8″ 5'5″	4'6″ 5'7″	4'4″ 5'10″	0'8″×0'6″
4	4'0″ 4'1″	3'11″ 4'1″	3'11″ 4'1″	3'11″ 4'1″	3'10″ 4'2″	3'9″ 4'3″	3'8″ 4'4″	3'7″ 4'6″	0'6″×0'4″

Lens focal length: 100.0mm   Circle of confusion = .001″ (1/1000″)

	f/2	f/2.8	f/4	f/5.6	f/8	f/11	f/16	f/22	
(Field of view is based on full 16mm aperture: .402″ × .292″)									
Hyperfocal dist.	646′2″	461′8″	323′3″	231′0″	161′9″	117′9″	81′1″	59′0″	
Lens focus (feet)	Near Far	Near Far	Near Far	Near Far	Near Far	Near Far	Near Far	Near Far	Field of view
100	86′8″ 118′3″	82′3″ 127′6″	76′5″ 144′7″	69′10″ 175′11″	61′11″ 260′6″	54′2″ 651′3″	44′10″ INF.	37′2″ INF.	10′2″ × 7′5″
50	46′5″ 54′2″	45′2″ 56′0″	43′4″ 59′1″	41′2″ 63′8″	38′3″ 72′2″	35′2″ 86′6″	31′0″ 129′2″	27′2″ 315′1″	5′1″ × 3′8″
25	24′1″ 26′0″	23′9″ 26′5″	23′3″ 27′1″	22′7″ 28′0″	21′8″ 29′6″	20′8″ 31′8″	19′2″ 35′11″	17′8″ 42′11″	2′6″ × 1′10″
15	14′8″ 15′4″	14′6″ 15′6″	14′4″ 15′9″	14′1″ 16′0″	13′9″ 16′6″	13′4″ 17′2″	12′8″ 18′4″	12′0″ 20′0″	1′6″ × 1′1″
10	9′10″ 10′2″	9′10″ 10′3″	9′9″ 10′4″	9′7″ 10′5″	9′5″ 10′8″	9′3″ 10′11″	8′11″ 11′4″	8′7″ 12′0″	1′0″ × 0′9″
8	7′11″ 8′1″	7′10″ 8′2″	7′10″ 8′2″	7′9″ 8′3″	7′8″ 8′5″	7′6″ 8′7″	7′4″ 8′10″	7′1″ 9′2″	0′9″ × 0′7″
7	6′11″ 7′1″	6′11″ 7′1″	6′10″ 7′2″	6′10″ 7′2″	6′9″ 7′4″	6′7″ 7′5″	6′6″ 7′8″	6′3″ 7′11″	0′8″ × 0′6″
6	5′11″ 6′1″	5′11″ 6′1	5′11″ 6′1″	5′10″ 6′2″	5′10″ 6′3″	5′9″ 6′4″	5′7″ 6′5″	5′6″ 6′8″	0′7″ × 0′5″
5	5′0″ 5′0″	4′1 ″ 5′1″	4′11″ 5′1″	4′11″ 5′1″	4′10″ 5′2″	4′10″ 5′ 2″	4′9″ 5′4″	4′8″ 5′5″	0′6″ × 0′4″
4	4′0″ 4′0″	4′0″ 4′0″	3′11″ 4′1″	3′11″ 4′1″	3′11″ 4′1″	3′11″ 4′2″	3′10″ 4′2″	3′9″ 4′3″	0′4″ × 0′3″

4-15. *(cont'd)*

Another important factor in obtaining proper focus is the lens opening. Two hints: opening the lens to its maximum aperture decreases depth of field, making the focus far more precise. Also, the image is much brighter and easier to see with wide-open aperture. (The problem is remembering to stop the lens back down to the working aperture when focus is established.)

An additional helpful hint: carefully choose the portion of the scene to be focused on. All too often a hurried cameraman will simply turn the focus ring until the overall scene looks sharp, forgetting that the main subject of the scene is closer than the background. A specific area of each scene must be selected as the part to be focused on. With ultraclose-ups of people, it is important to select a part of the face. Usually the eye closest to the camera is the proper place for sharp focus.

Often the documentary cameraman must select a point of focus that will provide the best compromise in the hope that the existing depth of field will be adequate. For example, when filming a medium long shot of a small crowd of people inside a restaurant, a clear difference in focus can be detected between the close table and the far table. Where is the best compromise for focus? The rule of thumb most often used is to focus about one-third of the way from the front. Depth of field tables indicate that there is always greater depth of field behind the focal point, and so "splitting" the focus at one-third to two-thirds usually yields the best results.

Extension and compression

Lenses of different focal lengths can be used to distort or enhance a particular subject by altering the perspective. *Perspective* means the apparent distance between objects in a scene; in a photograph, perspective is related only to the camera's distance from the scene itself. False perspective can be created with specially painted backdrops or props that are constructed with "built-in perspective." But telephoto and wide-angle lenses can be used to extend or compress the apparent perspective of a scene.

Consider the following example: three people are sitting on a fence. The top picture in figure 4-16 was made with a normal lens and the perspective seems to be realistic. The middle picture was photographed with a wide-angle lens, from closer in. The "cropping" or framing of the three heads is about the same, but notice the exaggerated difference in size (or distance) between the first person and the third. The bottom picture was taken with a telephoto lens, from a great distance. Now the three heads are the same size and there appears to be little or no space between them. By moving in very close but using a wide-angle lens, a scene can be photographed with exaggerated or extended perspective. By moving back from the scene but using a telephoto lens, the perspective can be reduced or "compressed."

The same principle can be applied to filming objects moving toward or away from the camera. With a telephoto lens, a person 35 feet from

4-16. Top: normal lens photo; middle: wide-angle lens photo; bottom: telephoto lens photo.

the camera with an extended fist would appear compressed as in the first picture in figure 4-17. In the second example, the framing is the same, but made with a wide-angle lens from a distance of five feet. When the person's hand is again extended, the action looks as it does in that photograph. Briefly, then: to exaggerate a particular movement, use a wide-angle lens and move very close to the subject. To make a given movement seem almost imperceptible, use a telephoto lens from a great distance.

4-17. Top: telephoto lens photo; bottom: wide-angle photo.

Zoom lenses

The focal length of the zoom lens is changed during shooting or between takes by moving groups of elements within the lens. The effect of this change is, of course, to change the magnification and image size. When focal length is increased during shooting, the center of the scene seems to grow or "zoom" toward the camera; when the length is decreased, parts of a scene will get smaller and "zoom" away.

Although the zoom lens can be used to take a wide-angle to a telephoto shot, the effect is not the same as moving closer with a fixed-focal-length lens. A zoom is accomplished from an unchanged camera position, and so the perspective is not altered as the cropping changes from wide to close. During a moving-camera shot from wide to close, the camera moves past objects, and the perspective changes as it does.

It is important that a zoom be smooth, and any unevenness of speed can look worse than a jerky pan. Making a smooth zoom and at the same time avoiding camera shake is a technique that requires practice. Please refer to chapter 2 for several important tips regarding zooming.

The use of zoom lenses

Some modern zoom lenses are of sufficient quality to be used in place of "prime" or fixed-focal-length lenses. A popular lens for 16mm cameras, for example, is the Angenieux 12 to 120. At 12mm it is a good all-around wide angle, and at 120mm it is a fairly long telephoto. And it can also be used at every focal length in between. It is possible to work with the zoom lens as if it were a very complete assortment of fixed-focal-length lenses. There are even a few advantages.

First, the change from one focal length to another can be done very quickly. A zoom is accomplished much faster than rotating a turret; the focus and aperture remain the same under normal circumstances, and a change in cropping can be accomplished with almost no delay. Second, set-up time for different shots

4-18. Top: a typical 10X zoom lens. Note crank handle for zooming. Middle: wide view of possible zoom shot. Bottom: close view of zoom shot showing unaltered perspective.

is less, because slight adjustments can be made in cropping without moving the whole camera back and forth. Third, if the zoom is the only lens being used, it is the only lens to filter, the only lens to shade from the sun, the only lens to focus, and the only lens on which to set the aperture. All these things generally mean more efficient shooting and fewer mistakes—particularly for a fast-moving documentary cameraman.

Considering that a zoom lens may not cost much more than three or four fixed-focus lenses, it begins to seem like the cameraman's panacea. But there are a few disadvantages. Zoom lenses are large and heavy. On cameras with "C" mounts, they need extra support in the form of an additional arm, support bracket, or "cradle" that attaches to the camera. Their added weight also tends to make some cameras front-heavy for handholding. In addition, their complexity means that zoom lenses are rarely as sharp as high-quality fixed-focus lenses of the same focal length. Also, zoom lenses usually have modest maximum apertures, making them suitable only where adequate light levels are found. Fixed-focus lenses often have greater maximum openings than zoom lenses; they should be carried in case filming in a low available light situation becomes necessary.

Zoom lenses tend to offer more at the telephoto end of the range and less at the wide-angle end. So although many zoom lenses are very long telephoto lenses, the wide-angle extreme may be rather moderate or hardly wide angle at all. For this reason the cameraman relying on the zoom lens will usually want to carry a good fixed-focal-length wide- or ultra-wide-angle lens as well.

Focusing the zoom lens

Since telephoto lenses have less depth of field than wide-angle lenses and the zoom lens is both a long-focal-length and wide-angle lens, the safest and most often recommended method of establishing focus is to zoom the lens to its longest focal length, focus on the subject, and then zoom the lens back to the desired focal length for shooting. In this way, should a change in focal length be required during the shot, focus will carry throughout the entire length of the zoom. If the lens had been focused at a wide-angle position, the less critical focus would not usually be good enough when the lens is zoomed to a telephoto position. Remember that a zoom lens will hold focus throughout its zoom range but depth of field will change as the zoom is made. Also remember that any lens at its maximum aperture allows for the brightest and most critical focusing.

Focusing a zoom lens is a six-step process.

1. Open the aperture

2. Select the subject or area within the scene to be focused on

3. Zoom the lens to its longest focal length and aim at the selected subject

4. Focus carefully

5. Zoom back to the focal length required for the shot

6. Close the aperture back down to the proper f-stop for exposure

Ultraclose-up photography

Most lenses have a rather moderate focusing range. The focus ring goes from infinity to around three feet at the closest. Although some focus at less, very few can focus closer than one foot. What does the cameraman do to get extreme close-up or "macro" shots of tiny objects?

Extension tubes and bellows

With fixed-focal-length lenses, the answer is usually *extension tubes* or *bellows*. Since a lens must move away from the film to focus close, it may be removed from the camera and a tube of a given length attached to the camera while the lens in turn is attached to it. This extension tube remounts the lens at a greater distance from the film, allowing much closer focus than normal. Tubes of various lengths (usually from about one-quarter inch to one inch) can be used singly or in groups to bring the focus within an inch or two.

4-19. Extension tubes, which can be used singly or in groups to provide close focus.

The *bellows* is simply an adjustable extension tube—also installed between the camera and lens.

When a lens is mounted to the camera via extension tubes or bellows, it can no longer reach infinity and its footage markings no longer apply. Also, many lenses are not corrected for close focus and show edge softness and other faults when moved too far from their usual focus mounts. In addition, the use of extension tubes or bellows requires exposure compensation. This is because the lens is moved to great distances from the infinity position, which establishes aperture numbers for a given focal-length lens. Theoretically, the aperture is correct only at the infinity position and would have to be recalibrated as the lens moves away from the film to focus closer. In practice, the usual focus range of a lens does not permit enough displacement from infinity for this discrepancy to show up in actual net exposure. But bellows or extension tubes make a significant difference in exposure and must be compensated for. This exposure difference is calculated by the following formula:

$$\frac{\text{Distance of lens to film}^2}{\text{Focal length of lens}^2} = \frac{\text{Exposure}}{\text{Factor}}$$

For example: given a 50mm lens and a two-inch extension tube, first convert all numbers to inches or millimeters. With approximately 25mm to the inch, the 50mm lens can be called a two-inch lens. The combination of the two-inch focal length and the two-inch extension tube equals the total distance of the lens to the film when the tube is in place.

Therefore:

$$\frac{(2 + 2)^2}{2^2} = \frac{4^2}{4} = \frac{16}{4} = 4$$

Four is the exposure factor, or the number of times the light must be increased. A factor of 4 equals two f-stops. This would be the correct exposure compensation for a 50mm lens with a two-inch extension tube.

Although computations such as the one above should lead to a suitable exposure, it is always a good idea to *bracket* the exposures just to be safe. Bracketing simply means shooting additional takes at one or two stops over and under the computed exposure as a backup. In fact, it is always a good idea to bracket shots of unusual scenes no matter how the exposure is calculated.

Another answer to the ultraclose-up focus problem is the *macro lens*. These specially corrected lenses are mounted in a focusing barrel that extends beyond the normal range. Some macro lenses can focus from infinity to just one or two inches without additional extenders. They are usually marked to show the exposure factors necessary when the focusing barrel is set in various positions. If the macro lens does not have exposure-increase markings, unless the iris is coupled for automatic compensation, an exposure computation like the one described for the bellows may be necessary.

Diopters

Zoom lenses will not work properly if moved even slightly from their correct seating on the camera. They are focused by moving only the front set of elements. If extension tubes were inserted behind the zoom lens, focus on a close object would not carry through the zoom range. With zoom lenses—and fixed focal-length lenses if desired—the use of additional *diopter lenses* makes ultraclose focus possible. These positive supplemental elements are available in various strengths and diameters. They are screwed onto the front of the camera lens or held in the sunshade or filter holder. Diopters with zoom lenses allow for extreme close-up work with the full zoom range. Diopters have the added advantage of requiring no exposure compensation.

A "diopter" is a mathematical reciprocal of the focal length in meters. A meter is 39.3 inches, and diopters come in designations of $+1$, $+2$, and $+3$. A $+3$ diopter has a focal length of one-third meter,

4-20. Top: diopter lens magnification effect when held about six inches above newsprint; bottom: label on a typical close-up lens.

or about 13 inches. A +2 diopter has a focal length of one-half meter, or about 20 inches. A +1 diopter has a focal length equal to one meter. The +3 diopter is the strongest and allows the closest focus. The three may be combined for even closer focus.

Another useful attachment is the split-field diopter, one that covers only a portion of the taking lens. It is similar to the human bifocal lens in that it allows the camera to focus on very close and very distant objects in the same shot. The objects must be carefully placed so that they are within the different focal areas covered. Also, the edge of the split may be visible unless it can be lined up with a straight edge in the background.

Split-field diopter shots, as well as other shots involving extreme close-ups, require very careful setup and balanced lighting if satisfactory results are to be obtained.

Additional lenses

Besides diopters for close-up photography, there are a wide variety of attachments to alter focal length. The most common are the telephoto lens extenders. These provide inexpensive additional focal lengths for fixed-focus and some zoom lenses. They require exposure compensation, however, equivalent to the square of the focal length change. If a telephoto extender doubles the focal length of the lens, it will probably have an exposure factor of 4. This means the lens needs to be opened up enough to allow four times the light, or two stops.

Zoom lenses and fixed-focal-length lenses that have relatively small front element diameters (about two inches) can be fitted with retrofocus wide-angle attachments. These have the opposite optical effect from the telephoto extenders. Wide-angle attachments reduce the focal-length lenses; they allow shorter focal-length zoom ranges. They do not require major exposure compensations. Lens attachments of this kind always cause some loss of image sharpness.

As a general rule, closing the aperture one, two, or even more f-stops will reduce the optical faults that are inevitably introduced with all attachments. Stopping down is also helpful simply because the smaller aperture significantly reduces the area of glass through which the light can pass. Optical problems, aberrations, faults, and defects all seem to be worst at or near the edges of the lenses, where the curvature is the greatest. When the lens is stopped down, these areas are no longer being used. Minimizing optical problems by stopping down applies to any and all lenses, whether used with attachments or not.

Lens faults

Nothing is more frustrating to the cameraman than to find that some or all of the film from a day's shooting is "soft" or out of focus. It is particularly upsetting to the professional who knows the importance of sharp focus, knows how to focus his lenses correctly, and was at all times concerned about achieving proper focus. Frequently, when all or most of the footage is soft, the fault is not the cameraman's.

Lenses vary widely in quality. If the lens is rented or has not been performance tested, a major problem may occur. Standards of quality in lenses and, to an even greater degree, standards of real image definition are difficult to observe, test, and measure. A given lens may seem to provide satisfactory focus when the lighting of the scene is very contrasty; the sharp shadows give a deceiving look of sharpness.

But the same lens with soft lighting or a "flat" subject may look very "fuzzy" indeed.

Almost all lenses perform better at small apertures. By stopping down, any faults are minimized. Stopping down also increases the depth of field, which helps compensate for any slight inaccuracies of focus. A few lenses actually begin to lose resolving power, however, when they are stopped down too far. All lenses have an optimum aperture for maximum sharpness, but with any good lens this optimum is difficult to identify in the footage.

Zoom lenses have an especially difficult set of focus problems, and internal maladjustments as well as improper positioning on the camera can cause so many different difficulties that the cameraman may lose his job before the real trouble is found. Since the proper way to focus a zoom lens is to focus at its maximum focal length and then zoom out to the desired focal length before shooting, a shift in focus can occur if the lens is not precisely adjusted. A simple test is to shoot a sharply defined target or subject. While the camera is running, focus at the maximum focal length and then slowly pull back to the wider focal lengths. The projected footage will show if the viewfinder is allowing accurate focus and if it is carrying throughout the zoom range. Sometimes a burr, nick, or piece of dirt on the rear of the lens mount or on the turret of the camera will prevent the lens from locking into its proper position or seat. Improper seating may be the most common cause of a lens suddenly giving poor results. Whenever a zoom lens is purchased, the camera and the lens should be checked by an expert on an optical device called a collimator to see if the internal adjustments and seating are correct.

Sometimes actual focus does not correspond to the footage markings on the lens barrel. This fact alone has increased the popularity of the

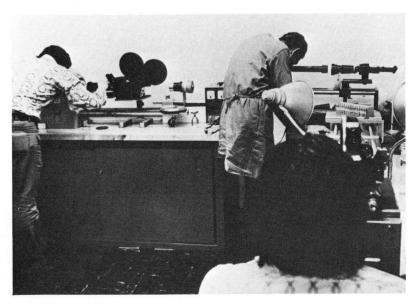

4-21. Lenses being checked for optical alignment and proper camera seating in lens department of Camera Mart, New York, New York. (Camera Mart)

reflex cameras, where footage inscriptions are seldom needed. If a lens shows a consistent difference between the footage markings and the actual focus distance, it may still perform satisfactorily if focused by reflex. But there is a good chance that the lens is incorrectly assembled, has been dropped, or is not seated correctly. Do not take the chance. Get the lens repaired.

Inexpensive lenses often have poor edge sharpness. A manufacturer may boast that the lens can resolve a certain number of lines per millimeter (a test that proves little, because it depends on the contrast of the chart photographed, film quality, graininess, development, and so on) but the lens may be capable of this resolution only in the center of the image.

Although not very scientific, the best test of a lens is simply to use it. It should be tried out under all of the normal conditions with the most commonly used film and projected on a reliable and familiar machine. Sometimes several days of shooting are required before the real "character" of a lens becomes obvious.

The conditions under which the picture is screened can also make a difference. In some studios a high-contrast, high-resolution chart is photographed, and footage is inserted into rolls of original before work-printing. This way the evaluators can check the projector (its lens and registration have a very important effect on the sharpness of the picture) immediately before evaluating the footage.

Lens care

The glass used in lenses is considerably softer than the glass used for bottles, windows, and the like. The coating on the lens elements is softer still. For these reasons they scratch easily and the image rendering ability is noticeably diminished. Moisture, particularly the acid in perspiration from fingerprints, can also etch and permanently damage the delicate coating.

Scratches, smudges, and specks of dust and dirt all diminish image quality. Keep lenses in impeccably clean condition. First use a soft, clean lens brush and air squeegee to remove dust and dirt. This may be all the cleaning that is necessary. If smudges or fingerprints remain, use lens tissues to wipe them away. Do not use cloth or regular tissues. Never wipe a lens without brushing and dusting it first, because the tissue will grind the tiny grit particles right through the coating. If a fingerprint has been left on the lens for more than a few minutes, permanent damage may already have taken place and no amount of rubbing will remove the trace. For this reason it is a good idea to check lenses not only when setting up but also when packing up. Do not overlook such care with rented equipment—you may be the next person to rent the same lens. There is no need to get jumpy about every speck of dust, however: if the lens is pulled off the camera and given a thorough rubdown every two takes, its coating will soon be rubbed right off.

When zoom lenses are put back in their cases, be sure to place the zoom control at the full telephoto position. This will prevent possible slight dents in the internal zoom guides caused by accidents like dropping the case. Such dents or other imperfections in the zoom guides may cause slight bumps or shifts in the moving elements and show up as image jumps, and the like.

In terms of the final results obtained from shooting film under all conditions, no other component of the shooting package is as important as the lens. Even though it is not uncommon for one of the new, imported, high-quality zoom lenses to cost as much or more than the camera on which it is mounted, the most inexpensive 16mm cameras can deliver beautiful images on the screen—if the optics are capable of producing a sharp image, and if the cameraman correctly applies the basic rules of focus and depth of field. By making informed choices among the many exciting new optics available and by using these devices with creativity and intelligence, today's filmmaker has unparalleled opportunities for visual communication.

chapter 5
Lighting

In the field of cinematography nothing separates the talented professionals from the inexperienced amateurs more than the ability to do good lighting. Part of the reason is that beginners can learn to load, aim, shoot smooth zooms, get decent exposures, and gain similar experience by using relatively simple and inexpensive cameras and film. Professionals and amateurs alike have learned to operate a camera and its lenses skillfully and successfully.

But lighting—the equipment, the power, the personnel, and the studio all cost money. For this reason, many beginners have few opportunities to gain experience in this area. Even professionals sometimes avoid producing films when they know that extensive lighting requirements will drive the costs higher and higher.

But documentaries are being made today about subjects that were never before attempted because of their inherent lighting problems. The current trend toward realism is without question possible at least partly because of the new fast film emulsions and the increased portability of cameras and equipment. Films like those of Frederick Wiseman could not have been made had additional lighting been required, so it is tempting to believe that learning to do good lighting is outmoded and unnecessary.

But experienced directors know that in film, as well as in any form of communication, there is one principle which is never successfully violated: select and use the elements that will produce and enhance the desired total effect, and see that all conflicting elements are kept below the awareness level of the audience. Filmmakers sometimes find that when they achieve the ultranatural "This is exactly the way it happened" look in their footage, they succeed only in distracting their audience. With the necessary time and effort, one can learn to use good lighting to create and sustain the moods that will be the very essence of a film.

When deciding whether or not to use auxiliary lighting on locations, remember that although fast films make exposures possible in locations not previously photographable without extra lights, the existing light is often not suitable for photography and will not give the desired effect. Also cameras and recorders are not the only pieces of equipment that have gotten lighter and more portable in recent years. Lighting equipment has had perhaps the greatest reduction in weight on a percentage basis of all motion picture equipment. It is easier to do good lighting today than it has ever been before.

The light around you

The best place to begin the study of lighting is the very place you are at this moment and all of the other places you go each day. Try to become aware of the light that is falling on the objects around you as you go from place to place. Look about your surroundings this very moment. What are the sources of light illuminating the things you can see? Are they producing shadows on surfaces behind the objects on which they fall? Are the shadows sharp and clear or are they soft and undefined? Look at round objects and compare their tones with flat objects; do the same with those that stand vertical and lie horizontal. Repeat this exercise in all the different rooms you enter and at all times of the day and night. Look around at breakfast, outside in different kinds of weather, and at the places you go at night. Memorize the sources of light and the direction and quality of the shadows they produce on the people and objects they illuminate. Carefully compare the brightest objects with the darkest ones, and watch how people look as they pass near or under different lighting fixtures. The next time you are at a party, in a bus, walking through a graveyard, sitting on the beach, or making love in front of a fireplace, stop and analyze the part light plays in establishing the prevailing mood.

It is vitally important to become aware of the role that light plays in the world in order to be successful in duplicating these effects on film. Trying to light a scene for film without regard for the way the scene looks in real life will result in a confused lighting approach that ultimately will confuse the audience as well. One must develop a conscious and systematic way of viewing the world before the world can be effectively duplicated for others. When this is successfully learned, the world can be recreated through the use of light.

Five aspects of lighting

This discussion of motion picture lighting begins by examining the functions of natural light sources and the ways artificial sources can simulate them. It will be divided into five sections: quantity, quality, direction, balance, and color temperature.

Quantity

The selection of various light sources for photographic illumination, the balance of these sources for aesthetics and contrast control, and the determination of film exposure are all dependent upon *photometry*, the science of the measurement of light intensities. Systems for measuring light must be based on a known unit, just as systems for measuring distance and volume are. In earlier times, the visible radiation emitted by a single given candle was used as the standard unit, and was called the *standard candle*. This delightful, simple, and easily understood concept has been replaced by the *candela*, which is defined as one-sixtieth of the luminous intensity of a black body radiator maintained at the temperature of melting platinum. Terms such as candlepower and footcandles are still used, but the candela is the actual reference used today.

Definition of terms

To avoid confusion it is important to distinguish between and among terms applied to the intensity of the light-emitting source itself; the quantity of light falling *on* a given surface; and the brightness of the light reflected *from* the surface being lighted.

The radiation that emits from a source of light is called *luminous intensity* and is rated in *candela,* or *candlepower.*

The light falling on a subject is called *incident light.* The light that is reflected from a subject is called *reflected light.* Thus, the light emanating from a light source, be it the sun, the sky, or an incandescent lamp, is incident to the objects being illuminated. It can be measured with a light-sensitive device (described in detail in chapter 6) called an incident light meter. Objects being illuminated reflect back to the viewer some of the light incident to them. The light reflected from the objects can be measured with another light-sensitive device (also described in chapter 6) called a reflected light meter.

The terms *luminous intensity* and *illumination* refer to systems for measuring *incident light.* The terms *luminance* and *brightness* refer to systems for measuring reflected light.

The most common unit of illumination refers to the luminous intensity at the *surface being illuminated* and is called the *footcandle.* The footcandle is defined as the intensity of illumination at the surface of a sphere at a one-foot radius from a theoretical pinpoint light source, with a luminous intensity of one candela. In other words, the illumination at any point on an imaginary one-foot radius sphere from one centrally located candela is equal to one footcandle. Most professional incident light meters give readings in footcandles, and most exposure conversion charts will use the term as well. The metric system uses meter-candles, which are called *lux;* one footcandle equals 10.764 lux.

The total footcandles of illumination that fall on a surface depend on at least four factors.

The luminous intensity of the source (candlepower of the sun, arc light, incandescent bulb, or other source of illumination)

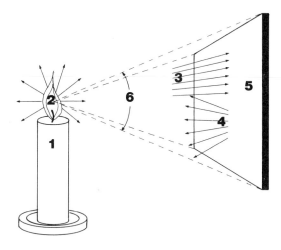

5-1. *(1) A light source of one candela. (2) Luminous intensity, or candlepower, the amount of light emitted in all directions by one candela. (3) Illumination falling on surface, incident light, measured in footcandles or lumens per square foot. (4) Light reflected from surface, luminance, measured in foot lamberts. (5) A surface of given reflectivity. (6) One lumen, or unit of luminous flux.*

The efficiency of the reflector and/or optical system employed in the lamp and fixture

The distance between the source and the surface being illuminated

The absorption of the air or medium through which the light travels (smoke, haze, smog, water, etc.)

A powerful light source can not only produce a given amount of light at a certain distance from the source but also can provide equal amounts of that intensity over a relatively large area. In terms of sheer quantity, nothing can equal the sun. The intensity is very high, and it can cover half the earth with nearly equal amounts of light. Small light sources can provide usable levels of illumination only when placed very close to the subject or when a system of reflectors or lenses focuses all the light into a narrow beam.

The total illumination on a surface in a given amount of time is called *luminous flux* and is measured in terms of *lumens per square foot* or simply *lumens* (lm). Remember that one footcandle is equal to the illumination at a one-foot radius sphere with a one candlepower source at the center. The lumen is equal to a one-foot-square portion of this sphere. To figure the total lumen output the expression $\pi(3.1416)$ is used as a multiplier to compute the total area of the sphere. So, one candela produces one footcandle, or 4π lumens, or 12.57 lumens.

A hypothetical example might make things clearer. According to the manufacturer of a 650-watt quartz halogen lighting unit, the bulb has a luminous intensity of about 16,500 candela—quite a birthday cake! This lamp can provide 16,500 footcandles of illumination measured one foot from the bulb, or 1,314 lumens of luminous flux. At 12 feet from the source, this particular lighting unit can provide about 125 footcandles. The reading takes into account the efficiency of the reflector in the unit housing, the absorption of the air, and so forth.

If the area covered by 125 footcandles of illumination is, say, 10 feet by 10 feet—100 square feet—the total illumination is 12,500 lumens.

To measure light reflected from a surface (called *luminance* or *brightness*), four factors need to be considered:

1. The lumens per square foot falling on the surface

2. The ability of the surface to reflect light, called *reflectance*

3. The kind of reflectance, whether *diffuse* from flat or matte surfaces, or *specular* from glossy or mirrored surfaces

4. The angle from which the measurement is taken, especially when measuring specular surfaces.

The luminance is measured in units that refer diretly to lumens or candles per square foot and are called *footlamberts*. A footlambert of reflected light is equal to one lumen of incident light, when that lumen is reflected from a perfectly diffuse ideal (100 percent) reflecting surface, with the source of light placed on a 90-degree angle to the surface. In other words, the ideal surface illuminated with one lumen per square foot reflects one footlambert. Under the metric system, one meter candle or *lux* reflects one *nit*. Professional reflected-light meters are usually calibrated in lamberts per square foot; like all meters, they give readings that can be converted directly to f-stops.

A brief glossary
This list will help clarify the confusing similarity between lighting terms.

Brightness: The amount of light reflected from a subject

Candela: Unit of luminous intensity, formerly the standard candle

Candlepower: The total luminous intensity of a light source

Diffuse: Scattered or spread light; also, a matte or flat reflecting surface

Footcandle: The unit of measurement of illumination

Footlambert: The unit of measurement of reflected light

Illumination: The amount of light falling on a subject

Incident light: Light falling onto a subject

Lumen: Unit of illumination per square foot

Luminance: The amount of light reflected from a subject

Luminaries: Light sources, particularly studio lights, consisting of lamp and housing

Luminous flux: The amount of light in terms of area

Luminous intensity: The amount of light emitted from a source

Photometry: The measurement of the intensity of light

Reflected light: Light reflected from a subject

Specular: A glossy or mirrored reflecting surface

Inverse square law of light
There are two important laws the cinematographer uses constantly in lighting. One has to do with quantities of incident light, and the other

with quantities of reflected light. The first is called the *inverse square law of light*. The law states that "the intensity of illumination at a given surface is inversely proportional to the *square* of the distance between the source and the surface."

The obvious fact was stated earlier that the distance between the source of light and the surface being illuminated was one of the prime factors in determining the intensity of illumination. The inverse square law of light states that when the distance from the light source is changed, the illumination is increased or reduced by a square of that amount. Place an object four feet from a light source; a light meter measures 500 footcandles of illumination falling on the object. But if the object is moved to eight feet, thereby doubling the distance, the surface does not receive one-half the illumination but only one-quarter, or 125 footcandles. The illustration shows why. When the distance, #1, is doubled, #2, the light is effectively covering four times the unit area with one-quarter the intensity of illumination on any given portion.

In the earlier example, the subject illumination falls to one quarter its intensity with only a four-foot change in position. It is easy to see how the inverse square law is an important factor when equal amounts of illumination are needed for subjects both close and far from a given luminary. This effect is minimized if a brighter lamp is placed at a greater distance. For example: a large light source provides, say, 500 footcandles at a distance of 16 feet from the source. Now, move back four feet further—the light will fall off only to 375 footcandles. In the previous example three-quarters of the light was lost with a four-foot change in position and, in this example, only one-quarter of the light is lost.

To light a set where an actor enters through a door on the left and

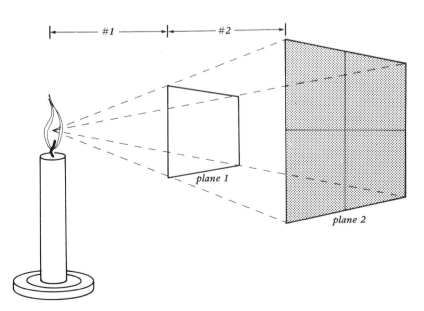

#1   #2

plane 1

plane 2

5-2. *Inverse square law.*

sits in a chair on the right, and where bright overall illumination is desired, use either several small sources placed so that he walks from one area of illumination to another, or a powerful single source placed a relatively great distance from either position. Otherwise, the intensity of the lighting would change drastically as the actor moved across the set.

In practice, many lighting schemes are greatly simplified when powerful lights can be used and placed at relatively great distances. The advantages to working this way include complete freedom of action (there are no "dark" spots), the lack of duplicate and overlapping shadows (these usually attract attention and are displeasing), easier microphone placement (again, fewer shadow problems), and less setup time (fewer lights to fiddle with).

Multiple small light sources are used to produce bright overall lighting when more powerful sources, large amounts of current, and space are unavailable, and when they will do a better job of giving the desired effect. But when several smaller lights must be used to cover a given piece of action, more setup time is usually required to establish the proper balance between all the lights and eliminate "hot spots" when several lights overlap. Actors must be careful to stop and deliver lines in the precise places where the lighting is right, and microphone and background shadows are usually more of a problem.

Later in this chapter specific lighting problems will be discussed such as duplicating the appearance of daylight in the studio and producing nighttime lighting moods; it will be obvious that the sqaure law is an underlying principle in the solution of many lighting problems.

The cosine law
A second law of importance that deals with the quantity of light reflected from surfaces is called the *cosine law*. It states that "the brightness of a surface decreases in an amount proportional to the cosine of the angle of incidence of the light source illuminating it." This means that if a surface has a given amount of luminance when light is striking it at an angle of 90 degrees, it will have less luminance when the light strikes it at an angle of less than 90 degrees.

Figure 5-3 shows why. When the surface of a given size is placed at a 90-degree angle to the light source, it is intercepting a given quantity of light shown by the angle of rays emanating from the source. When the same-size surface is angled to 150 degrees, a narrow angle of rays is intercepted; with continued rotation, no rays at all would be intercepted.

The cinematographer will employ lighting closer to a 90-degree angle to the surface when he requires the greatest efficiency from his light sources. When the angle of incidence is very narrow, he will check the surface carefully to see if it is reflecting enough light for the desired exposure. To facilitate readings of this kind, a reflected-light meter or a flat surface disc on an incident-light meter can be used. The flat disc responds to the light in accordance with the cosine law and gives a properly calibrated exposure reading at any angle (see chapter 6).

Quality

Every light source, be it the sun, sky, desk lamp, streetlight, campfire, candle, or a motion picture studio lighting unit, has a specific character or *quality*. Part of this quality is the actual color of the light created by the source; this is discussed as "color temperature" later in this chapter. But the most important aspect of the quality of light has to do with how a given subject looks when illuminated by various sources. A properly exposed picture of someone taken outside on a cloudy day looks very different from a properly exposed picture of someone taken on a sunny day. A photograph of a person illuminated by the light from a large window looks very different from

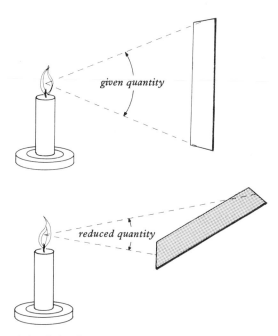

given quantity

reduced quantity

5-3. *Cosine law.*

5-4. *Top left: Spectra disc facing light source obtains reading of 125fc. Top right: turned about 30 degrees from light source, reading falls to 64fc. Bottom left: about 60 degrees from light source, reading falls to 32fc. Bottom right: at 90 degrees to light source, reading is negligible.*

a photograph of a person illuminated by a reading lamp, even when the two exposures are similar. This difference in quality has to do primarily with the nature and direction of the shadows on the subject and his background. On film, the highlights and shadows on the subject must communicate the desired lighting mood. All scenes contain form, color, and the textures of the subjects and backgrounds. But the quality of lighting in the shot will be seen in terms of highlights and shadows. These correspond not only to the direction from which the light is coming (shadows obviously fall in the opposite direction) but also will be "hard" or "soft" depending on the quality of the light source. The terms "hard" and "soft" refer respectively to sharp, well-defined shadows and highlights, and to diffused, poorly defined shadows. Do not confuse the terms hard and soft with lighting contrast (discussed later), because subjects can be lighted with sharp or diffused shadows and great or little contrast, in any combination.

The hardness or softness of shadows cast by any light source is dependent upon two factors. One is the distance between the shadow-

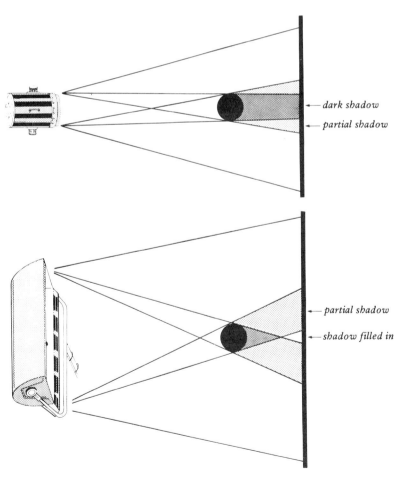

5-5. *Hard and soft light sources.*

dark shadow

partial shadow

partial shadow

shadow filled in

making subject and the background on which the shadow is cast. All other things being equal, when the distance between the subject and the background is increased, the shadow softens. But in most shooting situations, subjects and backgrounds cannot be moved very much in relation to each other—such as the nose on someone's face. Therefore it is the second factor that becomes most important—namely, the relative physical size of the light source. Other things being equal, lighting units with large areas from which the light emanates will cast soft shadows and those with small areas will cast hard shadows. Figure 5-5 helps to explain.

The large light sources simply fill in their own shadows, whereas the small light sources cannot do that. But it is important to remember that this is relative size, and that means the distance from the light source to the subject is a critical factor. Notice figure 5-6. When a lighting unit is very close to a given subject, it is also relatively large; however, when the light is moved to a great distance from the subject, it becomes relatively small. Consider the sun. With a diameter of 864,000 miles, it is surely one of the largest light sources going. However, it is usually about 93,000,000 miles from earthly subjects

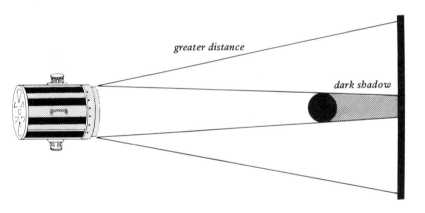

greater distance

dark shadow

5-6. *The same source produces softer shadows at reduced distances.*

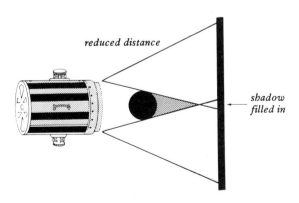

reduced distance

shadow
filled in

and therefore casts very well-defined shadows. Alternately, the atmosphere is so large and relatively close that it can fill in the sun's shadows with completely even illumination—on a cloudy day only large objects very close to their background cast any shadows at all.

Lighting units are selected for their ability to create or eliminate shadows, depending on their intended use. Occasionally the cinematographer will have to illuminate a subject with completely shadowless lighting. This may be the case where shadows would interfere with an already intricate pattern, where shadows would distract from the primary subject (such as a product), or where soft, shadowless illumination suits the mood of the script. In these cases, the cinematographer should choose the physically largest lighting units available, and he will use his ingenuity to devise ways of producing broad surfaces of illumination. For example, he will "bounce" lights off white walls and ceilings. If an ordinary, hard, six-inch diameter quartz light is aimed at a wall adjacent to the subject, it may produce a bright area three feet in diameter. This bright spot becomes a large-diameter lighting source for the subject. By attaching pieces of diffusion material (such as spun glass) to large frames placed in front of the lights, the source diameter is also increased. Numerous small lights placed behind large sheets of spun glass produce very wide "shadowless" lighting units. Lights can be mounted to a ceiling or grid, and then large strips of spun glass can be suspended below the lights to create soft lighting similar to the fluorescent illumination in some office and public buildings. Highly reflective plastic "space blankets" may be taped to the wall to create a large reflector for soft "bounce" lighting.

In many, perhaps most, lighting setups, "hard" sources of light are called for to give shape, form, and character to the subjects. If a plain ball is illuminated with completely shadowless light, it photographs as a flat disk. When a hard spotlight is used, its round shape is immediately apparent. The shape of faces, bodies, and objects of all descriptions are revealed with clarity and vitality by directional luminaries.

For motion picture purposes, the "hard" lights that provide clearly defined shadows include all types of open and lens-covered spotlights from tiny 150-watt "dinkys" up to 250-amp Brutes. The "soft" lights that provide fill and shadowless illumination include many forms of flood lights—"broads," "bathtubs," "umbrellas," or bounce-light setups.

Hard lighting units provide the directionality and characteristic look of the shot; soft lighting units raise overall illumination levels and fill in dark shadows. In theory the lighting quality of "real" settings can be duplicated by selecting units that cast the same kind of shadows as the sources that illuminate the real settings. They should be placed at similar angles and distances from the subject, with additional soft lighting units to raise the illumination in the shadows for an acceptable contrast level (more on contrast control to follow). In practice, the selection of units will be modified to suit space, distance, and power requirements for shooting as well as other factors that will be described as we go.

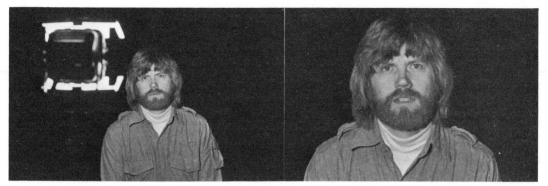

5-7. *Direct front lighting.*

Direction

The direction of the light is fundamental to the mood and communicative power of the shot. The skillfull cinematographer can change a bright, cheery daytime dining room to a mysterious midnight meeting place just by shifting the placement of the same few lights. With similar changes, the friendly salesman becomes a sinister extortionist.

Generally speaking, motion picture lighting directions or angles may be analyzed in four ways: front to back, high to low, top to bottom, and flat to texture. Such positions will be considered for each shot, each desired effect, and the placement of each light. The lighting units themselves begin to take on names as they assume various roles. For example, there are front lights, back lights, high, low, top, bottom, flat, and texture lights. The primary source of illumination—that which establishes the perceived direction of the light—is called the main light, or the *key light*. Its placement will always fall into one or more of the four categories—front to back, high to low, top to bottom, and flat to texture.

Figures 5-7, 5-8, 5-9, and 5-10 show the effects on a person created by moving a key light through these categories. The direct *front light* gives no distinct modeling to the subject, and all shadows are cast almost directly behind. Except for special effects, this treatment is unsatisfactory for people and is used only in situations where shadows

5-8. *Light at about 45 degrees produces shadows on face.*

5-10. *Light behind subject produces rim-lighted hair effect with face in shadow.*

would interfere. Special *ring lights* that are designed to surround the lens act as key lights and give shadowless illumination to medical subjects such as operations. Front lights of this sort are also useful not as key lights, but for filling in shadows cast by other key lights.

As the key light is moved to the side, shadows become more distinct on the subject, and the shape of the face begins to emerge. When the angle approaches 90 degrees from the camera, strong lines and highly defined features are produced. When the light moves behind the imaginary 90 degree line, the front of the face is predominantly in shadow. This important key light position is a primary technique for creating nighttime effects. While the illumination necessary for exposure is maintained, the predominant shadows produce the feeling of night. When the light is placed directly behind the subject, only a bright rim of detail remains. This "rim light" separates subjects distinctly from the background, and in conjunction with other lights can produce an almost spiritual radiance.

Back light, any light source farther than 90 degrees from the camera position, is almost always used. Back lights are often called *kicker lights* because of the hot "kicks" of light that are reflected strongly toward the camera. They are used in addition to key lights for scenes of virtually all moods. Back light adds a special brilliance that makes subjects stand out from the background.

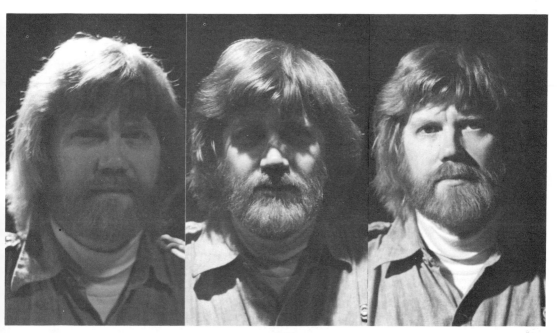

5-11. *Kicker light.*   5-12. *Light top light.*   5-13. *Typical key light position.*

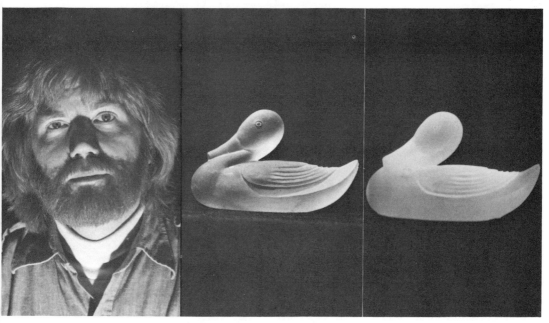

5-14. *Low key light produces mystery effect.*

5-15. *Top light on glass figurine produces pleasant modeling.*

5-16. *Illumination from underneath (often used with glass objects) causes figurine to "glow" and reduces detail.*

The *high front light* produces generally unpleasant nose and eyesocket shadows similar to direct overhead sunlighting; most cameramen try to avoid allowing the nose shadow to cross the lips if a pleasant rendering of the subject is desired. But when the key light is placed lower than eye level, strange and sinister upward shadows are cast. With exaggerated low front light positions features become distorted and unrecognizable; the effect can be used for strong mystery and supernatural effects.

Top light is used to help simulate daylight—it represents the effect of the sky. It is usually not considered a key light placement but as an overall illumination booster or fill light. *Bottom light* is successful with products such as glassware and bottles: lights are positioned below objects that have been placed on a glass shelf. A notable example of bottom light with human subjects is the illuminated floor in the closing bedroom scenes of Stanley Kubrick's *2001: A Space Odyssey*.

5-17. *Front light (top) and texture light (bottom) on cedar shingles. (Harvey "T" Thompson)*

When the surfaces of objects and walls are illuminated by lights placed near the camera, the surfaces will be rendered even and flat. As the light is moved toward a 90-degree angle from the camera, texture begins to appear and eventually becomes exaggerated. Shapes as well as textures and variations in backgrounds, sets, and landscapes, have greater strength and interest with the use of such lighting. This is another one of the cameraman's useful controls.

Since key light placement plays such an important role in the photographic rendering of the subject, the most experienced cameramen will, whenever possible, wait until the actors are actually on the set to freeze final lighting positions. While subtle differences in key light positions are relatively unimportant on long shots, the shape of every individual face requires consideration when shooting close-ups. Lighting is frequently adjusted to create this kind of personal tailoring.

Traditional key light angles for close-ups are about 45 degrees from the camera right or left, and about 30 to 45 degrees above the horizontal axis. They vary widely depending on the camera angle, tilt of the head in the close-up, and desired effect. Figure 5-18 shows the traditional Rembrandt cheek patch, often used as a guide to the best modeling position for the key light. "Modeling" in this context refers to the pattern of light and shadows that reveals the shapes of the head and face; it is frequently used to describe the play of light on forms.

When a shot is being lighted, move the key light back and forth from camera position to the right and left at various heights until the best effect is achieved. When lighting people, it is important ordinarily that only one key light be used for a given subject or position. When two or more hard lights overlap on a person's face and cast double and triple shadows, the lighting becomes distracting, confusing, and unpleasant. This is why shadows are illuminated and softened not by additional hard lighting but by large, soft, fill lights. Only when lights are more than 90 degrees from the camera do multiple hard

5-18. Cheek patch.

lights of equal intensity have a useful role in lighting the subject. For example, "cross lighting," spotlights placed 90 degrees from the camera at both sides of the subject, is often used for full-figure dance photography because of the way the dancer's entire form is revealed against the background.

Balance

As implied throughout this chapter, luminaries are rarely used alone. Single lights may be powerful enough to bring the illumination level up to the needed value for exposure and a single hard key light may give the proper modeling to the subject, but there are other factors that must always be considered.

The most important of these factors is the scene contrast, which must be controlled by careful lighting balance. This is a problem because, as discussed in chapter 3, films have a limited ability to reproduce bright and dark subjects. Figure 5-19 is the exposure range for a hypothetical black-and-white film and figure 5-20 is for a hypothetical color film.

The values across the bottom indicate f-stops or equivalent amounts of light. The values up the side indicate density on the film. The black-and-white film has a tolerance range from white to black—or from minimum-density-producing exposure to maximum-density-pro-

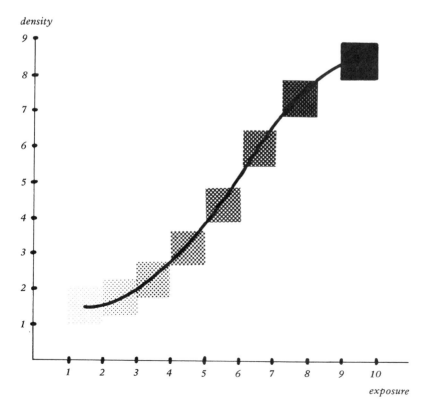

5-19. *Black-and-white film exposure range.*

density

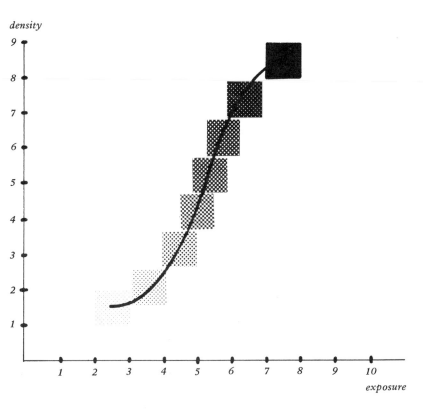

exposure

ducing exposure—of about eight stops. Color film can handle a max-imum of about six stops. Human eyes can handle twenty or more stops under most conditions. An average sunlit scene has a range of about seven stops if no extremely black or white subjects are included. The conclusions to be drawn from this information are, first, that the eyes can easily handle the contrast range of the average sunlit scene. Second, that black-and-white films can barely squeeze the contrast range of sunlit scenes into their limited exposure latitudes. Third, that color films will often not be able to handle the full contrast range of sunlit subjects at all.

The ability of objects to reflect light plays an important part in the contrast range within a given scene. Fortunately, few scenes contain a 100 percent white reflector and a 0 percent black reflector. A reflected light reading of a white fence post is only about five stops brighter than the reading of a black auto tire when both are illuminated by sunlight at the same angle. So the average scene's luminance is not, in itself, outside the range of color or black-and-white film. It is the additional problem of shadows that makes the black details drop below the acceptable exposure range. Films exposed on cloudy days show plenty of detail in the brightest whites and in the darkest blacks, assuming proper exposure. And, if extremely large "shadowless" light-ing units are exclusively used to light an indoor scene, whites and blacks in the scene also fall easily within the film's exposure latitude. The problem of lighting balance is, therefore, to keep the contrast range within the film's latitude while still allowing for directionality, interest, and shadows. The balance of lights—or *lighting ratio,* as it is usually called—will be changed in accordance with three variables.

The first variable is the *film type*—color or black-and-white, and the specific kind. As discussed in chapter 3, some color and black-and-white films have significantly greater inherent contrast than others. Experience—and the recommendations found in this book—will teach what kinds of lighting ratios are acceptable for each film.

The second variable is the built-in *contrast* of the scene itself. Exterior and interior scenes can vary widely in colors and gray-scale values, as well as their ability to diffuse light and fill in their own shadows. If an interior location is being illuminated for photography and in the long shot there are objects such as white walls and very dark furniture, or if the actor is wearing a clean white shirt and a black suit, lighting ratios must be narrower than usual. This is why the brightness of the colors selected for the set, as well as actors' clothing, should be controlled for photography. If all the objects within the scene are of controlled reflectance, stronger, more interesting, and dramatic lighting ratios can be used without sacrificing too much detail.

Certain exterior and interior scenes have the ability to diffuse and reflect some of the light and fill in their own shadows to a certain degree. For example, when the sun and the subject are at the proper angle, snow or white beaches can reflect enough light into the shadows for a decent-looking exposure. White walls and floors usually bounce a certain amount of light back into shadows as well. But generally the shadows are still rendered too strongly to allow for photography without some additional fill light.

The third lighting ratio variable is the *relative size of the shot* and the *respective shadow predominance* within the shot. In a wide exterior scene, for example, the shadows under bushes, distant lawn furniture, and under the chin of a person walking through are small and of no particular concern. But when the person moves

5-21. Top: long shot made in sunlight is acceptable; bottom: close-up has strong shadows that need fill for acceptable exposure range.

toward the camera and stops in close-up, the shadows are now clearly visible and have become a predominant element. The strong lighting ratio that was perfectly acceptable in the long shot becomes objectionable when a close-up is made under the same conditions. With long shots where the shadows are a predominant factor as in the city when the sun is at a strong angle to all the buildings, exposure must be adjusted in their favor. This is assuming that a normal rendering of the scene is desired. The predominance of shadows in scenes where the lighting ratio cannot be controlled always calls for consideration and exposure adjustment.

In close-ups of people, shadows must be filled in with the use of reflectors or fill lights. In practice this means the key light (or lights) is usually set up first, each area of the set is covered with the needed quantity of illumination, and double shadows or other problems are eliminated. Then large, soft fill lights are added, placed relatively near the camera so that any shadows they create will be cast behind the subjects and be invisible. Enough fill light must be added as well to bring the shadows to a tolerable exposure range. This ratio is expressed in terms such as 2 to 1, 3 to 1, 4 to 1, and so forth. It means that the fill light is one-half, one-third, or one-quarter as bright as the key light.

The lighting contrast ratio is measured with an incident-light meter, or with a reflected-light meter used in conjunction with a 18 percent neutral gray card. The incident-light meter is preferred because in order to read the intensity of each individual light source, the others must be blocked from affecting the reading. With the gray card and the reflected-light meter, it is awkward to block off the key light. With the incident-light meter, the key light can be blocked with a free hand. Figures 5-22 and 5-23 show how this is accomplished.

When the key light is less than 90 degrees from the camera position, first use the meter at the subject position to read the combined intensities of the key and fill lights together. This combination is the brightest total key

5-22. *Reading with reflected-light meter and gray card.*

5-23. *Reading with incident-light meter.*

light illumination on the subject. Next, block out the key light but allow the fill light to illuminate the dome on the incident meter. With a reflected meter and a gray card, try blocking the key light with your body, or turn the key light off.

When the key light is set at a greater angle from the camera, such as past the 90 degree position, the fill light no longer effectively illuminates the same surfaces as the key light; they do not combine for greater brightness on the subject. Simply read the key light and the fill light separately.

The ratio can be read in footcandles or in f-stops, depending on how the meter is calibrated. If the desired ratio is, say, 4 to 1, and the key-plus-fill combined reading is 500 footcandles or, say, f/5.6, then the fill light should be set so that it alone reads 125 footcandles or f/2.8. Moving two f-stops quarters or quadruples the light (see chapter 6). If the desired lighting ratio is 2 to 1 and the key-plus-fill light reads 250 footcandles, the fill light alone should be set to 125 footcandles. If the desired ratio is 2 to 1 and, because of the type of film, the key-plus-fill light reads f/8, then the fill light should be set to read one f-stop less, or f/5.6. Remember that a ratio of 3 to 1 means a difference of one and a half f-stops, not three f-stops. For a more detailed discussion of f-stops, see chapter 6.

The proper ratio depends on at least four things, as mentioned earlier: the inherent contrast of gray tones in the subject; the size of the shot (long or close) and the predominance of shadows; the inherent contrast or latitude of the film; and, most important, the desired effect. The recommed ratios can be relied on for most kinds of photography. Those for normal long shots and normal close-ups on both tables are fairly accepted standards. The others can vary depending on just how contrasty or flat the subjects really are.

A contrast viewing filter for pan (black-and-white) or color is helpful for examining the lighting ratios. These devices are reliable, however, only when used from camera position in the following manner. Close one eye and examine shadow details with the other. Then

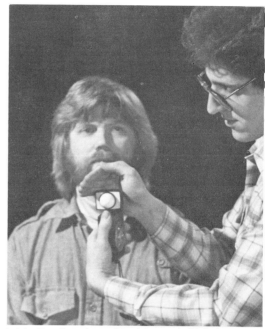

5-24. *Reading the combined key and fill light.*

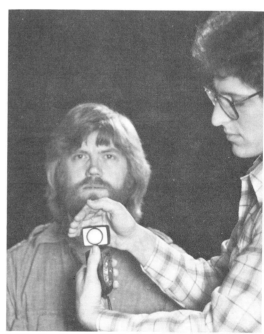

5-25. *Reading the fill light with the key turned off.*

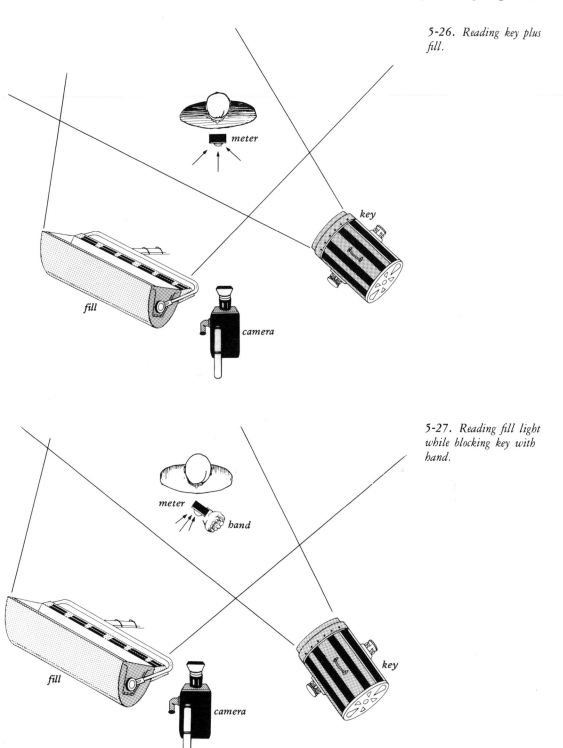

5-26. *Reading key plus fill.*

5-27. *Reading fill light while blocking key with hand.*

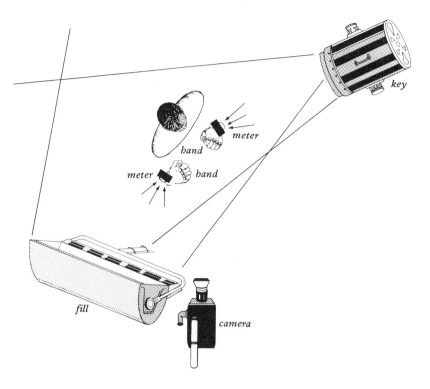

5-28. *When key and fill are more than 90 degrees apart, it is necessary to read the key and fill separately as shown.*

5-29. *Maximum lighting ratios for black-and-white and color films.*

Maximum ratio table for normal renditions		
	B&W	Color
Contrasty subject LS	5-1	3-1
Normal subject LS	6-1	4-1
Flat subject LS	8-1	5-1
Contrasty subject CU	2-1	1.5-1
Normal subject CU	3-1	2-1
Flat subject CU	4-1	3-1

Maximum ratio table for night, dramatic, and low-key renditions		
	B&W	Color
Contrasty subject LS	5-1	5-1
Normal subject LS	7-1	6-1
Flat subject LS	10-1	7-1
Contrasty subject CU	4-1	3-1
Normal subject CU	5-1	4-1
Flat subject CU	6-1	5-1

quickly place the filter over the open eye and continue to examine shadow detail through the filter. Leave the filter in front of the eye only for a few moments, because the eye adjusts in a short time to the diminished level provided by the filter. Viewed through the filter, a certain amount of shadow detail disappears. This causes perceptible boost in contrast, which is supposed to be similar to that of the film being used. If shadows appear to go black or lose detail altogether through the filter, the lighting ratio must be checked.

The properly used incident-light meter is the most accurate way of setting the lighting ratio. But it is important to remember that even a perfect ratio can be rendered too flat or contrasty by an improper film exposure or faulty development and printing.

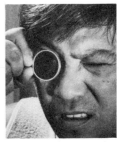

5-30. Cinematographer using contrast viewing filter.

Separation light

Kicker light, also called *separation light, hair light, back light,* and *top light,* depending mostly on the cameraman using it, is the third important light to set. It is used for every kind of photography: day, night, mystery, high level, or low key (predominant shadow).

As implied in the use of key and fill light, it is the sun and sky that serve as a basis for understanding most kinds of lighting requirements. And it is the light from the sky, which surrounds subjects and illuminates them from behind and gives them highlights and separation, that inspires the use of kicker light. In photography the effect is usually exaggerated to give life and depth to each shot. Bright or high key scenes will look too flat without kicker light, and with night or mystery lighting the subject simply disappears into the background without it.

The kicker light is usually set high on the side opposite the key light and behind the subject at around 45 degrees from the vertical. Relatively hard bright-light sources, like the spotlights used for key lights, are used for separation light. They are usually arranged to cover the entire playing area of the set with even illumination so the actors

5-31. Strong kicker light, combined with low key. (American Cinematographer, February, 1977, reprinted by permission)

normal high
kicker position (2)

low kicker
position (3)

key
light (1)

fill
light (4)

will never be without it. If the actor is bald, the intensity must be reduced or the kicker moved to a lower position, such as number 3 in figure 5-32, to avoid producing a hot spot in the middle of his head. Set this way, the kicker creates a bright rim on the cheek, neck, and sleeve, and is often called a *cheek light*.

Separation lights are usually set to about the same level of illumination as the key light—and sometimes even higher. Be careful not to let the kicker light hit the meter and adversely affect the exposure readings for the key and fill lights. The separation light does not illuminate the surface facing the camera and therefore does not affect the key-to-fill lighting ratio and film exposure. Figure 5-33 shows how to shield the incident meter dome when making such readings.

Background light

The lighting discussed so far has been concerned with the illumination of the subjects or actors within the set or location. But when visible, the set walls, background, and floors are predominant elements in the composition of the shot, and they must be given lighting consideration as well.

The quantity of illumination for backgrounds depends on two factors: the reflective quality and color brightness of the background itself, and the desired mood or effect of the lighting. Strong or saturated colors are usually avoided in set wall finishes because of their tendency to distract from the subjects. In brightly painted locations where the background colors cannot be controlled, background illumination may have to be kept very low to avoid such distraction. Locations with white walls often pick up enough illumination from stray key and fill lighting and do not need additional illumination; in fact, when the subject is very near a white wall it is difficult to keep the wall from getting too "hot" and overexposing the film. But the desired mood of the shot is of primary importance, and overlighting the background by two or three stops and "washing out" detail altogether may be just right for certain effects. For night and mystery effects, keep extraneous light off the background and control exposure carefully so that only a few textures and details are revealed.

It is difficult to be specific about suggested quantities of light for backgrounds since the variables are so broad. Generally speaking, however, the ratios between the foreground or subject illumination and the background illumination are very similar to the ratios between key and fill light when backgrounds are painted with midrange color values. In other words, for long shots of general subjects with normal contrast and light-colored backgrounds, a ratio of 4 to 1 between the total illumination on the subject and the total illumination of the background is typical. Ordinarily, the background illumination is not increased (or the ratio lessened) for close-ups.

5-33. *Shielding kicker from incident meter.*

The exception to this is a night or mystery lighting situation when background illumination is so low that only a few highlights and tones are revealed in the long shot. Switch to a close-up, and the background will be entirely black unless the angle includes a few of these background highlights. Chances are that the close-up will be more interesting if a few of these highlights are deliberately included, either by careful angle selection or lighting adjustment.

The direction of lighting for backgrounds is usually the same as the general key light direction. Shadows cast by picture frames, furniture, doors and the like should fall in the same direction as those on the actor's face and cast by the actor's body. Background lights are placed near the sides of the set beyond the key light positions or clamped to the tops of the adjacent set walls or both. Small lights may sometimes be hidden behind furniture or outside of open doorways to illuminate parts of the set, but they must be controlled carefully so that no stray "hot spots" that would reveal their placement are produced on close door frames or furniture parts.

It is extremely important that set lighting and location walls be illuminated with "shape" and varieties of tone to avoid the tendency of walls to reproduce as the flat, boring surfaces that they often are. Barn doors should be used to keep excess light off parts of the walls. Let the walls get slightly darker at the top, bottom, and in the corners. Use focused spotlights to highlight paintings on the wall, tables, and dark furniture. Use the incident-light meter, or reflected-light meter with gray card, to measure the intensity of light *at* illuminated walls and surfaces. Ideally the incident meter should be fitted with a flat disc for this kind of reading. The disc (or gray card) is held in a position corresponding to the flat surface being lighted. This practice automatically compensates for falloff due to the cosine law.

When visible sources of illumination, such as desk or table lamps, are a part of the shot, hang a small focused spotlight overhead to create a circle of illumination on the adjacent wall or table to enhance its effect. The light bulb in the desk or table lamp should provide just enough intensity to make the shade appear bright. But it will probably not cause the desired extra brightness on the surrounding surfaces, so the additional spot lighting is added. The illumination of highlight areas such as this should be about the same as the foreground or subject illumination. They are easily checked with a reflected-light meter.

Cycloramas are backgrounds with curved corners and sloping bottoms that eliminate visible floor edges, thus allowing subjects to be photographed as if floating in space. When they or large sheets of *backdrop paper* are used

5-34. *Note how background illumination is darker at top of set.* (American Cinematographer, *December, 1979, reprinted by permission*)

5-35. *Floor lamp and illumination on wall provide interest.*

as backgrounds, illumination is usually either a problem of providing extremely even and flat lighting or of breaking up the flatness to provide a sort of abstract interest behind the subject.

When the problem is providing even exposure over the entire background, special lighting units called *skypans* or the essentially equivalent *striplights* are usually selected. These are hung every few feet across the entire width of the background and several feet away from the top front edge so that they may be tilted down to illuminate the entire surface. When the background is serving as a "sky" seen through set windows or behind scenery, the pans or striplights can be placed along the bottom edge and sides as well.

When the problem is breaking up large, flat backdrops and set walls, a dappled or variegated pattern of light and dark is cast by using tree branches or cutouts called *cukolorises* or *cookies*. Cookies may be homemade from sheet metal, cardboard, plywood, or framed foil; their size depends on the light used and the set wall to be illuminated. Usually, cookies and their lights are placed near both edges of the wall so that more or less even amounts of patterned light will cover the area. The size and intensity of the pattern is changed by shifting lamp-to-cookie-to-wall distances. Hard light sources are used to cast relatively distinct shadows. Be sure to view the pattern and foreground with a contrast viewing filter to be certain that the contrast is not too strong or distracting.

Color temperature

As described in chapter 3, color-film emulsions are balanced for use with light of specific color temperatures. Professional films are of two types: tungsten films, balanced for a Kelvin temperature of 3,200°, and daylight films, balanced for about 5,400°K. Theoretically, accurate color rendering in photography means absolute adherence to the use of light sources that match the color temperature of the film. Tungsten and daylight films can be converted from one to the other by placing color-conversion filters on the camera. However, the

5-36. *Illuminated cyclorama.* (American Cinematographer, *November, 1979, reprinted by permission*)

5-37. *A cookie is placed in front of the background light to give some texture to the plain wall behind the subject.*

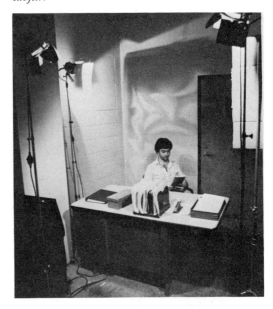

conversion of daylight films to tungsten illumination is not a standard practice for reasons mentioned in chapter 3. Briefly, the problem is the very large exposure factor required by the filter, which drastically reduces the film's speed.

The laboratory can compensate for overall mismatches in color temperature to a significantly greater degree when printing color negative emulsions than when printing color reversal films. Stray light bouncing from colored ceilings and walls may have a marked effect, and the redness of morning and evening sun is reproduced distinctly.

Available light is considered acceptable for an increasingly large number of applications (consider the subway sequence in *The French Connection,* photographed under existing fluorescent illumination), but there are still numerous educational, industrial, and scientific films where an exact color rendering is important.

Scenes illuminated entirely with studio lamps

Quartz lights and photoflood bulbs can be obtained in either 3,200°K or 3,400°K. Professional 16mm color films balanced for tungsten are for 3,200°K. In the studio, where supposedly sufficient amounts of current are available, only the eventual darkening of the glass globe on standard large tungsten lamps or the yellowing of reflectors and lenses because of heat and age can cause drops in color temperature. With occasional spot checks of reflector, bulb, and lens condition, color temperature problems are virtually nonexistent in studios with ample power.

The color-temperature meter is a good gadget to have on hand when lights are suspected of being off-color. It is not difficult to pick one reddish light from the rest and change the bulb to correct its color,

5-38. *Sequence in subway station and train interiors for* The French Connection, *filmed in available light. (Memory House)*

but when they are all consistently off-color because of voltage drop, check the color with a meter and use a light-balancing filter on the camera lens to make an overall correction. Remember that slight corrections may be made by the laboratory.

Studio lamps mixed with arc lights or HMI daylight lamps

There are five commonly available arc lights. All are made by the venerable Mole-Richardson Company, whose luminaries enjoy a worldwide reputation not only for quality but also for sheer weight. A fully equipped number 450 Brute weighs in at a hefty 420 pounds.

Carbon arc flames produce light between 5,000°K and 6,000°K. They are actually a little cooler (bluer) than daylight equipped with *white flame carbons*. *Yellow flame carbons* are also available for most models, and these produce light closer to 3,200°K. Arc lights are color-corrected with gelatin or plastic filters in frames attached to the front. A yellow Y-1 filter is needed with white-flame carbons to warm the light to daylight. Then a salmon-colored MT-2 (similar in color to the #85 color conversion filter) can be added to the lamp to bring the Kelvin temperature down to 3,200° to match tungsten films. The yellow-flame carbons are corrected to 3,200°K with a pale yellowish-greenish YF-101 filter. Use of the Y-1 filter results in a 10 percent light loss. Use of the MT-2 results in a 30 to 35 percent loss. Use them together, and the loss is about 40 percent. The YF-101 filter absorbs about 15 percent. The precise amount of light loss with filters is of no particular concern because lights themselves vary a bit, depending on the age and quality of carbons, the focus of carbons when burning, and the condition of the lens and reflector.

5-39 *(left). Mole-Richardson 225 Amp Literwate Brute Molearc with stand, ballast, and cables. (Mole-Richardson Company)*

5-40 *(right). Arc lights providing fill on typical feature location.*

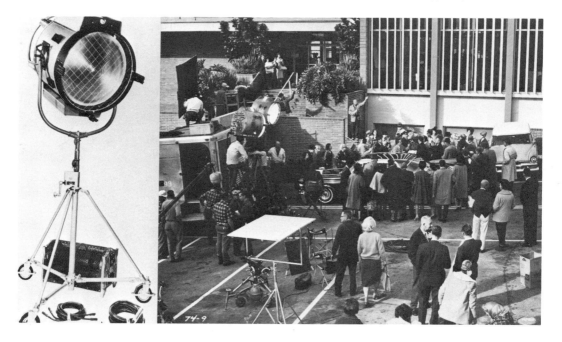

HMI and CID lights, which use a sealed arc bulb and are powered by special ballasts, produce a highly consistent 5,500°K illumination. Since even the largest (4,000 watt) HMI luminaries have only about one-quarter of the output of a large carbon arc lamp, they are not as likely to be used to simulate sunlight and the like. Although they may be filtered for 3,200°K and mixed with tungsten lamps, they are a rather inefficient source of simulated daylight in the studio.

Because of the closeness of their natural color temperature to daylight, arcs and HMI lights make ideal sources for filling in shadows outdoors. Arcs tend to be too tightly focused for many shots, however, and care must be taken that actors do not walk right out of the fill light area provided. On feature lots and on locations several arcs or large HMI lights are frequently placed in a row to cover playing areas evenly with shadow illumination. Filters are generally used to keep the arcs at daylight Kelvin or even slightly lower, because most cameramen prefer warm rather than cool shadows on people's flesh tones. The film, of course, is either balanced for or converted to daylight.

Arc lights are also used color-uncorrected at a substantial distance to simulate moonlight. The arc's great power makes them ideal sources for this purpose since, as mentioned, the square law of light requires that sources be placed at greater distances from the action whenever even illumination is required. The light from the moon does not have a tendency to fall off at the edges of a scene, and an arc light with its great intensity can usually be placed so that it does not fall off very much either. The bluish color helps create the "night" quality, and arc light mixes nicely with tungsten lamps filling in as torches, oil lamps, desk lamps, firelight, candle flames, flashlights, streetlights, match flames, and the like. In cases like this, with 3,200°K lamps filling in the shadows, the film is balanced for tungsten.

When arcs and HMIs are used as key lights in studios, they are usually converted to 3,200°K with the filters mentioned previously. The only alternative that will result in color-balanced lighting is to place blue filters over all the other tungsten sources, leave the arc uncovered, and use daylight balanced film. But since the arc is so much more powerful to begin with than studio tungsten lights, it makes more sense to filter the arcs and use supplementary tungsten lamps and tungsten film. Arc lights, incidentally, require a DC power supply, produced in most studios by motor generators, and on location by generator trucks.

In daylight

In order to understand the problems of shifting color temperature in daylight, which accompanies changes in weather, time of day, and locality, it is necessary to take a brief look at the elements that comprise the earth's source of illumination. Pure sunlight reaches the earth's atmosphere at about 6,000°K to 7,000°K. The layers of atmosphere through which the sunlight travels to reach earth scatter and diffuse the short wavelength—blue and ultraviolet—portions of the spectrum. The filtered sunlight arrives at about 5,400°K. Meanwhile the atmosphere diffuses the blue wavelengths it has filtered from the sunlight, and radiates light of between 10,000°K and 25,000°K. On a clear day the total daylight intensity is made up of 7 parts 5,400°K sunlight and 1 part cool sky light, producing a sunlight-skylight mixture of about 6,400°K at noon in ideal conditions of weather, haze, humidity, latitude, and lack of pollution. Sunlight must travel through more and more miles of atmosphere as the day approaches sunset. Since the atmosphere filters out blue light, the sunlight color temperature falls to about 2,000°K just before the sun goes down. While the sunlight-skylight combination is much redder at sunset, at twilight the sun's intensity falls off to the point where the blue skylight is responsible for a greater proportion of total light. At noon, the ratio of sun to sky is about 7 to 1; at sunset it may fall as low as 1 to 1 or 1/2 to 1. Twilight may be cooler (bluer, and thus a higher color temperature) than noontime daylight.

The color rendering of a subject also depends on how great a measure of illumination is by sunlight and how great a measure by blue skylight.

While subject illumination by pure sunlight is uncommon, subjects are frequently photographed entirely by skylight, resulting in a distinctly bluish rendering. City streets free of direct sunlight are deceivingly blue. An ultraviolet (UV) filter or small amounts of yellowish light-balancing filters are therefore recommended for shadow photography.

Overcast skies, which act as sunlight diffusers, also have a tendency to lower the sunlight-skylight ratio and produce bluish, diffused light at the earth's surface. The height of the clouds and degree of cover are important variables, but fully overcast skies provide light of about 6,800°K, which can be corrected with light-balancing filters such as a #81 or #81A.

The spectral energy curves (graphs that show individual color intensities) of daylight differ considerably from those of radiating black bodies, which are explained in chapter 3. The curves of radiating black bodies are the basis for measuring color temperature in degrees Kelvin, so color-temperature meters (which employ the Kelvin system) do not give accurate readings in daylight situations.

Fortunately, most slight out-of-door color shifts seem perfectly natural when reproduced on film, and individual color pictures made at all times of the day are, in themselves, quite acceptable. The problem in motion pictures arises when the day is ending and important shots still remain to be made. While isolated reddish scenes may be acceptable, shots made with late afternoon sun will not intercut smoothly with the midday photography. The reddish afternoon sun also casts longer shadows, giving many kinds of shots a distinctly different look from those made at noon. Needless to say, shooting schedules must take these important factors into consideration.

Mixtures of daylight and studio lamps

A frequent problem for the filmmaker is photography in interior locations where daylighted windows either included or not included in the shots, provide high levels of daylight illumination. Modern buildings with entire walls made of glass—cafeterias, classrooms, offices, libraries—are common locations of this kind. Because of the square law of light, there is seldom enough daylight illumination for photography on the far side of the room from the windows. If the corners are bright enough, the subjects near the windows are several times brighter, creating a problem of evenness. And if the camera must be turned toward the window, the sky and objects illuminated by direct sunlight outside are several stops brighter still, causing overexposure when shot with a proper setting for the subjects inside.

In other situations, daylighted windows do not provide enough light for exposure and the exterior view through the window is extremely bright. It is difficult to raise the brightness of the room to an equivalent of the exterior daylight with tungsten lamps, and even if successful, the color temperature would not match the exterior illumination.

There are three possible solutions to these problems. First, when the windows are not to be included or can be included with drapes drawn or blinds closed, simply block all the light by taping black paper over the windows, light the location with studio lamps, and use tungsten-balanced film. This is often the easiest solution to the daylight problem.

Second, when the windows must be included in the background, cover them with #85 or MT2 gelatin or plastic film. These filters convert the daylight to 3,200°K and allow for tungsten lights to be used to provide the interior illumination.

The flexible gelatin or plastic is usually cut and taped on the outside of the windows to eliminate time wasted cutting to match window frames. Rigid plastic sheets such as Roscolex can simply be propped in place. The rigid sheets are, by the way, optically clear enough to give a satisfactory rendering of views outside the window. (For actual point of view shots, remove the window entirely and use #85 camera filter). These salmon-colored sheets cut the light by about one stop and may be combined with gray-colored neutral-density sheets to reduce light levels further and match the interior illumination. It is possible to find soft self-sticking filter materials available in one, two, three, and three and a half stop neutral densities when combined with the #85 conversion control. Large windows that provide useful levels of illumination may also be converted to tungsten through the use of #85 filter sheets. This allows for supplementary tungsten lighting and the use of tungsten film.

The use of filter sheets is a good solution to these shooting problems, considering that about a hundred dollars worth of material will cover the equivalent of windows eight feet high and twenty-five feet wide and allow you to take advantage of all that nice soft illumination. Remember, however, that your lighting in this situation depends in part on the weather and on the direction of the window exposure. Clouds on shooting day may make the location much darker than on the scouting day. Moreover, direct sunlight may come splashing in during the afternoon on a location with western exposures, creating problematic hot spots. These problems are certainly reduced with a

low-contrast color negative film such as the improved Eastman Color Negative Type 7247, which often can handle overexposed windows quite satisfactorily.

The third solution to filming interiors with daylighted windows is to leave the windows uncorrected for color. Use daylight-balanced film and arcs, filtered tungsten lamps, or daylight HMI or CID lights to provide illumination. However, their size, weight, and DC power requirements make arcs not exactly the choice of the fast-moving, lightweight documentary film crew. Blue-glass and gelatin filters that convert 3,200°K tungsten lamps to daylight steal 64 percent of the light and add heavily to the number of lighting units and power requirements.

The newer *dichroic filters* that remove red light are considerably more efficient, reducing the light only by about 30 percent. Extremely thin transparent layers of metal on heat-resistant glass selectively reflect the light of certain wavelengths. But dichroic filters are expensive to buy or rent, costing nearly as much as some quartz lighting units themselves.

The newest and most efficient solution to daylight illumination problems is HMI or CID lights. HMI lights utilize a metal-vapor discharge lamp in a suitable housing and produce daylight illumination far more efficiently and with less heat than conventional filament lamps. CID lights are also metal-discharge but use slightly different formulations to produce much the same result. These lamps are available from several manufacturers in lightweight as well as heavy studio versions, and come with the required high-voltage transformers. The chief advantage of HMI lighting is the tremendous output of light per unit of power required, averaging almost four times the illumination per watt of tungsten halogen quartz lights. The 5,600°K color temperature of HMI lights is highly stable and perfectly compatible with daylight-balanced color film. The two major drawbacks with HMI lights are, first, the problem of 60-Hertz intermittent light pulses that must be synchronized with the camera shutter, and second, the relatively high cost.

Ultimately, depending on the style of movie production complications, time available, and various costs, the usual question will be asked: "How much can we get away with?" If there's a pan past a hot, unconverted window in the long shot, will the audience go on watching the picture or will it lose interest completely? If the rear corners of the classroom are a little dark and all of the main action has to be shot up front, will it ruin the scene or not? Will the style of the film lend itself to the "all-natural look" of occasional hot spots or uncorrected daylight? The answers lie in experience and good guessing.

Scenes illuminated with fluorescent lamps

In many new buildings, the high illumination levels produced by fluorescent lamps are sufficient for photography. They are not ideal luminaries for color photography, however, because they produce invisible (to you, but not to your film) intensities of particular wavelengths that are not conducive to creating the balanced spectrum required by color films. The color balance of fluorescent fixtures varies with the model, manufacturer, age, and style of bulb; voltage applied; degree of lamp warm-up; type of reflector; and portion of the AC cycle during which light is emitted. Acceptable color correction is a matter of guesswork, testing, and experience. Eastman Kodak recommends the color-correction filter combinations for their daylight and tungsten-balanced films show in figure 5-42. Actual exposure tests using incremental variations on all filters should be made in a particular shooting situation when time and budget permit.

Fluorescent lamps are actually blinking on and off 60 times per second as pulsed with the 60-cycle AC current. At running speeds much above 24 frames per second, the shutter speed approaches 1/60 second, and at these speeds drastic exposure fluctuations begin to appear.

The color rendering of scenes illuminated with fluorescent lamps may be improved greatly with the use of a few tungsten studio lamps,

5-42. Color-compensating filter recommendations for filming under fluorescent illumination.

Guide for initial test when exposing films with fluorescent lighting

Type of fluorescent lamp	Daylight films		Tungsten films	
	Kodak color-compensating filters	Effective exposure index	Kodak color-compensating filters	Effective exposure index
Daylight	40M + 30Y	80	85B + 30M + 10Y	64
White	20C + 30M	80	40M + 40Y	64
Warm white	40C + 40M	64	30M + 20Y	64
Deluxe warm white	60C + 30M	50	10Y	100
Cool white	30M	100	50M + 60Y	50
Deluxe cool white	30C + 20M	80	10M + 30Y	80

the light either bounced off the ceilings or used directly on the foreground subjects. They restore some of the missing color wavelengths and, when used in at least equal amounts with the fluorescent lighting, can provide the necessary illumination for acceptable color photography.

Location power problems

On location, the primary concern is the availability of power and the associated voltage and "line drop" problems. This is when the cinematographer reaches into his bag, pulls out his volt-ohm meter, and is transformed (zap!) into an electrician. In fact, electrical problems are so enormous on many locations that the filmmaker often becomes willing to sacrifice accurate color temperature, film grain, and good lighting by using fast films, forced development, few lights, and overloaded lines. The cinematographer should be given an opportunity to scout the location and check available power before deciding if the location will be satisfactory or if a generator truck should be brought along for the shoot.

To check on location power availability, search the basement or utility closet for the power distribution box. These boxes are of all sorts and description, depending on the age of the electrical installation and the amount of power installed. Some are sealed and only the fuse portion can be reached conveniently. Others are not only open but also downright dangerous.

Never touch any leads, fuse posts, boxes, or connectors until you have determined whether the parts are "hot" or not.

The production lighting kit should contain a wide variety of extra fuses for all types of fuse boxes, and if the fuse layout is not indicated by a list or chart near the box or inside the lid, you may as well just start plugging in and lighting up until the fuses or breakers begin to blow. Cinematographers have been observed turning off unneeded household appliances and installing higher-ampere fuses on a temporary basis when the normal ones fail.

Clipping in

If the fused circuits cannot handle your requirements, you will have to *clip in* or "tie in" to the building feeders. This requires a set of cables, usually rubber-insulated, three- or four-wire flexible copper #6 or heavier, equipped with insulated giant alligator clips on one end and a fused split-down box with standard outlets on the other.

Clipping-in is a dangerous procedure and must be done with a great deal of care. The dangers of improper hookup include blowing out all your lights, burning up the power box, burning out the building feeders or supply transformer, and electrocuting yourself.

In order to clip in you will need an electrical tool called the *amp probe* equipped with voltage reading dial. You should also have insulated gloves, lashing cords, pieces of asbestos, and strong tape.

5-43. Typical 220v household power box with clip cables tied in. Upper left cable is neutral connected to grounding strip, lower left cable is ground clamped to case, center cable is connected to a 110v power bus, right-hand cable is clipped to other 110v power bus.

5-44. Clip cables lead to fused outlet box where lights may be plugged in.

First, the box type must be determined. Unscrew the lid of the power box and lay it aside. In order to ascertain the box type, use the voltage probes of the amp probe. In the two-wire 110/120-volt type, the meter will read about 110 or 120 volts when the probes are placed on the circuits. This type of box is usually found only as a submain or feeder box to farm outbuildings and other locations of this sort.

In the most common household three-wire 220/240-volt box, there will be three large supply leads, buss bars, fuses, or all three, in addition to an uninsulated ground lead. The probes from the volt meter will read 220/240 volts across two of them; either one of those two leads will read 100/120 volts when read against the third or ground lead, or, properly, "neutral." If the colored feeders are visible, they will usually be red, white, and black, with the red and black providing the 220 and either red and white or black and white providing 110.

The four-wire "delta" or three-phase box is commonly found in larger commercial buildings. It will have three circuits, any combination of which will read 220/240 volts, and any of these three will read 110/120 when used with the fourth, "neutral" lead. In the three-phase box, as well as the two-wire 110/120-volt box, the *ground, or neutral lead,* is the one that gives no voltage reading when compared with the metal case.

Sometimes there will be a 440-volt three-phase box; they are generally used to feed elevators and large motors. The building will use transformers to step down to 220 volts, which is split further for the lighting and wall boxes. Look for feeder boxes near the lighting fuse panels. The appropriate clip cables should be marked, numbered, or color coded, with a ground lead and the proper number of hot phase leads. These color codes should be followed with all cables used until the current is split down into individual 110/120 volt "pockets" for the lights and camera.

W (watts)	E × I	I²R	E²/R
E (volts)	I × R	$\sqrt{W \times R}$	W/I
I (amperes)	E/R	$\sqrt{W/R}$	W/E
R (ohms)	E/I	E²/W	W/I²

It is a good idea to determine the acceptable load fairly early. The large buss-type fuses or main breaker in the distribution box give an indication of the total power available.

Then, use the formulas in figure 5-45 to determine how many lamps at given watt ratings can be used, how much power is needed for a given number of rated light sources, and other power requirements.

For example, the location has a 120-volt, two-line distribution box. The buss fuse or main breaker is rated for 150 amps of current. Use the formula:

$$W = E \times I$$
$$W = 120 \times 150$$
$$W = 18,000$$

It is immediately apparent that without other appliances plugged in a total of 18 1,000-watt lamps or its equivalent can be used.

Before clipping in, check to be sure there is ample space physically for the clips. Some boxes are too small and present a great danger of short circuits between clips and the metal box. If there is sufficient room, clip on carefully, and use strong cords to tie the clips in safe positions. Tape pieces of asbestos or insulated cardboard between clips to prevent wiggle and contact. Lash, tape, tie, and strap the cables so that they cannot be pulled loose by a clumsy passerby.

Be sure to clip in on the building side of the main breaker and turn off unneeded lights and appliances throughout the location.

The clip boxes should then be wired up to provide 110-volt pockets at the shooting location. Figure 5-46 shows how to do it. Ideally, individual heavy cables for each clip run all the way to the shooting location, and the 100-volt pockets are provided there. All cables and strips of pockets should be color coded so that the feeders carrying the heaviest loads are always known.

A problem may arise when cables are run from the box or generator truck to a shooting location many yards away. The color temperature of the light sources will be affected by a line voltage drop caused by the resistance of the cables. A power drop of only 10 volts will lower the Kelvin temperature by 100°. For this reason, as well as because camera motors lose significant amounts of power and problems start with tape recorder motors and amplifiers, a 5 percent voltage drop is usually the maximum allowed. Use the formulas and wire reference table or the list of recommended cable size in Figure 5-47 to keep line voltage within the 5 percent tolerance. The power should be measured at the box where the lamps are plugged in while the load is on.

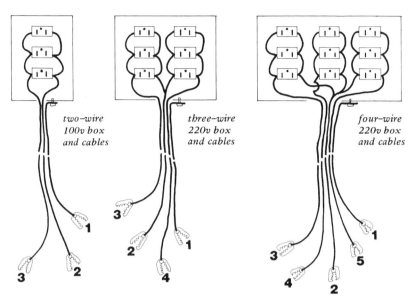

two–wire
100v box
and cables

three–wire
220v box
and cables

four–wire
220v box
and cables

5-46. Wiring diagrams for pocket boxes. Cable 1 is ground lead, which is connected to the power box case. Cable 2 is the neutral lead in each box. Cables 3, 4, and 5 are the "hot" feeders.

Notice that voltage drop formulas are based on amperes. Amperes are arrived at by dividing watts by volts. When higher voltage is run through the lines to split-down boxes, the voltage drop will be less. For example, ten 1,000-watt quartz lights or a total of 10,000 watts are required. At 110 volts this is equal to about 90 amps. At 220 volts it is equal to about 45 amps. Lower amperage means less resistance, and less resistance means a lighter wire can be used. Reduced resistance also means less voltage drop; therefore, whenever possible, run 220/ 240 volt current from the power panel or generator and split the current to 110 at the shooting location.

Lighting equipment and accessories

In recent years many new developments have drastically changed the look and operation of many lighting units and attachments. While this has made possible such things as shooting in previously difficult locations and permitted some handy substitutions of smaller, lighter units for heavy old klunkers, in general the principles of design and function have not changed. For example, instead of taking a 106-pound 2,000-watt Fresnel spotlight to the location, a 15-pound 2,000-watt focusing quartz light might be chosen instead. Both can provide a well-defined beam of light used for the same purposes—key light, kicker, whatever. A brief examination of the latest tools, with emphasis on design and function, follows.

Tungsten halogen quartz lamps

Tungsten halogen quartz lamps use tungsten filaments, as did their ancestors; however, by using quartz (and similar high melting point materials) rather than glass envelopes, much smaller sizes have been

Wire reference table

Wire size A.W.G.	Allowable current capacity (Amperes)	Area in circular mills (C.M.)
18 GA.	3 A.	1,624
16 GA.	6 A.	2,583
14 GA.	15 A.	4,107
12 GA.	20 A.	6,530
10 GA.	30 A.	10,380
8 GA.	45 A.	16,510
6 GA.	65 A.	26,250
4 GA.	85 A.	41,740
2 GA.	115 A.	66,370
1 GA.	130 A.	83,690
0 GA.	150 A.	105,500
00 GA.	175 A.	133,100

5-47. Wire references, voltage drops, and cable sizes.

Voltage drop of copper wire
(DC or 100% power factor AC circuits)

Single phase (1φ)

$$\text{Voltage drop} = \frac{\text{amperes} \times \text{feet} \times 21.6}{\text{circular mills}}$$

Three phase (3φ)

$$\text{Voltage drop} = \frac{\text{amperes} \times \text{feet} \times 18.7}{\text{circular mills}}$$

Recommended cable size

Lamps or heaters	100 ft. cable	200 ft. cable
500 Watt (4.3 A.)	16 GA.	14 GA.
750 Watt (6.3 A.)	16 GA.	12 GA.
1 KW (8.5 A.)	14 GA.	12 GA.
2 KW (17 A.)	12 GA.	8 GA.
5 KW (43 A.)	8 GA.	6 GA.
10 KW (85 A.)	4 GA.	2 GA.
AC motors	100 ft. cable	200 ft. cable
¼ H.P. (4.6 A.)	16 GA.	14 GA.
⅓ H.P. (5.8 A.)	16 GA.	14 GA.
½ H.P. (7.4 A.)	16 GA.	12 GA.
¾ H.P. (10.2 A.)	14 GA.	12 GA.
1 H.P. (13 A.)	12 GA.	10 GA.

obtained. The small size is in fact necessary, because the quartz lamps are filled with a halogen gas, which regenerates the oxidized tungsten from the glowing filament. Halogen is a gas that provides an atmosphere conducive to the constant redeposit of tungsten back onto the filament. The envelopes are very small so that they will operate at a temperature hot enough for the regeneration cycle to function.

When the tungsten filaments in ordinary lamps oxidize, the evaporated particles collect on the glass walls of the bulb, causing a diminished light output and a corresponding drop in color temperature. In tungsten-halogen quartz lamps, the particles are redeposited on the filament.

All these facts are responsible for the quartz lamp's small size, constant color temperature, and extremely long life.

The reduced size of the envelope has made possible the production of small, lightweight lamp housings that are not only much more portable but also more efficient in terms of light output per pound. A traditional focusing 1,000-watt studio light, for example, weighs 31 pounds and uses a stand that weighs 25 pounds, for a total of 56 pounds. Compare that to a 1,000-watt focusing quartz light that weighs 4.5 pounds, uses a 2.5 pound stand, and probably puts out more light because of its efficient little reflector. Eight 1,000-watt quartz lights with stands can be packed in a suitcase that weighs less than one standard studio lamp. To take advantage of the quartz-halogen bulb's size and efficiency, the large tungsten bulbs in traditional studio lamps have been replaced with quartz bulbs by using adapters and bipost bases that fit the older receptacles. Newly manufactured large studio spotlights are designed to accept quartz bulbs, and the huge once-standard tungsten globes are now virtually extinct.

Convenience factors like size and weight are not the primary criteria for selecting lighting units. Obviously, when both a heavyweight and a lightweight lamp are capable of performing identical functions, the lightweight unit will be chosen, especially when travel is involved. But the most important considera-

5-48. *Various typical quartz bulbs: top, bipost bulbs, 1,000 to 10,000 watts; left center, installation of bipost bulb in a focusing Fresnel lamphouse; right center, clear and frosted double-end bulbs, 500 to 1,000 watts; bottom, double-end bulb in open quartz housing.*

tions must begin with the scene being lighted, the nature of the illumination needed, and the demands of the style and mood of the film being made. If a scene calls for shadowless high-level illumination, large, flat fill lights and yards of spun glass diffusion material may be needed. If a scene calls for simulated moonlight or sunlight, powerful arc lights may be required. When a theatrical filmmaker decides on the effect he wants to create through lighting, he chooses the particular spotlights, fill lights, and accessories that will achieve this effect. On the other hand, a filmmaker going on a documentary location with no foreknowledge of the problems that may arise takes along a variety of lightweight units and accessories that will give him maximum versatility.

HMI daylight lamps, CSI 4,200°K lamps, and CID daylight lamps

The most significant recent advance in the field of illumination is the highly acclaimed HMI daylight lamp. Using Osram metallogen bulbs, Mole-Richardson of Hollywood, Arnold & Richter (Arriflex) and Kobold in Germany, Ianiro in Italy, LTM and Cremer in France, and Ryudensha of Japan, manufacture HMI lamp and ballast systems.

In addition, even newer "compact iodide daylight" (CID) lamps also provide 5,500°K illumination. Similar in operating principle are the "compact source iodide" (CSI) lamps, which provide illumination at 4,200°K.

The major reason for the interest in HMI, CSI, and CID lights is their tremendous efficiency, which is usually expressed in terms of lumens per watt of light. A typical 2,000-watt quartz bulb has an output of 50,000 lumens, providing 25 lumens per watt. An Osram HMI metallogen 2,500-watt bulb produces 240,000 lumens, for an amazing 96 lumens per watt of power required. To the filmmaker this means four times the light or two extra f-stops compared with the already efficient quartz halogen lamps. Even if daylight conversion filtering is required for tungsten film, approximately one f-stop gain is still realized.

5-49. An LTM Ambiarc 2500 HMI floodlight. (LTM Corporation of America)

Because of their daylight color temperature and high efficiency, HMI and CID lights are being used rather than standard arc lights for exterior fill and key applications. The light from a four-KW HMI luminary at 50 feet measures about 65 footcandles over a 6,500 square foot area, using about 40 amps of current. A 225 amp brute produces 70 footcandles at 100 feet (twice the distance) over a 12,500 square foot area. So although the HMI light is more efficient electrically, the big arcs are still very useful indeed for massive lighting jobs such as simulating sun- or moonlight. Also, the ballasts needed to provide current to HMI, CSI, and CID lamps are heavy items. For example, while the HMI Fresnel head weighs about 60 pounds and the Baby Brute head weighs 126 pounds, when the 67-pound grid (transformer) for the brute and the 145-pound ballast for the HMI are added, their weight is almost equal: 205 pounds for the HMI and 193 for the arc.

HMI, CSI, and CID lights present two other problems for film-makers. First, the HMI bulb is an enclosed arc that pulses on and off at a rate equal to twice the input current frequency. An HMI system operating on 120V 60Hz current pulses at 120Hz. If this pulse is not synchronized with the camera shutter, a noticeable flicker will result in the footage obtained. Sync between shutter and lamp must be established by using a shutter speed that is an even multiple of the 120Hz pulse rate: for example, a 144-degree shutter operating at 24 fps has speed of 1/60 second (see chapter 6). The standard 180-degree shutter found in most cameras will not perform satisfactorily. Also, camera speed must remain very stable, either through the use of crystal-controlled or AC camera motors. Generators used to provide power for the lamps must also be precisely controlled or disaster will result. CSI and CID lamps have a reduced "decay flux" that results in less of a camera synchronization problem. When these lamps are used in con-junction with special, heavier, and more costly "square wave control" ballasts, flicker can *almost* be eliminated.

Finally, all of the new metal-vapor HMI lights, like so many other nifty pieces of hardware, are not inexpensive. A 1,200-watt Fresnel head from Mole-Richardson currently costs $3,875, and the bulb (extra) is $500. The estimated life of the bulb is 750 hours, for a cost per hour of about 67 cents, compared to a $26 quartz bulb that lasts for 150 hours and costs only about 17 cents per hour to operate.

Lighting unit design: spotlights

Spotlights are used for key lights, separation lights, background lights, and, with the proper accessories, even for fill lights; they are the most widely employed type of lighting unit. Any lamp that has a relatively high intensity, a focused or controlled light beam, and a relatively small output area or diameter, qualifies as a spotlight. Spotlights employ reflectors, lenses, or both to focus and control their light output. They have taken many forms. The discussion that follows begins with the simplest designs and continues through the increasingly complex.

Reflector photofloods

Self-contained reflector photofloods are standard tungsten or tungsten halogen bulbs that contain their own reflectors and, in some cases, their own lenses. While individual bulbs cannot be focused, they can be inter-changed to provide wide, medium, and focused spot positions. Bulbs of this type may be used with inexpensive spring-clip sockets, screwed into other types of housings, or used with a complete system of highly portable units such as *Lowel-Lights*.

Lowel-Lights are designed with a versatile mounting plate that holds the focused bulb and may be hooked onto light stands, furniture or pipes, or taped to walls, ceilings, doors, floors, cameras, or any flat surface. The heavy cloth tape used with these units is called *gaffer tape*. This versatile product has more than usual stickiness. When gaffer tape is removed it can pull the paint right off the walls, ceilings, doors, floors, cameras—whatever surface it has been attached to. Use it with care or the friend's apartment borrowed for a location will be utterly destroyed. Lowel-Lights do not have tremendous luminous intensity but may nevertheless be used in cramped quarters to great advantage, especially when taped to ceilings and walls to provide kicker and background illumination.

Reflector flood

Reflector floods and *reflector spots* are photoflood bulbs in reflector housings. Photoflood bulbs (as opposed to reflector photofloods) look like ordinary household lamps, but they are rated for around 60 to 80 volts. When they are used with 110-volt household current, their filaments burn up to 3,200°K or 3,400°K at substantially increased luminous intensities. They are available in rather modest (300 watts) power ratings and do not last very long. Their use in color motion picture production is limited to low intensity fill lighting and close work.

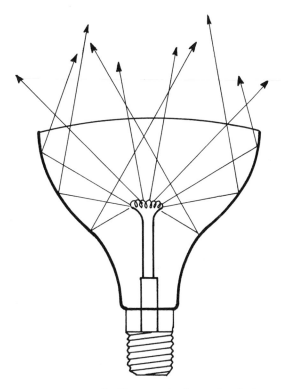

5-50. *Diagram of self-contained reflector photoflood.*

5-52. *Diagram of reflector photoflood lamp.*

5-51. *Lowel-Light and Lowel lighting kit. (Lowel-Light Photo Engineering)*

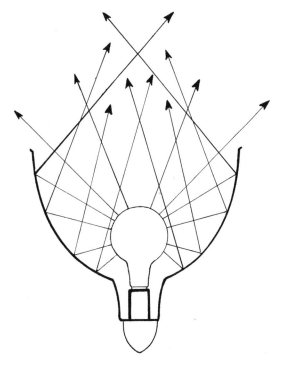

Quartz lights

Most *quartz spotlights* are of simple design as well. They usually consist of a quartz halogen lamp mounted in front of a bright aluminum reflector designed to distribute the tiny bulb's great intensity smoothly over a given area. Quartz lights are available with both fixed and focusing (variable) bulb positions. They provide intense, sharp, hard illumination, and because of their light weight and efficiency they are a popular and versatile light source. Average bulb life is often 150 hours, but it may be as little as 20 hours or as much as several thousand hours, depending on particular type and Kelvin rating.

Quartz lights are not without some disadvantages. The highly concentrated light output is accompanied by highly concentrated heat, and when quartz lights are placed too near draperies, walls, wood, door frames or (heaven help you) sprinkler systems, all sorts of unpleasant things begin to happen. Carry insurance! Because of the intense heat, the units are difficult to handle and adjust even after they have been turned on for only a few seconds. (Of course, all lighting units get hot and a good pair or insulated asbestos gloves will save time and blisters.) Only special heat-resistant glass and plastic sheets can survive in front of quartz lights—ordinary gelatin filters go up in smoke.

Quartz halogen bulbs are available with up to 10,000 watts rated output; however, most open-style quartz spotlights are supplied with a maximum 2,000-watt bulb. Focusing models offer only modest beam variations, but their ease of movement and placement helps make up for this limitation.

Fresnel spotlights

Standard large studio lights are called *Fresnel spotlights*. They are available in ratings of 50, 250, 500, 750, 1,000, 2,000, 5,000, and 10,000 watts with proportionate sizes ranging from a 3-inch diameter at four pounds to 24 inches at 125 pounds. These luminaries, though large and heavy, offer the greatest control of the light by employing a moving bulb and

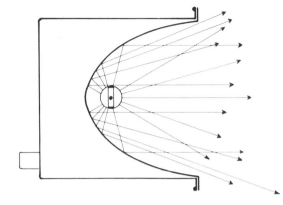

5-53. *Diagram of open quartz light.*

5-54. *Lowel-Quartz Model D is typical of modern open quartz housing. (Lowel-Light Photo Engineering)*

5-55. *Diagram of typical focusing Fresnel lamp.*

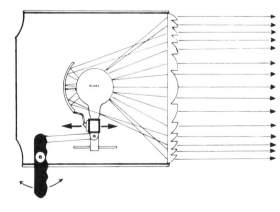

5-56. *A modern lightweight 10-inch ring-focusing Fresnel and folding-open quartz from Colortran. (Berkey Colortran, Inc.)*

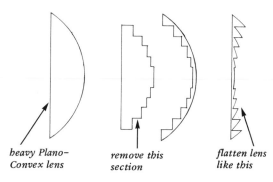

heavy Plano–
Convex lens

remove this
section

flatten lens
like this

5-57. *The construction of a Fresnel lens.*

reflector behind a Fresnel lens that focuses the light beam.

Fresnel lenses are actually "compressed" condenser lenses, designed that way to reduce weight. They are produced with textured rather than optically flat surfaces, which diffuse and soften the light beam to a slight degree. Among incandescent fixtures, their excellent light control, great power in large models, and smooth illumination is unexcelled. For studio lighting, where size and weight are not considered major disadvantages, focusing Fresnel spotlights are the ideal choice.

Daylight HMI lights are available in the focusing Fresnel style from several manufacturers and also offer smooth, versatile light beam control.

Arc lights

Arc lights also use Fresnel lenses to focus and control the intense arc flame, but they do not use reflectors because of the intense heat and smoke inside the housing.

Depending on how well the arc light is working, smoke may become a problem outside the housing and all over the studio as well. Arcs produce great quantities of light, but they are in need of almost constant supervision while shooting. The carbon rods need changing at regular intervals, and this

5-58. *Fresnel lens on a Mole-Richardson spotlight. Notice textured rear surface of lens to further soften light beam.*

5-59. *Diagram of arc light. Notice lack of reflector because of intense heat and smoke.*

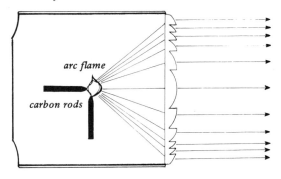

arc flame

carbon rods

operation alone is akin to doing a heart transplant inside of a furnace. Asbestos gloves are essential, as well as pliers and wrenches to suit particular models and their states of condition. Rods must be properly "struck" (touched together quickly to start the electrical arc while, hopefully, not chipping or breaking one) and properly focused if the light beam is to be of consistent color and intensity. Most models are fitted with automatic feed on the carbons to move them ever closer as they burn, but the lamp still needs regular monitoring while shooting is taking place.

Fill lights

Fill lights are used for two important purposes. One, as mentioned earlier, is to provide enough illumination in the shadows cast by the key light for acceptable rendering of contrast on the film. The second is to provide overall set and background illumination. These two purposes are related, and both require light sources that do not cast distinct shadows of their own. The larger the physical dimensions or the output portion of a fill light, the softer the shadows that will be created by the luminary. Two means are employed to produce the required large surface and luminous intensity that make a good fill light: fixtures for direct and indirect light.

Direct housings are nothing more than a large reflector with a bulb in the middle. There is no baffle or guard of any sort in front of the bulb. The reflector is not, however, a highly polished and efficient reflector but rather a flat-white diffusing surface. Large frosted lamp globes work best in these fixtures because they do not produce a hard and shadow-producing light source in themselves.

Indirect housings have opaque guards in front of the bulbs so that all of the light is indirect and therefore very soft. Some direct reflector fill lights are converted to indirect by attaching a light shield in front of the bulb.

Large direct and indirect fixtures are often fitted with several bulbs for additional luminous intensity. They are necessary because of the relative inefficiency of the diffuse reflectors.

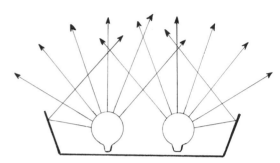

5-60. *Diagram of direct-reflector fill light.*

5-61. *Thousand-watt Mole-Richardson Molequartz direct-reflector fill lights. (Mole-Richardson Company)*

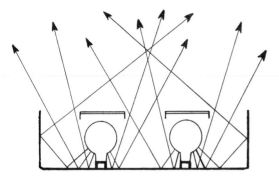

5-62. *Diagram of indirect-reflector fill light. Note baffles to prevent direct rays.*

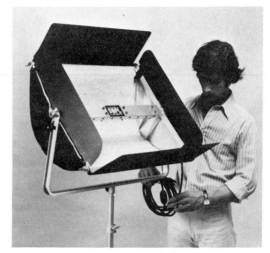

5-63. *A folding Lowel indirect-reflector fill light. (Lowel-Light Photo Engineering)*

Special purpose lights and accessories

Strip lights are used along the tops and bottoms of backgrounds to provide wide illumination over broad surfaces such as cycloramas and sky backdrops.

Focused *follow spots* provide accurately defined and focused light beams useful for following onstage action. Round- and square-shaped light beams are projected through a system of lenses. Some fixtures have a built-in series of filter slots which allow the operator to drop-in colors as desired.

Pans are large-diameter diffused reflectors that are also used to illuminate background and cycloramas. When used with diffusion sheets, they make excellent fill lights as well.

Accessories

Spotlights, almost as a matter of course, are fitted with *barn doors*. These hinged and rotating baffles may be either two- or four-sided. They generally control and contain light output as well as give shape and dimension to the light beam. Common uses include the following: keeping separate key lights for different actor positions from overlapping, confining light on set walls to specific areas (particularly off the top edges), conforming a light beam to fit, say, a framed picture on a set wall without overilluminating the surrounding area, and shielding back lights and kickers from the camera lens. Barn doors usually attach to lamps with brackets on the front of the fixtures and depend on gravity to stay in place. Safety chains or lock-in clips should be used whenever available, especially when lamps are greatly tilted. Barn doors are somewhat more effective when the lights are in the flood position;

they are not very effective on large, diffuse fill lights, because the shadows caused by the barn doors are, as one should fully expect, filled in.

Scrims are frames containing cloth or wire screen mesh. They are used in primarily two ways. Scrims (sometimes made of screening material and called *screens*) are used close to the key or other spotlight to reduce the intensity of all or part of the light beam. They may be one-quarter, one-half, three-quarter, or full scrims, depending on how

5-64. *Top left: Mole-lipso spotlight, 2,000 watts, for producing sharply defined light beams; lower left: Mole-quartz overhead strip light, 5,000 watts, for illuminating cycloramas, etc.; center: skypan, 5,000 watts, for illuminating cycloramas, etc.; right top and bottom: barn doors closed, open, and mounted on a Colortran quartz light. (Mole-Richardson Company and author)*

5-65. *Use of half scrim to produce even lighting.*

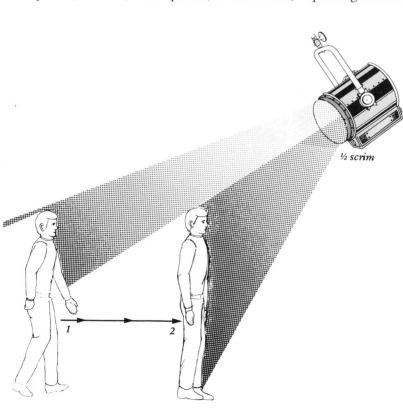

½ **scrim**

much of the beam they are to affect, and are made up in single, double, and even triple thicknesses. They are sized either to be dropped directly into the barn door brackets on the front of the fixtures or to be clamped to stands some distance in front of the light. Their effectiveness increases the farther they are placed from the light source. This may or may not be an advantage, depending on specific situations.

Scrims are often used to help even out the intensity of a key or background light as it illuminates an angled surface or area of action. Since the actor at position #1 in figure 5-65 is farther from the key light and illuminated with less intensity, a half scrim at the bottom of the light beam prevents overexposure when the actor moves to position #2. With the scrim close to the source, no distinct line between the scrimmed and unscrimmed portion of the light is visible.

Figure 5-66 shows how three-quarter, one-half, and one-quarter scrims used together will further even out a light beam. When scrims are placed in frames farther in front of the light, it is usually to diminish the key light on specific objects.

Diffusers are framed pieces of spun glass or frosted plastic placed in front of light sources to diminish their hardness. When diffusers are the same size as the spotlights they are attached to, they actually do very little to soften shadows other than to reduce the intensity of the light that may be causing the shadow. Since only large-diameter sources are relatively shadowless, it is understandable why large diffusers may be placed some distance in front of a spotlight to produce a soft fill

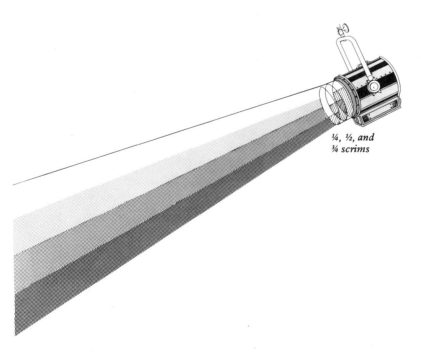

¼, ½, and
¾ scrims

5-66. *Use of combined scrims.*

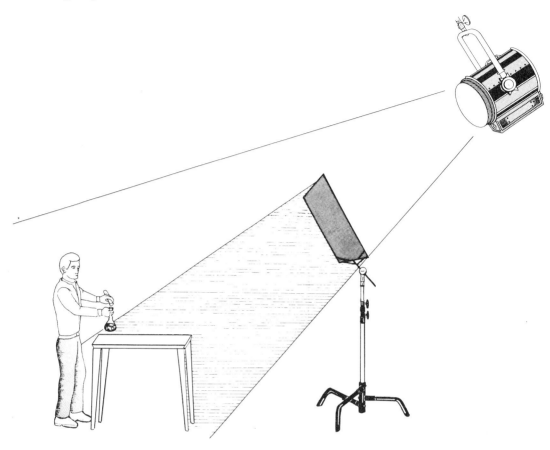

5-67. *Using large scrim to prevent overexposure of foreground objects.*

5-68. *Two gobos, a cookie, and a large scrim, with stand and clamps. (Mole-Richardson Company)*

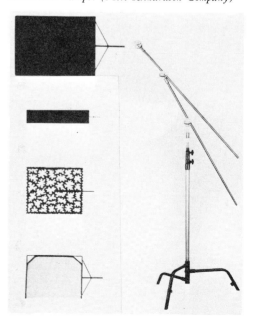

light. Huge shadowless lighting units may be created by suspending large sheets of diffusion material in the positions where fill lights are needed, and then aiming several spotlights at the rear surface of the diffuser. Alternatively, diffusing and reflecting "tents," "space blankets," or "umbrellas" can be set up and the spotlights bounced from the front side to provide soft illumination.

Gobos, flags, teasers, dots, targets, blades, and clips are names used to describe opaque black fixtures of all imaginable shapes and sizes that are used to keep light off surfaces, skin, clothing, props, cameras, and crew. *Gobos, flags,* and *teasers,* usually square or rectangular, are generally used for shading portions of the set and keeping kickers out of the camera lens. The larger ones are usually held in place with their own stands and adjustable arms. *Dots* and *targets,* round or custom-shaped, are often small enough to shade faces, white shirts, and other small areas. *Blades* and *clips* have their own clamps and can be attached directly to lights to augment the barn doors, or to the front of the camera to act as sunshades.

Cukalorises, or "cookies," as well as tree branches and other abstract shapes, may be placed on stands held in front of lights to give mottled textures to background or other surfaces. Cookies are often homemade—the various shapes and patterns are cut into an approximately two-foot square piece of thin plywood, masonite, or cardboard. Sheet metal is better since it does not burn, but it is much more difficult to cut. The great challenge has always been to create the perfect pattern—not too large or small, not too open or closed, but one that allows just the right amount of light to pass. The size and definition of the patterns can be controlled by changing the distance between the lights, the cookies, and the background.

Colored gelatin sheets or *gels,* in frames on the fronts of lights, produce special color effects, convert the color temperature to daylight, or provide slight color corrections. Two examples: a brightly colored key or kicker light can add interest to the rendition of machinery, consumer products, and glassware; a piece of red gelatin attached to a strip of wood, cut into vertical strips, and manually wiggled in front of a low key light can provide a firelight effect.

Solutions to typical lighting problems

The following are some typical set and location lighting problems and step-by-step suggestions not only for lighting them, but also to make the most of their potential mood and effect.

Day interiors: interviews

Filmmakers are frequently called upon to shoot interviews—the chairman of the board extolling his company, the writer discussing his new book, the announcer holding a box of detergent. If an interesting setting and mood to complement the interview come up, great. But all too often the interviews are fully intended to be totally nondescript, taking place against neutral office or household backgrounds, with no outstanding visual elements to distract from the words that come flowing out. Since these situations are not only extremely common but also serve as a very basic lighting example, what follows is a description of a typical lighting setup.

Ideally, have the subject "sit in" for a few moments, examine him or her, and find an ideal key light position. The person's face and special characteristics should determine the key light angle—look for pleasant modeling, a not too long nose shadow, a good Rembrandt cheek patch highlight, and so on. If the subject is not available, "rough in" the light on someone else and polish it up when the subject arrives. For the key light use a focusing spotlight, with barn doors attached,

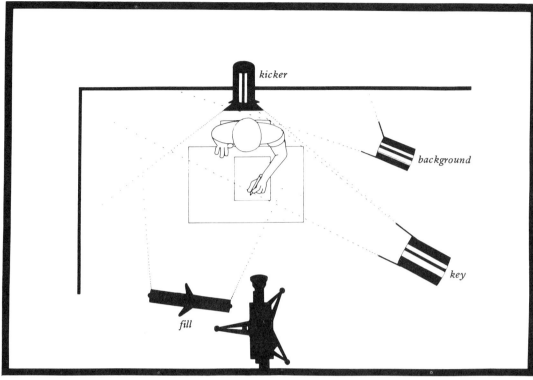

5-69. *Basic interview setup.*

5-70. *Basic interview setup.*

of sufficient power to give (or nearly give) the desired f-stop for shooting. Aim the light so that it covers the subject evenly within the camera angle to be used. Remember not to worry about portions of the set that will not be seen. Check the camera angle and use the barn doors to block the light off the background at the upper part of the shot. This creates dark edges around the frame that help lead the viewer's eye to the subject and avoids the overlighted look, where backgrounds seem to come forward and surround the subject. Scrim or gobo the key light off any hot foregrounds (desk, table).

Next, bring in a broad, diffused fill light and place it next to the camera on the side opposite the key light. It must be powerful enough to give the desired lighting ratio and should be set accordingly.

Hang, clamp, or tape up a kicker light of almost equal intensity to the key light. The proper angle is usually about 30 degrees from a vertical line above the subject's head. Watch out for rising hairlines and the hot spot on the forehead caused by a kicker light placed too directly overhead. Barn door the kicker light so that it does not shine directly into the camera lens, does not overilluminate a foreground desk or tabletop, and does not cause an inadvertent skim, or shine, down the wall behind the subject.

Take a good look at the background with all lights on. Is it light or dark? If it is dark and out of key light range, add a background light from a relatively high position outside of the camera angle. If space allows, place the background light on the same side as the key light. Shadows in the background will fall in the same direction as those in the foreground, with natural-looking results. If one light is insufficient to bring the background up to the desired illumination level, additional lights may be added from either side. Read the wall to be sure that it is covered relatively evenly from one side of the camera angle to the other. Point up interesting textures; barn door the light off the subject and off the top of the set as seen by the camera. If a plain background looks too even and dull, use a cookie or other appliance to break up the light and give it some texture. Set the background illumination to a suitable lighting ratio.

That completes the basic four-light setup—with the possible exception of an additional kicker light to pick up a nice cheek highlight, placed at eye level opposite the key light and 45 degrees behind the subject.

If the subject is to move about, modify the setup according to the amount of movement. If it only amounts to a few steps, cover the movement evenly by using a larger key light from farther away and adding any necessary scrimming. The kicker lights can be set for proper background separation throughout the move. If the subject is to walk a greater distance, use two key lights, one for each position. The slight falloff in intensity at the middle portion of the movement is all right as long as the subject does not stop to deliver an important line in this area. Just be sure to avoid the overlapping of key lights, where multiple shadows might occur. If the subject walks from the background into a close-up, you may need to set a large fill light off to one side to handle the long shot, and use another small fill light near or clamped onto the camera.

Daylight interiors: living room

While a lot depends on the particular set or location, the style of the room, and the desired effect, the first step in the daylight living room is to decide from what source the discernible light should be emanating. Usually one or two large windows will be the supposed primary source and any lamps in the room will be secondary. On location, filter the windows as discussed earlier. In the studio, paint a *flat*, a wall panel used in set construction to look like an exterior view and place it several feet beyond any windows seen by the camera. Illuminate the flat with a few sky pans or strip lights at the top, bottom, and sides to cover it with perfectly even, bright illumination. Put focusing spotlights on the top of the flat and aim them through the window, thus flooding the living room floor with light. Use additional broads (bright, direct-reflector fill lights) at the outside edges of the window to add to the effect of daylight coming through. Use this scheme for all the living room windows in the set. If desired, use an arc placed some distance outside the set to cast sun shadows of the window blinds or sash frames on the floor and furniture. A few thin curtains will help diffuse the incoming light, as well as render the exterior flat less distinct.

Check the action of the characters in the living room. Set the necessary key lighting to cover the main areas of action. If actors move all around the set, key lighting will necessarily be broad and general. If the action is localized, a single key may give a more dramatic feel. Remember to use the windows for clues on key light direction.

Turn on any *practical* lamps (props in the action area), focusing spotlights on the walls and furniture that surround the lamps to give the appearance of extra illumination coming from those sources. Kicker lights must be set to cover all areas of action.

With the addition of two or more large fill lights on both sides of the camera to bring the shadow illumination up to the proper ratio, the set should now be completely lighted.

Evening interior: living room with fireplace

The assumption is that the fireplace in the living room will be seen, at least in the long shot, and is an apparent source of light. If it is not seen from the front in a particular shot, spotlights may be placed inside to act as key lights on the subjects. Usually a roaring fire is called for, and focusing spotlights will have to be placed as near as possible to the fireplace. For close shots, these key lights may be placed down low, hidden behind furniture or the subjects themselves, and controlled with gobos so they do not flood the camera or walls with stray light.

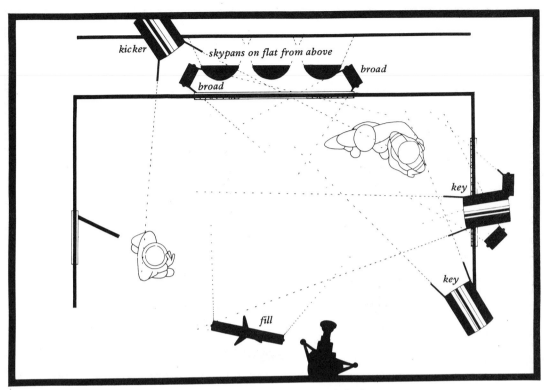

5-71. *Daylight living room setup.*

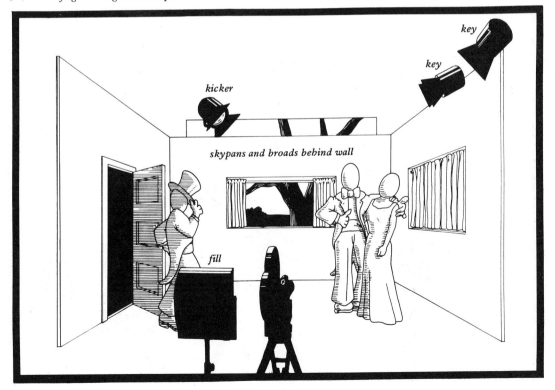

5-72. *Daylight living room setup.*

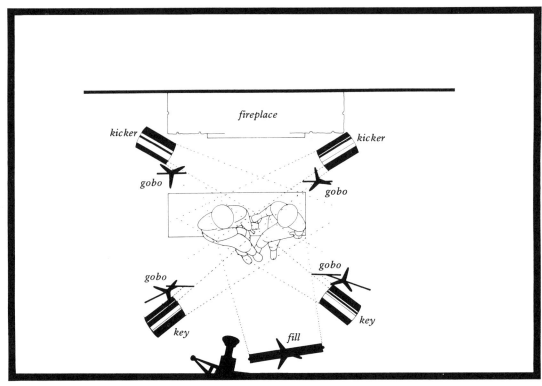

5-73. *Evening living room setup.*   5-74. *Evening living room setup.*

From some angles the fireplace key lights are almost directly behind the subjects and act only as kicker lights. That being so, use two additional key lights, one from each side, goboing them so that they illuminate only the faces and fronts of the subjects. This is a case where it is necessary to "cheat" the lighting direction to provide the necessary illumination. The crisscrossing keys illuminate the front of the actor facing them and provide hairlight to the other actor at the same time. Unless serious mystery is the purpose of the scene, the entire face should not be in shadow. An additional spotlight from either side should be barn doored and focused softly onto the fireplace to make its textures evident, but it must be kept at about 4 to 1 below the keylight-plus-fill-light (or total exposure) level.

The top and sides of the set as seen within the camera angle should be left quite dark and almost without detail—how much without depending on the desired mood. If there are other sources, such as visible table lamps, turn them on and spotlight the area surrounding them from above. Add the usual fill lights and keep the lighting ratio higher, perhaps 4 or 5 to 1, to sustain the evening mood.

Evening interiors: dining room

Use the chandelier in the dining room as the apparent source of light. Since it is high up and in the middle of the family group seated around the table, the people should be illuminated from their front side only, so use focused and barn-doored spotlights on the left and right set walls aimed across the table. Place about three spotlights on the far set wall to kick the heads of all seated.

The walls of the room and edges of the shot should be left quite dark. A large fill light suspended above the camera will soften the shadows but still sustain the warm center glow of the picture. People who come and go from the table should be allowed to enter and leave the full exposure of their seated position. Barn door all luminaries to control excess light and keep it out of the camera lens. Additional lights may be used to illuminate the walls if they are very dark, but these should be used judiciously, allowing perhaps for only a few areas to be illuminated while others remain dark.

Evening interior: den, study, office

When the location is a den, study, or office, a desk lamp can provide the key light with a high-intensity bulb installed. The desk light should be set so that it illuminates the desk and subject, placed just low enough to illuminate the face but be shaded from the hair. Use a kicker on the hair and shoulders, some background lights illuminating a few wall areas (kept at a contrast ratio of perhaps 6 to 1 below the exposure setting), and soft fill on the camera to bring face shadows up to a ratio of 3 or 4 to 1 for a pleasant rendering. Allow the actor to get "hot" if he leans close under the light and go dark as he backs away. If the desk lamp is unsatisfactory as a source (wrong type,

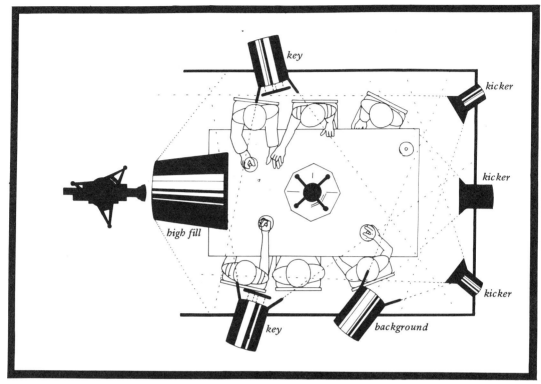

5-75. *Dining room setup.*

5-76. *Dining room setup.*

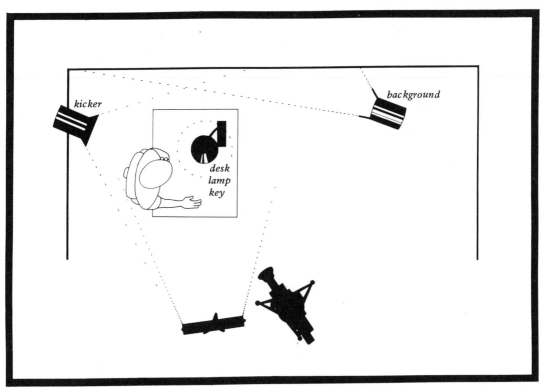

5-77. *Evening office setup.*

5-78. *Evening office setup.*

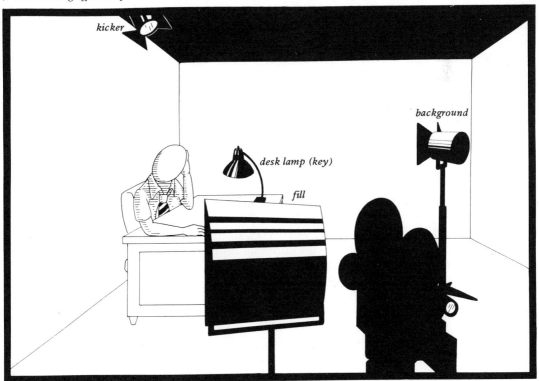

reflector, shade, and so on), use a small key light placed close to the subject from outside the camera angle but from the direction of the desk light to give the same effect.

Night mystery interiors: bedroom

The apparent source of light in a bedroom at night may be as much a mystery as the scene itself. Much depends on the action, locality, and mood and the scene may be enhanced with such things as a neon sign blinking outside and casting occasional soft-colored patterns through the window.

The action calls for two people to remain asleep in bed while a burglar enters through the window. The long shot shows the window, illuminated by a focused spotlight crossing it from the outside, with the resultant slight spill of light coming in to produce a well defined pattern on the wall above the bed. A closely barn-doored kicker is placed on the far wall and skims across the bed to reveal the texture of the heads and pillows only. One or two additional kickers hit walls or floors in goboed angular patterns. When the burglar comes through the window, highlights on his head and body are seen, but few face details. Inside, only his silhouette is visible against the window. As he moves through the bedroom, he passes through some focused kicker lights and he is rimlighted for a moment and then disappears again. If he carries a flashlight, it will be bright; a small hand-held follow-spot can simulate its effect in the point-of-view shots. Remember to keep the camera side of the burglar's face in shadow at virtually all times—use strongly angled and controlled lighting to pick up just enough details to make his outline recognizable.

If mystery scenes call for the inclusion of light sources such as table lamps, the light inside the refrigerator, matches, and so forth, use small low-intensity spots placed very close to the subjects. This will cause a quick falloff of light when the subject moves his head farther from the light and a slight overexposure when the subject gets very near. Such an effect adds to the feeling of night illumination.

Simulating daylight in the studio

Frequently, the establishing shot for a dialogue sequence will be made on location or on an exterior lot and the close-ups with dialogue will be shot in the studio on a matching set, where good-quality sound can be recorded. The cowboy rides into town and ties up his horse in front of the saloon, and as he steps up on the sidewalk, the camera cuts to a medium shot where he meets Miss Kitty and proceeds to make arrangements for the evening. The medium shot and close-ups must be made on a set with lighting similar in contrast, quality, and direction to the daylight in the long shot.

Hopefully, someone took a Polaroid of the exterior scene as it was being shot to show the exact direction of the light at the time. Select the largest lighting unit available (preferably an arc) and hang it at

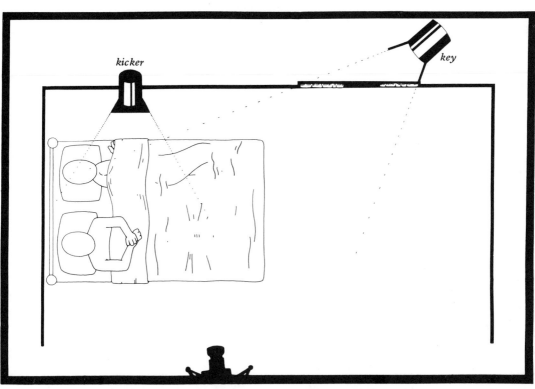

5-79. *Mystery bedroom setup.*   **5-80.** *Mystery bedroom setup.*

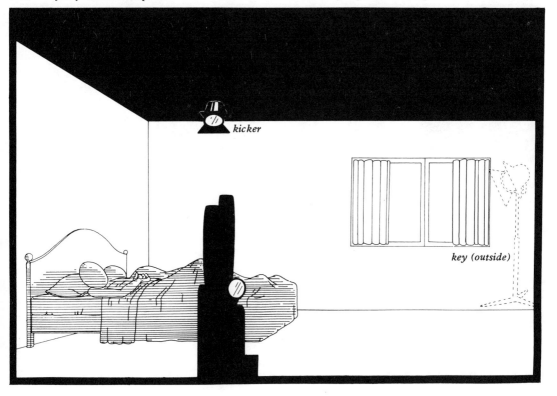

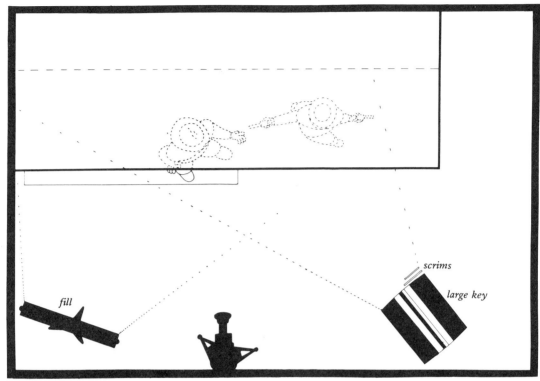

5-81. *Simulating daylight.*   5-82. *Simulating daylight.*

the proper angle and at the greatest distance to give the needed exposure value in the corner of the shot farthest from the luminary. Because of the inverse square law of light, the difference in intensity from the areas close to the key light to areas distant will be diminished by keeping the luminary as far away as possible. Use scrims to even further the level of light across the set. Use a light meter to check everywhere, especially the corners of the shot, to be certain that the light from the key is absolutely even. Sunlight does not fall off at the edges of a shot, and this is one time when everything must be lighted evenly.

After the keylight has been set, bring on the largest fill lights. Since sky light is naturally very shadowless, the fill lighting on the set must not cast multiple shadows either.

Depending on the angle of the sun in relation to the subject, the key-plus-fill to fill-light ratio on a sunlit exterior is about 4 or 5 to 1. Color medium shots in the studio should be made with a ratio of about 4 to 1 and close-ups at about 3 to 1, the exact ratio depending on taste, film used, and the desired effect.

A few top kickers may be used, but their intensities must be kept down to 3 or 4 to 1 and the source must be kept undetectable. Be careful of any hot spots on the walls or surfaces near the kickers themselves.

Simulating moonlight and night exteriors

As with daylight, simulating moonlight requires a large light source placed at a great distance from the set to minimize illumination falloff. An uncolor-corrected arc light is ideal when shooting in color, since its blue light adds nicely to the night effect. But to sustain the effect, the arc must be placed at a position farther than 90 degrees from the camera for most subjects. This causes shadows to be cast on the front surfaces of the actors, which helps create the night feeling. Fill light ratio is kept at least 4 to 1 for close shots and even greater for long shots.

Firelight can be simulated by waving strips of red or orange gelatin in front of closely placed spots. The lighting can be frontal, but it is augmented by the moonlight and must be controlled so that only those close to the "fire" will be up to exposure.

Such effects as photoflood bulbs inside lanterns, small spots turned on with the striking of a match, a panning pair of focused spotlights coordinated with the sound effect of a passing car, all add to the mood being created.

In the city, slanted spotlight beams goboed into angular shapes may be aimed on walls and sidewalks through which the actors pass. With arc-powered "moonlight" providing kicker to rimlight the subjects, actors may be further illuminated by tightly focused spotlights that supposedly originate from streetlights, store windows, passing cars, and flashing signs.

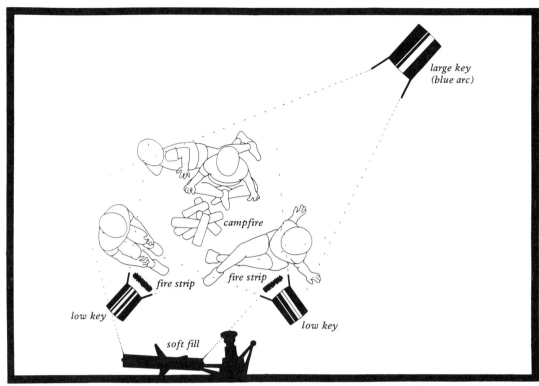

5-83. *Simulating moonlit campfire.*   5-84. *Simulating moonlit campfire.*

Illuminating titles and flat art

When titles or flat art are to be shot, there are two major lighting considerations. First, the lighting must be perfectly even from side to side and corner to corner. Second, it must not produce any distracting reflections or "kicks" from glossy or textured surfaces.

The usual procedure is to use two spot or floodlights, one on each side of the artwork at a 45-degree angle to the surface. If the lights are too near the camera (near 90 degrees to the artwork), the light on the surface will reflect directly back into the lens and cause hot spots. If the lights are placed at very shallow angles, the cosine law has a pronounced effect and very little surface brightness will occur; textures may also become visible. An incident-light meter with a flat disc or a reflected-light meter used with an 18 percent gray card will give the exposure readings that automatically compensate for the cosine effect; they should be used for making the light readings.

Focusing spotlights are usually selected for flat-art photography because even lighting may be obtained by focusing to the spot or flood positions and aiming carefully. Use a light meter in all the corners and pass it back and forth over the entire surface, shifting and adjusting the lights until there is less than a quarter-stop variation on any part.

When the art is large, several lights may be placed at each side, all at 45-degree angles, to spread illumination evenly across the surface. In an art museum the problem may be a painting in the corner that may not be removed from the wall. With several spotlights on one side even illumination may be obtained by using the arrangement shown in figures 5-87 and 5-88.

Some varnished oil paintings have glossy textured surfaces that would seem to defy illumination without glare and reflection. There are two schools of thought about this: some say that anyone who views the actual painting must see a certain amount of glare and so a very small amount is acceptable in the photograph; others say that all glare must be removed, because in the gallery it is possible to move from side to side and eventually see the true colors of each portion of the painting, not possible with projected film. The glare can be removed entirely, when desired, with polarized light (see chapter 6). Polarized sheets are put on the luminaries and set with matched polar directions. A polarizing filter is placed on the camera lens in the opposite direction. The polarizing sheets on the lights eliminate all light waves except those in one plane. The camera polarizer is rotated to the opposite plane, which theoretically should prevent all light from reaching the film. But in actual practice enough polarized light leaks through the filters to make photography possible. This polarizing system will eliminate glare and reproduce the painting in the purest possible color, but careful exposure compensation for the filters on the lights and camera must be made. The best way to determine exposure for this setup is with a through-the-lens exposure meter used when all filters are in place.

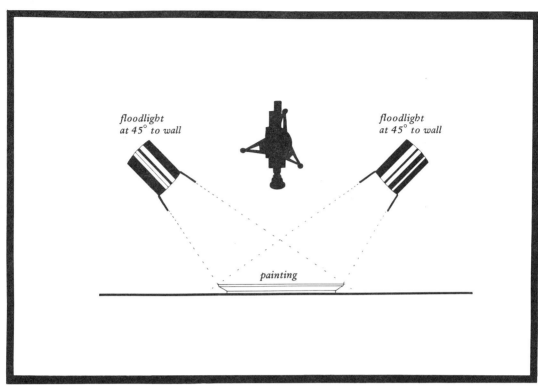

5-85. *Illuminating artwork.*   5-86. *Illuminating artwork.*

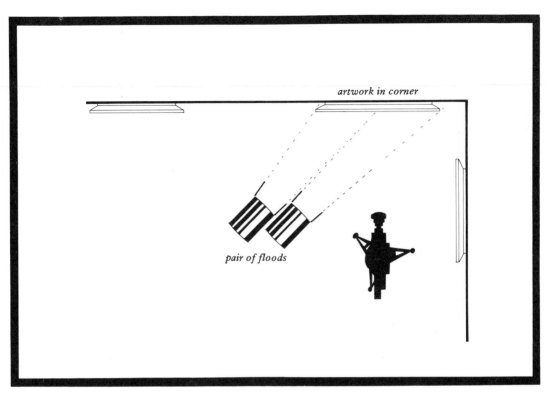

5-87. *Artwork in corner.*

5-88. *Artwork in corner.*

Care must be taken so that the heat from the lights (especially open-style quartz lights) does not cause overheating and bubbling of the painted surfaces to be photographed.

It is, of course, beyond the range of any book to teach lighting completely. The guidelines given in this chapter, however, should permit the beginning filmmaker to observe analytically the role light plays in daily life and in the filmic representations of life seen on the screen. By combining an increased awareness of light with the suggestions in this chapter, the student will be able to approach the many lighting challenges that are a fundamental part of cinematography in a sensitive and sensible way.

chapter 6

Exposure

Ask three different cameramen for the best method of computing exposure for a given shot and chances are three different answers will emerge. But strangely enough, all these answers may be correct when the desired effect, film type, nature of scene illumination, and a host of other factors are considered. In a field where even the experts occasionally offer conflicting viewpoints, this discussion will hold to the facts and allow the reader to make the final choices. Making the proper exposure is primarily a matter of learning to make a well-informed choice of the tools and system available for calculating the exposure in a wide variety of filming situations.

Determining correct exposure

Before it is possible to talk about how to find the correct exposure, the word "correct" itself must be understood. An exposure that is correct in theory may not be correct in practice because of elements of taste, desired effect, the way it will be developed and printed, how the scene fits into the overall story, and even the final projection conditions. "Desired effect" will be dealt with throughout this section, but suffice it to say now that there are subjective elements that must be decided in each individual case.

In most filming situations "correct exposure" will be determined in one of two ways. First, the correct exposure renders the flesh tones of the subjects in the shot consistently and as normal. Since motion pictures are most often made about people, this is usually the most important exposure consideration. Audiences expect people in films to look realistic, and the filmmaker must be certain that he exposes for normal flesh tones in a given shot and that the actors do not change color and complexion as they go from scene to scene or place to place.

The second way to define "correct exposure," especially for general scenes without people, is to say that it renders the full range of tones, colors, highlights, and shadows from the original scene onto film, with adequate detail remaining in the darkest and lightest areas as well. This concept accurately places the contrast range of the scene's essential tones within the exposure latitude of the film being used. If the film is given too much exposure on a scene with a normal range of bright and dark tones, the resulting overexposed film will render all the tones unnaturally light and there will be a complete lack of detail in what were the scene's important highlights. If the film is given too little exposure, the underexposed image will render all the tones too dark and there will be no detail in the areas corresponding to important dark or shadow tones in the scene. Underexposure and overexposure can be corrected somewhat in the printing and reproduction processes and a normal-looking balance to the middle values of the scene restored, but highlight or shadow details lost through over- or underexposure can never be corrected.

6-1. Top: overexposed light areas of original film have lost detail that can never be recovered; bottom: similarly, blocked shadows, such as interviewer's hair, will never have adequate detail.

When a scene has abnormally high contrast, the cameraman must choose those tones that are the most important and expose so that these will be reproduced with satisfactory detail. Brighter or darker highlights and shadows will, of necessity, be beyond the film's ability to reproduce.

The common conflict

The two ways of achieving correct exposure are frequently in conflict with one another. A good overall exposure balance for a particular scene may not give the best flesh tones, and at the same time a scene with a properly exposed flesh tone may have missing detail in highlights or shadows. The conflict is created in most cases by differences in brightness between the subject and the background. If the subject is standing in front of an extremely light or dark background and an overall balanced exposure is made, the flesh tone rendering will suffer badly. The reason is that if the film is given extra exposure to capture detail in the dark background, the flesh tone of the subject will be inadvertently overexposed (rendered too light). If the film is given less exposure to compenste for the light background, the flesh tones will be underexposed (rendered too dark).

Very few scenes contain a balanced range of bright and dark tones. There are four ways the cameraman may deal with this very common dilemma. First, he can simply decide that the most important thing is a good tone rendering on his subject and will expose accordingly, allowing the surrounding tones to fall where they may. Second, he can decide that the quality of the background (e.g., a lovely sunset) is more important than detail in the actor's face, so he will allow his subject to go into silhouette. Third, he can make a careful compromise, adjusting his exposure to favor an important background element while not allowing the flesh tone to be rendered too far from normal. Fourth, he can use lights and reflectors, or gobos and scrims to control the contrast so that a satisfactory rendering of both the subject's flesh tones and the important subtleties of the background will be included.

Determining the "correct exposure" for a given scene is, then, a matter of determining which portion, subject, or area of the shot is most important and choosing a system of determining exposure that will lead to the desired rendering of that area. Before these techniques are described, the variables common to all exposure considerations will be examined.

The five variables

There are five variables to be considered when determining exposure:

1. Film sensitivity
2. Exposure time (shutter speed)
3. Lens aperture
4. Brightness of the scene
5. Exposure compensation: filter factors

Variable 1: film sensitivity

As discussed in chapter 3, different films have different abilities to respond to light. This ability is called film sensitivity, film speed, exposure rating, exposure index, ASA rating, or ISO rating. For practical purposes the terms are interchangeable.

The most common film speed rating system in the United States is the American Standards Association Exposure Index, usually called the *ASA rating* or *exposure index*. As mentioned previously, this term is in the process of being changed to the *ISO rating* (for International Standards Organization), which has the same numerical value and will be used the world over. Eastman Kodak plans to continue using simply the term "exposure index" on their motion picture film packages and listings. In any case, the numbers are based, as described earlier, on the amount of exposure needed to produce a density on a given film that is just above the fog level of the film when it is developed to a specific contrast value called gamma. In the negative film emulsion Density Log Exposure Curve (see chapter 3), a 0.1 density above the fog level on the toe of the curve is used as the ASA rating reference point.

The toe of the curve is used as a reference point in speed rating systems because this is the area of least density in the negative—the point beyond which the photographer simply cannot go. In other words, the toe area is the most critical exposure cutoff point because it represents the threshold of density-producing exposure. The shoulder of the curve slopes off more gradually. Increases in exposure continue to produce slight increases in density over a more extended range. This detail in the dense areas of the negative can be reproduced by printing the negative with more light. But if no detail exists, as with exposures under the region of the toe on the D log E curve, no amount of printing control can help correct the problem. In reversal films, the critical area of the characteristic curve is found at the opposite end, where increase in exposure can produce no less density, the density eventually falling to the fog level. Therefore, with negative emulsions, the dark areas or shadow portion of the scene represent the most critical limitations of the exposure range and must be treated accordingly; with reversal films, the light areas or highlights in the scene represent the most critical exposure limits.

The ASA rating system uses each film's point of minimum density-producing exposure as the rating point. Based on these parameters, film sensitivities are measured and assigned a numerical value. The ASA rating numbers are structured so that film sensitivity doubles as the numbers also double. A film with an ASA rating of 400 is twice as fast (sensitive) as a film with an exposure index of 200 and requires half the amount of exposure. Or, conversely, a film with an exposure index of 50 is half as fast and requires twice the exposure of one rated at 100.

The exposure rating of a given film can be found in a number of places. Some rolls of film come with a package insert giving the index numbers as well as other manufacturer's recommendations. Sometimes index numbers are found imprinted on the outside of the film boxes.

Larger rolls are usually supplied without such information, possibly because the customers are presumed to be professionals who already know the exposure index of the materials they order. Manufacturers have film data sheets that indicate all the necessary information, and these can be requested when the film is ordered. Various sources, such as the *American Cinematograher Manual* and Appendix 5 in this book, also list the ASA ratings of commonly ordered professional emulsions. The actual use of the exposure index number will be explained later, when the use of exposure meters is discussed.

Variable 2: exposure time (shutter speed)

The *shutter speed* is actually the amount of time light is allowed to reach each frame of film to make an exposure. The longer the time or the lower the shutter speed, the greater the exposure and vice versa. The formula for calculating shutter speed is:

$$\text{Exposure time} = \frac{360 \times \text{frames per second}}{\text{shutter opening angle}}$$

As explained in chapter 2, the shutter angle on most cameras is 175 or 180 degrees, and the standard sound running speed is 24 frames per second. This yields an exposure time or shutter speed of about 1/50 second. The shutter speed may be shortened by decreasing the shutter angle on cameras with variable shutters. Some cameras have maximum shutter angles as wide as 235 degrees, which at 24 fps produces a shutter speed of 1/37 second. The shutter speed on these as well as other cameras may be further lengthened by a decrease in camera running speed. This fact is useful for filming static scenes with low light levels. Exposure meters have a range of shutter speeds marked on their dials, and meters designed particularly for motion picture use may have special pointers at the "standard" 1/50-second mark or can be preset for that speed.

Variable 3: lens aperture

Total exposure can be compared to filling a pail with water. A certain amount of water (light) is needed to fill the pail (cause sufficient exposure). The length of time the water is allowed to run into the bucket is the shutter speed; the size of the hose, which controls the quantity of water flowing, is comparable to the aperture. A greater quantity will fill the pail quickly; a smaller quantity will fill the pail in more time. During most filming the shutter speed is fixed at 1/50 second, and the quantity of light and the resulting exposure can be controlled by adjusting the lens aperture.

The "aperture" actually consists of two parts: an *iris diaphragm* located between the optical elements of the lens, which is capable of opening and closing to allow more or less light to pass through, and a *diaphragm control ring* which, when rotated, opens and closes the iris. The iris diaphragm is located near the optical center of the lens so that it causes an even overall light diminution rather than darkness at the edges of the image (called *vignetting*). The diaphragm control ring or aperture ring is marked with a series of numbers called "f-stops"; a similar series of numbers is used on light meter scales and other exposure devices. The range of control provided by the aperture is quite extensive, and a linear scale would be impractical. From the widest to the smallest opening, the light may be altered by a factor of more than 500 in a typical modern camera lens. For this reason the aperture control ring is calibrated in increments based on the square root of two, thus: f/1, f/1.4, f/2, f/2.8, f/4, f/5.6, f/8, f/11, f/16, f/22, f/32, f/45, f/64, and so forth.

With the possible exception of the space between the maximum and next adjacent f-stop, all other stops change the light passing through the lens by a factor of two. It is important to realize that this factor must be multiplied, not added, when changes of more than one f-stop are made. For example, stopping down from f/2.8 to f/4 allows half the light to pass. Stopping down another f-stop to f/5.6 allows one-quarter of the amount of light that passed at f/2.8. Move another stop to f/8, and only one-eighth the original light will pass.

The standard series of f-stop numbers must be memorized so that mental computations can be made quickly and easily. If the cameraman is shooting, say, at f/5.6 and decided to shoot some slow motion by increasing the camera running speed to 48 frames per second, without pencil and paper he should in effect be able to say: "I have doubled the running speed, which has effectively halved my shutter speed. I now need to double the light in order to maintain a consistent exposure."

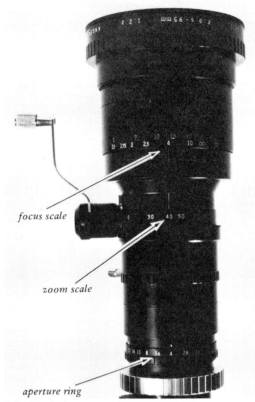

focus scale

zoom scale

aperture ring

6-2. *Typical aperture ring.*

This is the simplest possible example of the kind of mental computations that will be made constantly in the course of a shooting day. It is a good idea to take some spare time and rehearse hypothetical problems so that exposure computation errors will be avoided under the pressure of shooting.

Variable 4: brightness of the scene

At the beginning of chapter 5 it was explained that there are two ways to measure the quantities of light on a scene: the amount of light falling onto the scene, or the amount of light reflected by the objects in the scene. They are referred to respectively as the incident-light system (which measures light incident to, or falling on, the scene) and the reflected-light system (which measures light reflected back toward the viewer by the scene and its contents). The cameraman will measure light with one or both of these systems when calculating exposure.

There are various exposure meters designed to measure incident light, reflected light, or both.

How exposure meters work

Several basic designs have been used in constructing light measuring meters. An early type, called the *extinction meter,* was fitted with an eyepiece and sliding filter wedge and did little more than aid purely visual estimations of light levels. These extinction meters could give widely varying readings depending on the operator and other conditions and so today they are themselves virtually extinct.

Comparison meters removed some of the extinction meter's shortcomings by employing batteries, a calibrating rheostat, a tiny bulb, and an illuminated surface with which the subject could be compared. There is a modern and very sophisticated meter called the *exposure photometer* that utilizes the comparison method very effectively.

The vast majority of today's light-measuring instruments are of a type known as *photoelectric.* Photoelectric meters may be of two kinds, either photovoltaic or photoconductive.

Photovoltaic meters employ light-sensitive cells consisting of selenium bonded to a metal plate and surfaced with a thin translucent coating of platinum or gold. When struck by light, this cell produces a minute voltage charge that is measured with a microammeter wired in series to the cell. Meters made in this fashion are robust, simply constructed, long lasting, stable, and, above all, can be made to be very accurate. Only ordinary precautions, such as shading from extremely bright light and insulating from high temperatures, are necessary to maintain a long service life. The cells have a spectral sensitivity (sensitivity to color) similar to panchromatic and color films, so no special color compensation is necessary.

The major drawback of selenium photovoltaic meters is their relatively poor sensitivity to low light levels. This limits their usefulness in available-light photography and with reflected-light readings of dark

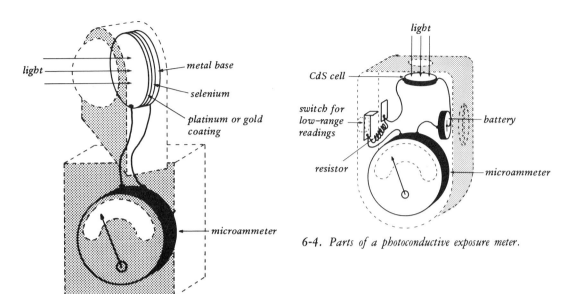

6-4. Parts of a photoconductive exposure meter.

6-3. Parts of a photovoltaic exposure meter.

objects. The problem has been partly solved through the use of several add-ons, including "booster elements," enlarged selenium cells, and more sensitive volt meters. But in fact the disadvantage is of little importance in motion picture work because, generally, if there is not enough light to move the needle on the light meter, there certainly is not enough light to shoot film.

The second type of photoelectric light meters are known as *photoconductive*. These are often called cadmium sulphide or CdS meters because that is the substance most frequently used in the construction of the light-sensitive cells. But unlike the selenium cell, which produces a minute voltage when struck by light, the CdS cell produces a drop in electrical resistance.

A battery produces the voltage that is semiconducted by the CdS cell and monitored by a microammeter. Since these cells are about ten times as sensitive as a selenium cell, a resistor and bypass switch are often added to take advantage of the low-light sensitivity and yet allow readings with high light levels as well.

Light meters of this type are extremely versatile; they are often sensitive enough to make readings in moonlight. But they do have a few disadvantages. For one, they use batteries and, like so many battery-operated instruments, frequently need recalibration because the battery has run down. Some meters are equipped with special voltage-regulating circuits to reduce the prolem, but it all adds to the bulk, weight, and complexity. The CdS cell also suffers from a certain amount of sensitivity lag at low light levels and requires some time to adjust to great changes in brightness. This problem is often evident if the meter has been used in a bright area and then is taken immediately to a rather dark location. The needle takes considerable time to settle down to the actual reading.

It is also prone to adaptation to the dark, and to give falsely high readings when brought into bright light after periods of storage. It is a phenomenon similar to what the eyes do when one awakens or enters a brightly lit room. CdS cells are not normally sensitive to the same color spectrum as panchromatic films and need color correcting for use with modern films.

Despite all these problems, CdS meters are nevertheless extremely useful and popular. The through-the-lens meters very commonly built into many modern still cameras are usually based on a CdS system, providing one good example of how the super-sensitivity of CdS can be used with great success.

Meter designs

Modern photovoltaic light meters fall into four design categories, with some models able to convert from one type to another with accessories: incident-light meters, reflected-light meters, spot reading reflected-light meters, and through-the-lens reflected-light meters.

Incident-Light Meters: Incident-light meters are always characterized by their round or conical white plastic domes, which act as light-acceptance regulators and diffusers. The selenium or CdS cell is located behind the dome and senses the total brightness of the light striking the dome.

The incident-light meter is used to measure light falling on the scene and is held at the subject position with the dome aimed toward the camera. The dome is designed primarily to simulate the shape of people's faces and other three-dimensional objects in the scene. The advantage of this design is that the dome will automatically give a balanced reading of one or more light sources striking the subject. In daylight, for example, the sun will fall on the upper portion of the dome while the lower portion will be in shadow, filled in somewhat by the ambient light from the sky. The sensitive cell behind the dome responds not only to the intensity of the light on the dome but also to the size of the area struck by that intensity. Thus the readings are integrated in a manner that corresponds to relative light and dark portions of the three-dimensional subjects in the scene. Since the meter is held at the subject with the dome pointed toward the camera, the dome gives a reading representative of both the intensity and the direction of the light; if the camera angle changes significantly, a new reading should be taken to compensate for the change. In this way the incident meter takes into account the conditions of illumination geometry. It will give an integrated reading of a front key light, a side key light, or a backlit subject, and will compute the effect of the fill light and other sources as well.

The incident-light meter may also be used to set light-level balance between the various luminaries. It can read the intensity, at the subject, of each source of illumination and calculate the desired balance between them. Such readings are done in one of two ways.

The meter is held at the subject position and aimed toward the

6-5. *Dome on incident meter automatically accounts for angle of lighting.*

luminaries as an assistant turns them on one by one. In this way the intensity of the key light, then the fill light, and then the backlight can be read and set. Multiple-location key lights can be checked to make sure they are all even, and the desired contrast ratio is achieved.

Another way is for the cameraman to use his hand and body to block the light from some luminaries while reading the intensity of others, which will achieve the same effect as having someone turn the lights on and off. Since the incident-light meter reads the light falling on the scene, it does not take into account the brightness or reflectance of the scene itself. A dark object in the scene will be rendered dark on the film, a white object as white, a 30 percent reflectance flesh tone will fall into the 30 percent value range on the film and look like a flesh tone. Consistent "real" flesh tones are one important way of recognizing correct exposure, and no other type of exposure meter will give more accurate readings for that purpose than the incident meter.

6-6. *Usual method of reading with incident meter.*

It is this simplicity that makes the incident meter the first choice of most motion picture cameramen. But the experienced user will watch for bright, white hot spots, large, dark shadow areas, and other background peculiarities that would make this theoretically correct exposure look bad. For example, a person is standing in front of a bright white wall. The incident meter gives an exposure reading that would indeed render the wall white on film and place the flesh tone in its proper position on the film's tonal scale. But the developed picture looks like a terrific mistake because no one wants to see a toneless, washed-out background (unless the effect is intended), no matter how correct the flesh tone is. A better solution would be to move the subject to a more suitable background, or to try to change the lighting a bit and get some tone into the whiteness. So while the incident meter is ideally suited for establishing illumination levels when a set is being lighted and for getting consistent flesh tones, in practice there are many shooting situations in which some exposure adjustment, based either on the cameraman's experience or on his readings with reflected-light meters, will be required for an overall good image.

The incident meter may also be fitted with a flat diffusion disc in place of the light-integrating dome. The disc, being two-dimensional, gives a reading that is accurate for two-dimensional objects—flat art, walls, table tops. The disc automatically incorporates the cosine law (see chapter 5) and gives a reading that corresponds accurately to the effective surface illumination due to the angle of incidence of the light source. To make readings of this kind, the meter is held with its back against the flat surface, the disc therefore parallel to it. The illumination angles and intensities on the meter will thus correspond accurately to the illumination geometry of the surface being measured.

Reflected-Light Meters: Reflected-light meters are designed with the light-sensitive cell located behind some sort of shield to control the light-acceptance angle. This shield may be a perforated grid, a simple narrow tube, or a lenticular magnifier. The idea is to produce a meter that is more or less directional so that it can be pointed toward a given object and not read light from all directions at once. As stated pre-

6-7. *Left: the Sekonic incident meter with flat disc attached; right: using meter to read illumination on artwork.*

viously, the reflected meter reads the brightness of the light reflected by the objects in the scene. It may be used in at least three important and different ways.

The *integrated reading of the scene as a whole* is undoubtedly the most common technique of using a reflected light meter, particularly among amateurs. People whip out the meter, wave it around with the front pointed toward the scene, read the results, and shoot away. If there happens to be a nicely balanced range of tones in the scene, if all the tones are about equal in size, and if the user avoided reading too much sky or his own feet, chances are the picture will be nicely exposed. But more often than not there are large walls, objects, or other backgrounds either too bright or too dark for this method to produce an acceptable overall exposure reading. A major drawback is that flesh tones are given no particular consideration and will change drastically from scene to scene. Another drawback is that the light-acceptance angle of the meter usually fails to match even remotely the acceptance angle of the camera lens, and objects not a part of the scene on film are allowed to have an effect on the exposure reading.

Measuring single tone areas of the scene will lead to more accurate exposure control. The scene is looked at with the camera angle in mind, and the brightest and darkest objects are noted. Reflected-light readings are then taken of these single bright and dark tones and an exposure value somewhere between these two extremes is chosen. Such an exposure will, as close as possible, capture the entire tonal range.

This method obviously disregards the notion of consistent flesh tones, but it does fall perfectly into the concept of the "correct exposure" as one that fits the scene's total range within the film's latitude. Because of the infinite variety of scenes and tonal ranges, it is impossible for the cinematographer to use this method and get consistent results from one scene to another. Some modify the method by taking reflected-light readings of the subject's flesh tones as well, but here again the results cannot be very consistent given the wide range of complexions among human beings.

A third system is to use the reflected-light meter to *read a subject of known and constant reflectance,* such as an 18 percent gray card. These medium-gray cards, of specific tone, correspond to the calibration of incident-light meters. In other words, a reflected-light meter, reading an 18 percent gray card, will give essentially the same reading as an incident meter held at the same angle and position. But to use the card successfully be sure to "read" it and nothing else, and be careful not to shadow the card with hand and meter.

In the final analysis, if an incident reading is called for, use an incident-light meter; it is a lot more convenient.

Spot Reading Reflected-Light Meters: Spot meters, as they are usually called, are reflected-light meters fitted with an optical system that permits restricting the reading to an extremely narrow acceptance angle (usually from .5 to 5 degrees). They are capable of giving accurate readings of small portions of the scene, and are ideal for the brightest highlight and darkest shadow method mentioned earlier. They will also measure flesh tones from great distances. Spot meters are especially suited for use with long telephoto lenses. Usually the area being measured is visible in the meter's viewfinder within a wider field of view for easier pinpointing. Recent versions are directly readable through the finder, have powered scales that move automatically and instantly in response to the light, and lighted scales that facilitate reading under dark conditions. Their range of sensitivity is wide, they have automatic transistorized voltage regulation, and they carry exorbitant price tags. They can be used for all types of reflected-light readings, except the wide integrated reading of an entire scene. Most motion picture cameramen use spot meters to check the brightness of particular tones that come into question and to take readings of objects a great distance away. At a sports event or concert, for example, the cameraman may be shooting from the dark sidelines with a long lens and have to expose for the brightly lighted ring or stage. It would

6-8. *A Minolta Auto-Spot spotreading reflected-light meter. (Harvey "T" Thompson)*

be extremely inconvenient to walk up front to make an incident-light reading, especially every time the lighting changed; an ordinary wide-viewing reflected meter would respond to the predominantly dark audience between the cameraman and subject and give a falsely low reading. The spot meter here allows accurate readings of the people and tones within the shot and is the best way to monitor the exposure in a situation of this kind.

Through-the-Lens Reflected-Light Meters: With the advent of reflex cameras and zoom lenses with reflex viewfinding systems, it was a natural step to place a tiny light-sensitive cell in the reflex light path and thus constantly monitor the brightness of the scene as viewed by the camera itself. This seemed to be such a wonderful idea that it was only a short time before someone added a few electronic circuits and a tiny motor coupled to the aperture ring and—voilà!—the fully automatic exposure system. Light passes through the lens, is reflected by the reflex system to the CdS cell, which controls a current that is used to instantly set the aperture. Marvelous—yes! A panacea for the professional cameraman—no!

There are at least two important drawbacks to this system. First, the through-the-lens system gives essentially an integrated reflected-light reading; this type of reading does not produce consistent flesh tones because of the changes in backgrounds and objects surrounding the subject. Second, when the camera with a fully automatic exposure system pans across a scene and lighter or darker objects are introduced, the aperture changes accordingly. If the camera is following a moving subject, the exposure on the subject varies within the shot as the backgrounds change. Manufacturers claim this can be an advantage in scenes where the subject walks from, say, direct sunlight into shadow. The problem is that with an automatic system generally, the exposure adjustment is too great and it happens too quickly, so the sudden resulting exposure jump calls attention to itself. (In situations like this, it is often better to give slightly less than the full amount of correction called for because the person who has walked into shadow should look, at least in the establishing shot, a little darker.) Footage exposed in a camera equipped with a fully automatic exposure system is therefore characterized by constant exposure fluctuations usually unacceptable to the professional cinematographer. The system is useful in documentary filming situations where the cameraman must move so fast that he cannot give any attention to his exposure requirements, but these are extremely rare.

Some professional cameras (specially equipped Arriflex BLs and Beaulieus) have through-the-lens meters that constantly monitor image brightness, but they are not coupled to the lens diaphragm. These semiautomatic manual systems read out with an indicator needle visible within the viewing area. The aperture is set by hand to a corresponding or needle-matching position. These systems give the cameraman final control. They are especially useful for filming distant subjects with telephoto lens, and in other situations when making incident-light readings at the position of the subject is impossible.

One advantage of through-the-lens systems is that they will automatically account for any filters, bellows extensions, or other lens attachments that have an effect on exposure. The exposure system settings are normal and the meter reads the effect of any lens attachments, giving a calculation-free reading.

The Light Meter Calculator Dial: The simple device that combines the four exposure variables described so far and produces an exposure setting is the calculator dial, found conveniently mounted on the exposure meter. These calculators are produced in a variety of forms, but all have at least four dials that correspond to the four variables—film sensitivity, exposure time, lens aperture, and scene brightness.

On each calculator is an exposure index dial, which has an indicator or window with which the ASA rating of the film may be set. Most dials use click stops or friction devices so that the involved wheels of the calculator will rotate together and maintain the ASA setting as exposure computations are made.

Next, there is a scale with numbers corresponding to those that appear on the light-measuring meter dial. When a light reading is made, the number the needle points to is noted and the calculator dial rotated until the appropriate pointer is aimed at the corresponding numer on the calculator scale.

Finally, there is a scale containing the standard series of f-stop numbers: f/1.4, 2, 2.8, 4, 5.6, 8, 11, 16, 22, 32, 45, 64, 90, and so on. This "aperture" scale is in direct proximity to a scale containing shutter speed numbers. These usually begin with a long exposure time of perhaps 60 seconds and, in increments equal to half the preceding time (30 seconds, 15 seconds, 8 seconds, 4 seconds, 2 seconds), move to one second in the middle of the scale, and then continue in fractions of a second. Fractions are usually indicated by a small slanted line. The series proceeds with reduced exposure times in multiples of two: 1/2 (second), 4 (one quarter second), 8, 15, 30, 60, 125, 250, 500, 1,000. When the calculator dial is set at the point corresponding to the needle reading, the f-stop number is located

6-9. *A typical exposure meter dial showing ASA window, meter scale, and shutter speed/aperture scales.*

directly adjacent to the shutter speed the camera is using. The lens on the camera is then set to this f-stop. All other matters settled, shooting can start.

Which Meter to Use: Finding the "correct exposure" is mostly a matter of first selecting the most important elements of a scene and then choosing a system of determining exposure that leads to the desired rendering of those elements. The "right" method will therefore vary according to the cinematographer's goals and the diretor's wishes—a common pattern in the process of filmmaking. Under most filming conditions: the incident meter is the first among the "equipment of choice." But properly equipped professionals will be prepared to utilize incident, reflective, spot, and through-the-lens metering systems as each of their special applications are required to deal with the ever-changing demands of most shooting situations.

Variable 5: exposure compensation: filter factors

The fifth and last exposure variable is the compensation factor of any filters being used. Since they absorb part of the light that would otherwise be received by the film, some compensation must be made when virtually any type of filter is used. The amount of adjustment needed is computed with the aid of a figure called the *filter factor*. It gives the number of times the exposure must be increased to compensate for the light absorbed by the filter. A filter factor of 2 requires that the exposure be doubled, which means opening the aperture one f-stop. A factor of 4 requires opening the aperture 2 stops, a factor of 8 means 3 stops, and a factor of 16 requires an aperture change of 4 stops.

Factors are supplied by the filter manufacturer. Generally they are accurate enough for most filming situations—where the filters are used with the type of film for which they were designed. Film manufacturers, however, sometimes recommend slightly different filter factors for the same filter when it is used with different emulsions. For example, a Wratten #21 orange filter used with black-and-white film to give haze penetration, darken skies, and lighten flesh tones is said by the filter manufacturer to have a factor of 3. According to Eastman's recommendations, this factor is fine for all black-and-white cine films except 4X negative film, for which they recommend a factor of 3.5. This is typical of the slight variances in recommended factors, but these are usually so slight that no discernible exposure error will be detected if one recommendation rather than the other is used.

Instead of compensating for the filter factor by changing the lens aperture after making the reading, which is too easy to forget, it may be incorporated in the ASA rating. In other words, if there is a filter factor of 2, instead of making the required one-stop aperture adjustment, reduce (in this case divide by 2) the ASA rating of the film as set on the light meter. The filter factor is therefore automatically taken into account by the meter, and the danger of forgetting to adjust the lens after the light reading is eliminated. It is to this end that many manufacturers list the adjusted ASA rating number on the film guide sheet for certain filters commonly used with that emulsion. For example, the Eastman guide sheet for Eastman Color Negative film type 7247 lists under the exposure index, "tungsten ASA 100, daylight ASA 64, with Kodak Wratten filter #85." In this way the precise filter factor for this combination of emulsion and filter is automatically computed when exposure readings are taken.

Filters are sometimes used in conjunction with other filters, such as using a polarizer in addition to a color-conversion filter. In cases like this the factors of the two filters are multiplied, not added, to give a factor that will compensate for both filters.

Motion picture camera filters

There are three basic kinds of motion picture camera filters: for use with black-and-white films; for use with color films; for use with either black-and-white or color.

These three kinds of filters are made in three different ways.

Gelatin filter sheets are made of pharmaceutically pure gelatin precisely dyed with the intended color. Color control is very accurate and the gelatin sheets, extremely thin and flat, have excellent optical properties. Of all filter types, gelatin diminishes image quality the least. This is an important consideration, but the gelatin is very soft and fragile, easily scratched, a collector of dirt and fingerprints, highly susceptible to moisture, and must be frequently replaced. Gelatin filters are therefore not usually mounted on the front of the lens where they can be so easily damaged. They are instead cut into small discs or squares and mounted on the back of lenses or, in cameras so equipped, placed in frames in the camera filter slot.

Cemented filters consist of two sheets of optically flat glass between which a gelatin filter has been cemented. These filters, the most common type for general photography, have the advantage of gelatin's accurate color combined with greater strength. They may be mounted on the front of the lens or in the matte box filter slots without risking permanent damage from fingerprints, raindrops, dust, and dirt. Cemented filters are available in a variety of sizes and shaped to screw directly into various lenses, to be mounted in filter holders and sunshades, and to be slid into matte box filter slots. They are usually far too bulky to be used behind the lens. Their main disadvantage is that light must pass through a sandwich of what was originally six surfaces (both sides of both pieces of glass plus the gelatin), reduced to two through cementing. The resulting thickness is believed to have a slightly negative effect on image quality.

Although there have been some recent advances in the manufacture of *solid glass filters,* they are available only in a limited color range because of the difficulty of controlling spectral absorption characteristics when the dyes are mixed with molten glass. They are easy to work with and may have an antireflection coating, similar to coated lenses, that improves image quality. If the proper color can be found, solid glass filters often make the best choice for many shooting situations.

There are strong differences of opinion among experienced cameramen as to which type of filter is best. Sometimes the choice is made for you by what is available; whether or not the camera has a gelatin filter slot; the size and type of lens; the adapters, filter rings, and sunshades available; and so forth. If shooting conditions are even slightly difficult (sandy beach, rain forest, dusty factory), the raw gelatin filters are most certainly a poor choice; even when mounted behind the lens they are a problem since moisture makes gelatin sticky and the slightest specks may show up on the film. But thick cemented filters can have a slight image-softening effect, especially when mounted on wide-angle and zoom lenses. They are also prone to "separating," a process by which moisture or microbes attack the center gelatin layer and render the filter cloudy and useless.

For these simple and practical reasons, it is best to use light and film that are balanced for each other and need the least filtration possible. Avoid multiple filters and use the same filter, same type of filter, or a matched set of filters when multiple lenses are being used in the shooting of a scene.

Black-and-White Photography: Filters for black-and-white photography are virtually always used in daylight and can accomplish a wide range of changes in image rendering. It is important to understand exactly how and why these filters affect tone rendering the way they do, so that it is possible to make the most useful choices of available filters.

The additive primary colors of red, blue, and green pass their own color (wavelength) of light and absorb (or stop) all others, while the subtractive primary color filters of yellow, cyan, and magenta have the ability to pass both of their related additive primaries. Yellow passes green and red, cyan passes green and blue, magenta passes blue and red. Most modern black-and-white films for general photography are *panchromatic,* or sensitive to all colors of the spectrum.

Thus it may be assumed that when a scene is shot, all of the colors in the scene will make equal exposures on the film if they are equal in brightness and reflectance. But in practical cinematography this condition does not exist. An "average" scene contains many shades of color. The objects in the scene not only have varying abilities to reflect light but also have varying amounts of light falling on them. A colored filter on the camera will pass, in accordance with its intensity of color saturation, more light from the portions of the scene that contain the same color as the filter and less light from the portions of the scene that contain the colors which the filter can best absorb.

For example: a woman in red pants is standing on a very green lawn, with a deep blue sky serving as the background. A red filter would pass a relatively great deal of light from the pants while greatly diminishing the light from the green grass and the blue sky. Black-and-white film would render the pants light and the sky and grass dark. A green filter would lighten the grass while darkening the sky and pants, and a blue filter would lighten the sky while darkening the pants and grass. All of this is assuming that the three areas of the scene are of equal brightness. But in reality they are not equal and a filter would be selected to accomplish some specific end. If the problem in this example is the sky, which, while blue, is too light (a common problem) and might overexpose and "wash out" on film, the goal is to select a filter that would pass relatively equal amounts of the red and green, but darken the bluish sky and thus help control scene contrast. Color theory makes it obvious that yellow is the proper choice. This subtractive primary color passes green and red but not blue. A yellow filter of greater intensity (toward orange) would be chosen if the sky was very pale and bright, and a filter of less intensity (pale lemon) if the sky was intensely blue and not as bright.

By applying this bit of color theory, the color rendering and contrast of many scenes can be adjusted to considerable advantage. Figure 6-10, a list of twelve commonly used filters for black-and-white pho-

Filter number	Color	Effect in daylight	Plus X neg 7231		Double X neg 7222		4 X neg 7227	
			Factor	Stops increase	Factor	Stops increase	Factor	Stops increase
No. 3 Aero 1	light yellow	slight haze penetration; slight contrast increase; slightly darker sky and lighter skin	1.5	1/2	1.5	1/2	1.5	1/2
No. 8 K-2	yellow	moderate haze penetration; darkens sky and lightens flesh tone	2	1	1.5	1/2	2	1
No. 12 minus blue	yellow	stronger haze penetration; darkens sky and lightens flesh tone	2	1	2	1	2.5	1 1/4
No. 15 G	deep yellow	heavy haze penetration; greater contrast; useful for aerial photos and telephoto lenses	2.5	1 1/4	3	1 1/2	3	1 1/2
No. 21	orange	increased haze penetration and contrast; especially good for aerial, mountain, telephoto photos	3	1 1/2	3	1 1/2	3.5	1 3/4

tography, contains a description of the filter, its factor with five black-and-white Eastman films, and its rendering of various colors.

Color Photography: Filters for color photography fall mainly into three categories: color conversion, light balancing, and color compensating.

Color-conversion filters are used to change the color of light so that it matches the color balance (or color temperature) of the film being used (see chapter 3). There are theoretically six filters needed, allowing films balanced for 3,200°K to be converted to 3,400°K and daylight; films balanced for 3,400°K to be converted to 3,200°K and daylight; and for films balanced for daylight to be converted to 3,200°K and 3,400°K. Figure 6-11 gives the Wratten number of the filters needed to accomplish these conversions. The filter factors are in the form of compensated ASA ratings on the film manufacturer's guide sheets.

Plus X reversal		Tri X reversal					
Factor	Stops increase	Factor	Stops increase	Renders blue	Renders green	Renders red	Renders yellow
1.5	1/2	1.5	1/2	very slightly darker	very slightly lighter	very slightly lighter	very slightly lighter
2	1	2	1	slightly darker	very slightly lighter	very slightly lighter	slightly lighter
2	1	2	1	fairly dark	fairly light	fairly light	light
2.5	1 1/4	2.5	1 1/4	dark	light	light	very light
3	1 1/2	3	1 1/2	dark	very slightly darker	very light	very light

6-10. Filters for black-and-white photography.

6-10. *(cont'd)*

Filter number	Color	Effect in daylight	Plus X neg 7231		Double X neg 7222		4 X neg 7227	
			Factor	Stops increase	Factor	Stops increase	Factor	Stops increase
No. 23A	red	darkens blue sky significantly; lightens faces; strong contrast on clouds, sky, water	5	2 1/4	5	2 1/4	5	2 1/4
No. 25	red	very strong contrast on skies, clouds, sunsets; too light on flesh tones	8	3	8	3	8	3
No. 29	deep red	extreme contrast and exaggerated rendering; sky and water reproduced black	16	4	20	4 1/4	25	4 1/2
No. 11 (X-1)	light green	useful for flowers and foliage; good flesh tones; darkens sky	4	2	4	2	4	2
No. 58	green	excellent for trees against sky; renders green lighter than red and blue	8	3	8	3	8	3
No. 47 C5	blue	renders blue subjects light; adds haze to produce "atmosphere," especially with telephoto	6	2 1/2	6	2 1/2	6	2 1/2
Nos. 23A and 56	red and green	combination filter for night effects in daylight; green is good for flesh tones; red darkens sky	normal, 20/efx 6	4 1/4 2 1/2	normal, 20/efx 6	4 1/4 2 1/2	normal, 20/efx 6	4 1/4 2 1/2

Plus X reversal		Tri X reversal					
Factor	Stops increase	Factor	Stops increase	Renders blue	Renders green	Renders red	Renders yellow
6	2 1/2	5	2 1/4	very dark	dark	very light	slightly lighter
10	3 1/4	10	3 1/4	black	very dark	very light	fairly light
40	5 1/4	40	5 1/4	black	black	white	very light
4	2	4	2	fairly dark	light	medium dark	fairly light
5	2 1/4	5	2 1/4	very dark	very light	very dark	light
8	3	8	3	white	dark	black	very dark
normal, 20/efx 6	4 1/4, 2 1/2	normal, 20/efx 6	4 1/4, 2 1/2	very dark	very dark	light	white

	When exposed in:		
	Daylight	3,400°K	3,200°K
Films balanced for daylight		80B blue	80A blue
Films balanced for 3,400°K	85 orange		82A bluish
Films balanced for 3,200°K	85 orange	81A yellowish	

6-12. *Light-balancing filters.*

Filter color	Color temperature of source		Wratten filter number	Exposure increase in stops*
	Converted to 3,200°K	Converted to 3,400°K		
Bluish	2,490°K	2,610°K	82C + 82C	1 1/3
	2,570°K	2,700°K	82C + 82B	1 1/3
	2,650°K	2,780°K	82C + 82A	1
	2,720°K	2,870°K	82C + 82	1
	2,800°K	2,950°K	82C	2/3
	2,900°K	3,060°K	82B	2/3
	3,000°K	3,180°K	82A	1/3
	3,100°K	3,290°K	82	1/3
	3,200°K	3,400°K	no filter necessary	
Yellowish	3,300°K	3,510°K	81	1/3
	3,400°K	3,630°K	81A	1/3
	3,500°K	3,740°K	81B	1/3
	3,600°K	3,850°K	81C	1/3
	3,700°K	3,970°K	81D	2/3
	3,850°K	4,140°K	81EF	2/3

* These values are approximate. For critical work they should be checked by practical test, especially if more than one filter is used.

The second major category of filters for color photography is intended for less drastic color temperature alteration than the color-conversion filters. *Light-balancing filters* are used on the camera to adjust the color of the illumination in order to obtain a warmer (yellow) or cooler (blue) rendering of the scene, or to correct for slight color temperature mismatches.

The color temperature of the illumination in a studio or location can be measured with *color-temperature meters.* These meters make color-temperature readings of light sources to provide filtration information. In their simplest form, they use rotating graduated red and blue filters.

As the meter dials are turned, the filters pass back and forth over a light-sensitive cell, and when a balance between red and blue is obtained the meter will indicate the Kelvin temperature of the light sources being measured. The meters are used in conjunction with tables that give the light-balancing or -compensating filter needed to make the necessary color temperature alteration. While these meters are useful in many specialized fields of lighting and photography, most filmmakers rely on the stated Kelvin rating of the light sources they are using to determine what, if any, color correction is required.

Color-compensating filters, the third category of filters for use with color films, are used to compensate for color alterations other than those which adhere to the Kelvin red-to-blue scale. In addition to CC red and blue, there are CCG (green), CCM (magenta), CCY (yellow), and CCC (cyan).

Figure 6-13 is a table of Kodak color-compensating filters and the necessary exposure increase in f-stops. According to Kodak, these exposure values are meant only as a guide, and both the exposure compensation and the color rendition should be checked by shooting a test. A typical recommended use of CC filters would be in underwater photography (see chapter 2).

There are also recommended filtrations for photography under fluorescent illumination, which does not fall within the parameters of the ordinary tungsten spectral pattern. Fluorescent lights, which come in

6-13. *Color-compensating filters.*

Yellow (absorbs blue)	Exposure increase in stops*	Magenta (absorbs green)	Exposure increase in stops*	Cyan (absorbs red)	Exposure increase in stops*
CC-05Y	—	CC-05M	1/3	CC-05C	1/3
CC-10Y	1/3	CC-10M	1/3	CC-10C	1/3
CC-20Y	1/3	CC-20M	1/3	CC-20C	1/3
CC-30Y	1/3	CC-30M	2/3	CC-30C	2/3
CC-40Y	1/3	CC-40M	2/3	CC-40C	2/3
CC-50Y	2/3	CC-50M	2/3	CC-50C	1

Red (absorbs blue and green)	Exposure increase in stops*	Green (absorbs blue and red)	Exposure increase in stops*	Blue (absorbs red and green)	Exposure increase in stops*
CC-05R	1/3	CC-05G	1/3	CC-05B	1/3
CC-10R	1/3	CC-10G	1/3	CC-10B	1/3
CC-20R	1/3	CC-20G	1/3	CC-20B	2/3
CC-30R	2/3	CC-30G	2/3	CC-30B	2/3
CC-40R	2/3	CC-40G	2/3	CC-40B	1
CC-50R	1	CC-50G	1	CC-50B	1 1/3

* These values are approximate. For critical work they should be checked by practical test, especially if more than one filter is used.

many varieties, tend to have a strong greenish cast that renders flesh tones poorly on color film. This problem and the recommended color filtration is discussed in detail in chapter 5.

General Purpose: There is a wide assortment of filters for all types of film that is neutral in color but provide for exposure control (neutral-density filters), glare and reflection control (polarizing filters), and special visual effects (diffusion, star, and gauze filters).

The chief purpose of *neutral-density filters* is to allow fast film emulsions to be exposed in bright sunlight at moderate lens aperture settings. Neutral density (N.D.) filters are gray, absorb light from all areas of the spectrum, and thus do not affect color rendition. They may be used in combination with other filters (and sometimes are sold in forms already combined, especially with conversion filters) and are useful when a large lens aperture is used to limit the depth of field. Figure 6-14 is a list of the variable N.D. filters, giving the Kodak number, density, transmission of light filter factor, and equivalent f-stop increase.

There are also graduated neutral-density filters, gray at one edge and blending slowly into clear glass at the other edge. These can be placed carefully in front of the lens (and reflex checked with the lens set at the operating aperture to be sure of alignment) to control bright snow, skies, and so on. Panning and tilting the camera during the shot may be impossible with the graduated N.D. filter, depending on the setup.

Polarizing Filters: Polarizers or polascreens have the ability to transmit light waves oscillating in only one axis.

Reflective surfaces also polarize the light. When they are viewed through a polarizing filter rotated into a 90-degree plane for the axis of light polarization, the reflection can be eliminated. The degree to which polarizing filters are successful depends primarily on the angle of the light source to the reflective surface.

Light sources may also be polarized with glass or plastic polarized

6-14. *Neutral-density filters.*

Kodak no.	Density	Transmission	Factor	Stops increase
	0.10	80%	1.3	¼
	0.20	63%	1.6	½
ND-1	0.30	50%	2.0	1
	0.40	40%	2.5	1¼
	0.50	32%	3.1	1½
ND-2	0.60	25%	4.0	2
	0.70	20%	5.0	2¼
	0.80	16%	6.3	2½
ND-3	0.90	13%	8.0	3
	1.00	10%	10.0	3¼
	2.00	1%	100	6¾
	3.00	.10%	1,000	10
	4.00	.010%	10,000	13¼

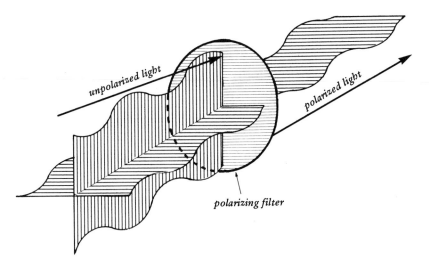

6-15. *The polarization of light through a polarizing filter.*

unpolarized light

polarized light

polarizing filter

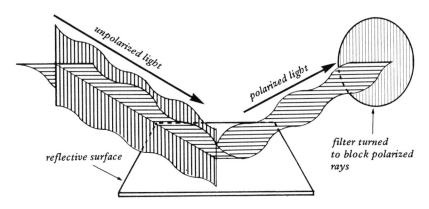

6-16. *Now filter blocks polarized, reflected light.*

unpolarized light

polarized light

reflective surface

filter turned to block polarized rays

sheets. When this polarized light is used in conjunction with a polarizer on the camera, virtually all glare is eliminated.

Through refraction, the light of the sky is also polarized. In these cases, the maximum effect is found in a blue sky photographed at a 90-degree angle to the sun. The polarizer has a significant effect in darkening skies and bringing out dramatic "postcard quality" cloud detail. The effect will always be maximized by using rotating filter rings equipped with an indicator or handle to facilitate alignment. The filter factor of polascreens is usually 2 or 3, depending on style and manufacturer.

Star filters, fog filters, gauze filters, diffusion filters: A large variety of special-effects filters modify the image to soften hard lines, disperse the image around highlights, and generally create ethereal effects. Nylon stockings and petroleum jelly smears on clear glass are also common and inexpensive image modifiers. Gauzes once were commonly used on close-ups of aging actresses in a more romantic era of film-making, but these effects are more frequently used today in commer-

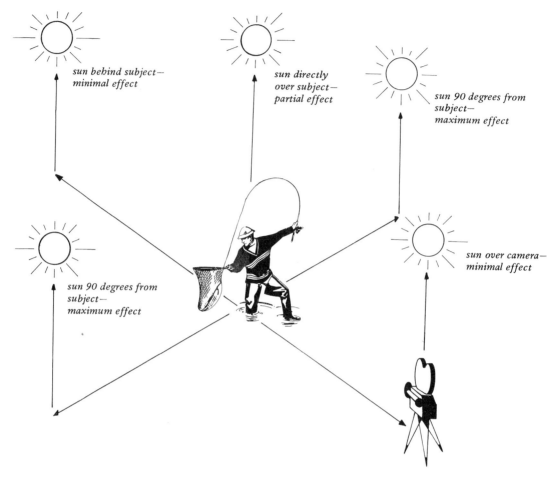

sun behind subject—
minimal effect

sun directly
over subject—
partial effect

sun 90 degrees from
subject—
maximum effect

sun 90 degrees from
subject—
maximum effect

sun over camera—
minimal effect

6-17. Effectiveness of polarizing filter depends on the angle of polarized light.

cials, dream sequences, flashbacks, and the like. Generally it is wise to shoot a test to determine if the desired effect is being achieved. No exposure compensation is usually necessary.

Exposure and the film lab

Anyone who has had slides or prints developed through the neighborhood drugstore has probably observed the inconsistent results. Unfortunately, despite great efforts to the contrary, even professional motion picture laboratories sometimes deliver results that range from poor to disastrous. All of the cinematographer's careful measurement and adjustment of exposure and lighting balance will have been completely wasted if the lab's quality controls are not rigidly maintained, and this is indeed a fitting topic for the closing paragraphs of this book.

How then does the filmmaker assure himself that the lab is delivering the best possible quality? The phrasing of this question is deliberate.

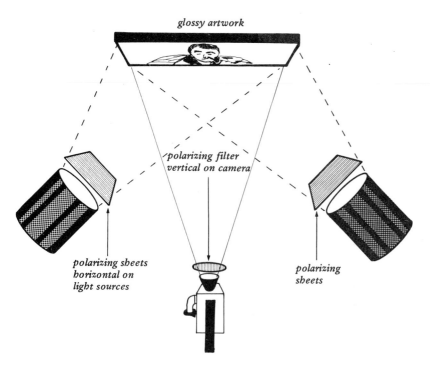

glossy artwork

polarizing filter
vertical on camera

polarizing sheets
horizontal on
light sources

polarizing
sheets

6-18. *Eliminating glare in photography of shiny objects.*

6-19. *Effect of petroleum jelly on glass filter.*

Sometimes (perhaps usually) the selection of a lab is made on the basis of criteria which should be ranked much lower than "best quality." Such factors as convenient location, better price, credit policies, and speed do help create a pleasant working relationship, but these aspects of lab service tend to change with time. Once a negative has been developed, all the pleasantries cannot change the result.

The recommended answer to the question of best quality involves spending a little money and certainly would not be sensible for every project—shoot a test and send out equivalent portions to the best-looking lab candidates. Doing that will definitely buy some peace of mind. Even producers deeply involved with a particular lab might be surprised—or very pleasantly reassured—with the results. Raw stock, various lighting conditions, and other variables should be reflected in the test footage. The length of each exposed sample may be determined by the lab's normal minimum charges. Do not forget the added benefit of lens and camera checkout at the same time.

Schedules or other problems may make such a test impractical, but it is extremely important for the filmmaker to be certain that he is obtaining the finest and most consistent lab results possible.

There seems to be a tradition among authors of film books to conclude with interesting predictions about the future of the medium. The all-time favorite, *Film and Its Techniques* by Raymond Spottiswoode (1951), undoubtedly set the pace with predictions of 3D, synthesized sound, and changes caused by television. Twenty years later Lenny Lipton wrote about wall-sized TV screens and films by computer in the wrap-up of his popular book *Independent Filmmaking*. Recently, Sony Corporation has announced a camera that records images on a computer chip, and it would be quite easy to fly off on the most prodigious heights of imagination.

But it is far more practical to state simply that much of what has been discussed in this book will undoubtedly have direct application to communicating effectively with whatever tools technology ultimately supplies. Production methods, pictorial continuity, mobilizing and using cameras, the principles and uses of lenses, everything on lighting—all are areas fundamental to every known and imagined visual motion-capturing and image-retrieval systems. It is hoped that the readers of this book will now have a better understanding of how to use the increasingly versatile, beautiful, exciting medium of film.

Glossary

action axis   An imaginary line in all staged action that can be used to maintain the established positions, movements, and directions of characters and objects to be filmed.

additive primary colors   The colors of red, green, and blue that, in the form of quantities of light, can be added together to produce white light or any color of the spectrum.

aerial image   The visible inverted image of a given subject formed within all positive lenses when the lens is positioned between the viewer and the subject.

antihalation backing   A dark-colored dye coating applied to the base of a photographic film in order to prevent light from passing through the film and reflecting off other sufaces, thus causing re-exposure, or halation.

aperture (camera and projector)   The opening in the film guideway or plate behind which the film travels during exposure or projection that determines the precise area of the film to be exposed or projected.

aperture (lens)   The adjustable opening for controlling the amount of light to pass through a photographic lens.

ASA speed rating   A system established by the American Standards Association for rating the sensitivity of photographic materials to light. See also **exposure index**.

back light   See **kicker light**.

barn doors   A set of two or four opaque shields that may be attached to the front of a lamp housing for the purpose of controlling the spread of the light output.

barney   Padded, close-fitting camera bags designed to reduce camera and magazine noise, or to keep the camera warm with battery-operated resistance heating coils built into the bag.

base (film)   The transparent flexible plastic support material (cellulose triacetate) on a photographic film that is coated with the light-sensitive emulsion layer.

beamsplitter   An optical device that combines or divides light and can be used inside cameras to provide reflex viewing or in front of lenses to combine separate images.

bellows   An attachment used between camera and lens to reposition the lens for extreme close-focus cinematography.

blade   See **gobo**.

blimp   A soundproof camera housing designed to silence the noise of a running camera so that simultaneous sound recordings can be made.

body brace   A support that rests on the cameraman's shoulders and waist for shooting with cameras too heavy to be supported by hand.

brightness   The amount of light reflected from a subject.

brute   A trade name of the Mole-Richardson Company for particular models of powerful carbon arc luminaries.

candela   Unit of luminous intensity, formerly the standard candle.

candlepower   The total luminous intensity of a light source.

cellulose triacetate   A transparent plastic material used as the support or base for the emulsion on photographic films.

changing bag   A lined, zippered, opaque cloth bag used for loading undeveloped film in cameras, magazines, and the like.

characteristic curve   A chart plotting the relationship of exposure and the resulting density of photographic films.

CID   See **HMI.**

cinéma vérité   The documentary filming technique of following and not overtly directing the action as it unfolds.

circle of confusion   A point of light that constitutes the optical image of a point object source as formed by a practical lens. In practice, the theoretical image point is rendered as a circle due to aberrations in the optical system, and limits on circle size are used to determine focus acceptability.

claw   The internal part of a camera that uses the film's perforations to advance the film for each exposure.

clip   See **gobo.**

close-up   A shot taken either with a long focal-length lens or from a relatively close distance from the subject, so as to make the portion photographed appear large on the screen.

color couplers   See **dye couplers.**

color temperature   The color of light as measured through the use of the Kelvin scale; the temperature is arrived at through a rating system based on the temperature to which a black body must be heated to match the color of the light source in question.

contrast   The difference between the lightest and darkest areas of a scene or the image of the scene after recording on film.

cookie   See **cucoloris.**

core   A usually plastic hub on which film may be wound and supplied. Required for certain camera magazines and other film-handling equipment.

cosine law   A principle of illumination that states that the brightness of a surface decreases in an amount proportional to the cosine of the angle of incidence of the light source illuminating it.

cradle   A camera attachment used to support large or heavy lenses for the purpose of avoiding strain on the lens mounting itself, and to provide additional image stability.

crane   A large, wheeled camera and operator support, characterized by a counterbalanced boom that permits the camera and operator to be raised, lowered, or moved about.

crop   A term used in cinematography to describe what portion of a given subject is included within the boundaries of the photographed scene.

CSI   See **HMI.**

cucoloris   An opaque sheet with a patterned cutout used in front of a light to create dappled backgrounds.

cut-away shot   Used to describe shots of characters not included in the initial scene but later inserted in the footage to provide a reaction or to bridge a gap in the main action.

cyclorama   A seamless backdrop, usually of cloth, that is streched across a studio, attached at a curve to the floor and sometimes the corners, that provides a horizonless sky or background.

daylight-loading spools   Various-sized film reels, usually of metal, with opaque sides that prevent light from reaching the inner layers of film during loading and unloading.

densitometry   The measurement of the quantity of the light transmitted through developed photographic films.

depth of field   The range of distances that will be in acceptable focus, with a given lens, focal length, aperture, and distance from the scene.

depth of focus   The range of distances that will be in acceptable focus in the space behind the lens and at the film plane for a given focal length, aperture, and distance from the scene.

development   The chemical process of converting a latent image recorded on film into a visible density or image.

diaphragm   See **aperture** (lens).

diffuse; diffusion   As a verb, to scatter, or spread light. As a noun or adjective, light characterized by being scattered or dispersed. Also, a matte or flat reflecting surface.

diffuser   A translucent light-modifier, usually of cloth, plastic, or spun glass, mounted or hung in front of luminaries to disperse and soften the light.

diopter   A unit of measurement of the refractive power of a lens equal to the reciprocal of the focal length in meters, used to calibrate the curvature and therefore magnifying power of lenses. Also applied to the simple lenses used as attachments to zoom and fixed focal-length lenses for the purpose of extra-close-up photography.

dissolve   A technique used to create transitions by fading out one scene while fading in another.

dolly   A wheeled camera support used to follow moving subjects or to create movement within static scenes.

dolly shot   A moving shot, created with the use of a rolling camera support.

dot   See **gobo.**

double-system sound   The camera captures only the visual, while the sound is recorded on a separate machine.

dye couplers   Compounds that ultimately produce the colored dyes in a developed negative or color reversal film. They may be built into the emulsion during manufacture or added during development, depending on film type, and convert the silver image to a dye record with appropriate density and color.

dye inhibition   A film-duplicating system that uses color dyes and three special relief-image printing masters to produce the composite print.

emulsion   The light-sensitive layer or layers coated onto the support base in a photographic film.

establishing shot   The often initial and usually wide-angle opening shot of a film sequence that establishes the relationships of characters and objects within the scene.

exposure   The process of subjecting a photographically sensitive material to light so as to create a latent image on the film, which may subsequently be made visible through development.

exposure index   A numeric value assigned to a given photographic emulsion based on its ability to respond to light. It is intended to be used in conjunction with light meters and exposure tables as a guide to subjecting the film material to light with predictable results.

extension tubes   Tubes of various lengths used singly or in groups and attached between lens and camera to create a greater than normal distance from the film plane, thereby permitting closer focus distances than normal.

fade-in, fade-out   A device to create transitions, often used at the beginning or end of films, that grad-ually change from a normal exposure to black or vice versa.

fiber optics   Optical systems employing very fine glass rods for light transmission.

film gate   See **gate.**

film plane   The location of the film surface in a camera or optical system.

filter   Transparent sheet of optically flat material that absorbs specific wavelengths or colors of light; intended for use on the camera in front of film during exposure.

filter factor   A numeric value by which the film exposure must be increased to compensate for the light absorbed by a given filter.

flag   See **gobo.**

flashback   The continuity technique of jumping back in time to an event that occurred before the "present time" of the initial story.

flashing   Exposing film to small quantities of white light before development, resulting in a small amount of fog on the developed film. Flashing may help produce tone in the shadow areas and a reduction of overall contrast in the scene.

fluid head   A camera-mounting device utilizing a highly viscous fluid to permit smooth panning and tilting of the camera. Designed for attachment to legs, dollies, and other camera supports.

focal length   The distance between the optical center of a lens and the focal plane when the lens is focused on infinity.

focal plane   The point behind a lens perpendicular to its optical axis where the image comes into principal focus; in cameras this is usually the location of the camera aperture and film.

fog   The background opacity of a developed film not produced by the exposure of the desired image.

footcandle   The unit of measurement of illumination.

footlambert   The unit of measurement of reflected light.

forced development   The use of higher temperatures or longer development times to produce greater density, contrast, or the effect of an increased sensitivity rating when developing film.

friction head   A camera-mounting device utilizing friction to permit smooth panning and tilting of the camera. Designed for attachment to various leg sets and other camera supports.

gamma   System for measuring and expressing contrast in the photographic reproduction process. On a D log E sensitometric chart it is the slope of the straight-line portion of the curve, expressed by the formula $y = \Delta d/\Delta$ Log E.

gate   The guideway for film inside a camera that properly aligns the film during exposure and advancement.

gear head   A camera-mounting device utilizing gears and crank-wheels to activate panning and tilting the camera. Designed for attachment to tripod legs, dollies, cranes, and other camera supports.

gelatin   A transparent colloidal protein used as the binder for the light-sensitive silver halides in film emulsions.

gels   Sheets of filter material, made of gelatin or plastic, placed in front of luminaries to alter color or otherwise modify light output.

gobo   Opaque black panel, made in various shapes and sizes, mounted in front of a luminary to shade light from specific areas of the subject, scene, or camera lens.

grain, graininess   The characteristic optical texture of film emulsions produced by the microscopic particles of silver (or, in certain color films, dyes); may be visible on enlargement or projection, especially when the particles are clustered together in clumps.

ground glass   Piece of flat glass on which one of the surfaces has been finely ground. The resulting translucent surface is used in camera viewing systems as a screen on which an image may be formed.

halide   Compounds such as silver bromide, chloride, or iodide which are used to form the light-sensitive substances in photographic film emulsions.

hi-hat   A short base usually made of metal to which various panning heads may be attached. Hi-hats are used to attach cameras to the floor or to any other desired surface with clamps, screws, nails, and so forth.

HMI   Term applied to a group of metal-discharge lamps, the luminaries that use the lamps, and the illumination provided therefrom.

hyperfocal distance   The closest focus distance at which a lens may be set and still include infinity at the far end of the acceptable depth of field.

illumination   The amount of light falling on a subject.

incident light   Light falling onto a subject.

insert shots   Isolated shot of an object or illustration, unrelated to the main action, inserted into the visuals to accomplish a desired communicative function.

instrumentation cameras   Special cameras used for scientific analysis of specific problems; often high speed, but may also be equipped for stop-motion or other techniques.

integral tripack   Color film using three different sensitized emulsion layers to produce the red, blue, and green record required to reproduce color.

intervalometer   A camera control system that operates the camera at a variety of preset single frame rates; may also control lights or other appliances. Commonly used for producing time-lapse photography.

inverted telephoto   Term applied to wide-angle lens designs in which the optical center of the lens is located behind the physical center of the lens, permitting more space for camera components and lens mounting.

iris   See **aperture** (lens).

ISO exposure index   International Standards Organization film sensitivity rating system. See also **exposure index**.

key light   The primary source of illumination on a given subject.

kicker light   A luminary or the light from the luminary directed toward a subject from an angle to the camera of greater than 90 degrees, to produce highlights and background separation.

lap dissolve   See **dissolve**.

latent image   The invisible record on an exposed, undeveloped photographic film.

lens, telephoto   See **telephoto lens**.

lens, wide-angle   See **wide-angle lens**.

lighting ratio   The balance of illumination levels between the key and fill lighting.

location camera   A relatively small, lightweight camera used for remote filming.

long shot   A wide view of the subject or scene, often made with a wide-angle lens, that shows a relatively large portion of the scene.

loop   The extra length of film that allows for intermittent film travel through a projector or camera gate.

lumen   Unit of illumination per square foot.

luminance   The amount of light reflected from a subject.

luminaries   Light sources, particularly studio lights, consisting of lamp and housing.

luminous flux   The amount of light in terms of area.

luminous intensity   The amount of light emitted from a source.

macro lens   A term applied in general to lenses mounted in specially designed focusing tubes, which permit greater than usual lens-to-film distances for extremely close-focus photography.

magazine   A camera attachment designed to contain rolls of film before, during, and after exposure.

magnetic stripe   A narrow band of magnetic recording material coated on the edge of film, intended for magnetic recording and playback.

master shot   A take intended for use in editing to cover all important action; can be used at any time during the sequence.

matte box   A sunshade and filter holder attached to the front of the camera.

medium shot   A shot usually made with a "normal" lens at a comfortable viewing distance from the subject in order to present the subject in what appears to be a normal size on the screen.

mirrored shutter   Used in reflex cameras, reflects light to the viewing system when the shutter is closed to the film.

monitoring viewfinder   A camera attachment that, after careful adjustment, allows the operator to see the scene as filmed.

multicam   The use of multiple cameras to cover an event or action from several angles.

neutral angle   A shot made from the center of the action-axis that can be used for special purposes within the sequence, such as to shift the camera to the opposite side of the action-axis.

normal lens   General term applied to lenses that have a focal length approximately equal to the diagonal of the film plane of the camera on which the lens is to be used.

optical sound   A method of reproducing sound used primarily for release prints in 16mm and 35mm. During recording, the light-sensitive film is exposed by a sound-modulated light beam that produces a variable area or a band of variable density along the nonperforated edge of the film. On the projector a constant light beam is caused to modulate as it passes through the moving film. These light-modulations are detected and amplified electronically to play back the sound.

overlapping action   Filming extra action at the beginning and end of each shot so that a smoothly flowing cut can be made during editing.

pan shot   Created by moving the camera on its horizontal axis during filming.

panchromatic   Emulsions that respond approximately equally to light of all visible wavelengths.

parallax   The problem in cameras with separate viewfinders, caused by the slightly differing alignment between the lens axis and the axis of the viewing device.

parallel action   A technique to create continuity by telling two or more stories at the same time by cutting back and forth from one to the other.

perforation   The equally sized and spaced holes punched in a row along one or both edges of films to allow for transport and registration purposes throughout exposure, editing, or reproduction.

perspective   The appearance of depth as perceived by human vision, rendered in photography by various combinations of lens focal length, camera distance, and viewing distance.

photoflood   A bulb, similar in shape to household lamps, distinguished by a filament rated for a lower voltage than that actually supplied, which causes the filament to burn at a higher Kelvin temperature and with increased light output.

photomation   Various techniques of filming still photos to give the illusion of watching full animation; characterized by numerous dissolves, pans, cuts, wipes, fades and so forth.

photometry   The measurement of the intensity of light.

pictorial continuity   The art of telling a story on film with separate shots that, when cut together, result in smooth-flowing, easily understood action.

pitch   The precise distance between perforations. Films are manufactured in long or short pitch, depending on their use in original photography or for duplication.

pixilation   See **photomation**.

polarization   The modification of light waves with special screens, filters, or sheets that have the ability to eliminate all waves oscillating in one plane but permit passage of waves oscillating in the plane 90 degrees from the absorbed plane.

prescore and playback   A technique for filming, usually a musical scene, without sound. The music is played through loudspeakers to the performers, who mouth the words while being filmed. The picture and track are later synchronized for editing and final mixing.

pressure plate   The often spring-loaded pad inside the camera that holds the film in the gate and against the camera aperture plate for proper positioning during exposure.

prism   An angular, transparent, usually glass solid used in cameras and optical devices to reflect light beams or break light into spectral components.

process camera   Used on animation stands and optical printers to provide especially accurate registration for precision cinematography.

pseudoanimation   See **photomation**.

pull-down claw   See **claw**.

pushing   See forced development.

quartz lamps   See tungsten halogen.

reaction shot   A take of a player within the main action, showing his or her response to the action within the scene.

reflected light   Light reflected from a subject.

reflex   Usually applied to a type of camera or viewing system that provides for cropping and focusing exactly as recorded on film.

refraction   The deflection of light waves that occurs at the boundary of two mediums with different refractive indices, or which occurs as light rays pass through a medium of uneven density.

registration pin   The internal part of a camera film-advance mechanism inserted into a perforation to maintain accurate positioning of the film during exposure.

reversal   The photographic reproduction process that employs positive, rather than negative, images. After initial development, the latent image is bleached away and the remaining sensitive emulsion is exposed and developed; this leaves a positive image on the film that may then be projected directly or reproduced through the use of other reversal or negative/positive duplicating systems.

ring light   A circular light source with a hole in the center so that it can be mounted over the taking lens of a camera and produce shadowless illumination.

scratch track   A sync-sound cue track made during shooting to be used as a reference for voice dubbing and editing.

screen direction   See action axis.

scrim   Frames with cloth or wire mesh placed in front of luminaries to modify and reduce the intensity of all or part of the light beam.

self-blimped   Silent running cameras contained in their own soundproof housing.

sensitometry   The measurement of the effect of light on photographic films.

separation light   See kicker light.

shock cut   A technique used to create transitions by a sudden, strong change in both picture and sound that alters pictorial continuity.

shutter   Internal part of a camera that opens to allow light to reach the film and then closes to allow the film to be advanced for the next exposure.

shutter speed   The exposure time permitted by a given shutter opening while the camera operates at a given running speed.

single-system sound   Recording sound with cameras that contain built-in recording modules. The resulting film, which may have a magnetic or optical track depending on the recording system, will play back directly on suitably equipped projectors.

skypan   A diffuse reflecting luminary shaped like a shallow dish, designed to illuminate large, flat surfaces and backgrounds.

slow motion   Reduced speed of subjects in projected film that is created by reduced projector speed or, more commonly, an increased camera speed at the time of shooting.

specular   A glossy or mirrored reflecting surface.

speeded-up motion   Increase in the speed of subjects in projected film that is produced by an increase in projector speed or, more commonly, by a reduced camera speed at the time of shooting.

spreaders   See triangle.

stage line   See action axis.

steadicam   The trade name of a unique camera-support system manufactured by Cinema Products Company that consists of a body mount, support arms, stabilizing system, and video viewer, and allows for smooth, flexible camera movements under a wide range of conditions.

strip lights   Type of photographic luminary characterized by a narrow, open, direct reflector, generally used in rows or strips along the top or bottom of backgrounds to provide wide, even illumination.

studio camera   Largest and most fully equipped camera, usually with such features as sound blimping for silent operation and follow-focus control attachments for the lens.

subcoat   A coating applied to both sides of the film base to prevent curl and provide a proper binder for the emulsion layer.

subtractive primary colors   Cyan, magenta, and yellow which, when used as filters, have the ability to remove (subtract) the additive primary colors.

supercoat   A tough coating to prevent scratching applied to the film surface.

target   See gobo.

teaser   See gobo.

telephoto lens   Positive front optical components combined with negative rear optical components to produce a long focal-length lens physically shorter than the focal length provided.

telephoto, inverted   See inverted telephoto.

tie-down   A set of chains, hooks, and turnbuckles

used to secure a tripod to a surface and prevent the camera from slipping or being knocked over.

time lapse   The effect of extremely speeded-up motion created with very reduced camera speed, such as one frame per minute or per hour.

tracking shot   A shot made by moving the camera behind, beside, or in front of a moving subject.

triangle   A three-legged folding device used under the legs of a tripod to prevent the tripod feet from slipping outward.

tungsten halogen   An electric light bulb with a tungsten filament in a quartz envelope filled with a halogen gas.

turret   A revolving lens mount for the front of cameras on which two or more lenses are attached at the same time; it allows the desired lens to be quickly and accurately moved in front of the film gate.

variable shutter   A motion picture camera shutter adjustable for longer or shorter exposure times while the running speed remains constant.

voice dubbing   Also known as post-sync; used to produce the dialogue for scenes in which satisfactory live sound has not been recorded. The actors rehearse their lines while watching the film in a sound studio. They then record the dialogue, making a careful attempt to synchronize their lips with the screen. Often used with foreign languages.

walking shot   A shot created by walking with the camera while filming.

wheelies   The caster-wheeled triangular tripod support that allows the camera to be rolled about.

wide-angle lens   Relative term applied to lenses with a shorter than normal focal length (equal to diagonal of film plane) for a given film format.

wipe   A technique used to create transition in which one scene appears to slide off the screen while another scene slides on to replace it.

zoom lens   A special type of camera lens with the ability to change focal length continuously within a given range.

zoom shot   Made with a zoom lens that changes focal length during the take. The result is a change in image size from small to large or large to small, depending on the direction of the zoom.

Sources

Cameras

Aaton Cameras Inc.
1697 Broadway
New York, NY 10019

Alan Gordon Enterprises Inc.
1430 North Cahuenga Boulevard
Hollywood, CA 90028

Arriflex Corporation
One Westchester Plaza
Elmsford, NY 10523

Bach Auricon Inc.
6950 Romaine Street
Hollywood, CA 90038

Beaulieu/Otto Hervic
4907 Valjean Avenue
Encino, CA 91436

Bolex (U.S.A.) Inc.
225 Community Drive
Great Neck, NY 11020

Canon U.S.A. Inc.
64-10 Queens Boulevard
Woodside, Queens, NY 11377

Cinema Products Corporation
2037 Granville Avenue
Los Angeles, CA 90025

Eclair
7262 Melrose Avenue
Los Angeles, CA 90046

Frezzolini Electronics Inc.
7 Valley Street
Hawthorne, NJ 07506

Instrumentation Marketing Corporation
820 South Mariposa Street
Burbank, CA 91506

Mitchell Camera Corporation
666 West Harvard Street
Glendale, CA 91209

Films

Agfa-Gevaert Inc.
Motion Picture Department
275 North Street
Teterboro, NJ 07608

Eastman Kodak
Eastern Region
1187 Ridge Road
West Rochester, NY 14650

Fuji Photo Film (USA) Inc.
350 Fifth Avenue
New York, NY 10001

Lenses

Angenieux Corporation of America
1500 Ocean Avenue
Bohemia, NY 11716

Arriflex Corporation
One Westchester Plaza
Elmsford, NY 10523

Bolex (U.S.A.) Inc.
250 Community Drive
Great Neck, NY 11020

Canon Optics & Business Machines Company Inc.
3113 Wilshire Boulevard
Los Angeles, CA 90005

Century Precision Cine/Optics
10661 Burbank Boulevard
North Hollywood, CA 91601

Questar
RD1
New Hope, PA 18938

Schneider Corporation of America
185 Willis Avenue
Mineola, NY 11501

Shotec Inc.
1717 Junction Avenue
San Jose, CA 95112

Taylor & Hobson
Stoughton Street
Leicester, England

Lighting

Bardwell & McAlister Inc.
12164 Sherman Way
North Hollywood, CA 91605

Berkey Colortran
1015 Chestnut Street
Burbank, CA 91502

Charles Ross Inc.
333 West 52nd Street
New York, NY 10019

Cine 60 Inc.
630 Ninth Avenue
New York, NY 10036

Cinema Products Corporation
2037 Granville Avenue
Los Angeles, CA 90025

General Electric Company/Lamp Division
General Offices
Nela Park
Cleveland, OH 44112

Lowel-Light Manufacturing Inc.
421 West 54th Street
New York, NY 10019

LTM
1160 North Las Palmas Avenue
Hollywood, CA 90038

Macbeth Sales Corporation
P.O. Box 7062
RD #3
Jeanne Drive
Newburgh, NY 12550

Mole-Richardson Lighting
937 North Sycamore Avenue
Hollywood, CA 90038

Strand Century Inc.
20 Bushes Lane
Elmwood Park, NJ 07407

Sylvania Lighting Center
Danvers, MA 01923

Thorn Lighting Inc.
Thorn House
23 Leslie Court
Whippany, NJ 07981

Filters

Belden Communications Inc.
534 West 25th Street
New York, NY 10001
(Lee filters)

Eastman Kodak
Eastern Region
1187 Ridge Road
West Rochester, NY 14650

Harrison & Harrison
6363 Santa Monica Boulevard
Hollywood, CA 90038

Rosco Laboratories Inc.
36 Bush Avenue
Port Chester, NY 10573

Tiffen Manufacturing Corporation
90 Oser Avenue
Hauppauge, NY 11787

Exposure meters

Asahi Optical America Inc. (Pentax)
15 East 26th Street
Suite 1710
New York, NY 10010

Copal Corporation of America (Sekonic)
58–25 Queens Boulevard
Woodside, NY 11377

Minolta Corporation
101 Williams Drive
Ramsey, NJ 07446

Photo Research Corporation (Spectra)
837 North Cahuenga Boulevard
Hollywood, CA 90038

Retail sales and rentals

Adolph Gasser Film Enterprises Inc.
181 Second Street
San Francisco, CA 94107

Atlanta Film Equipment Rentals
1848 Briarwood Road, N.E.
Atlanta, GA 30329

Behrend's Inc.
225 West Ohio Street
Chicago, IL 60610

Cam Rent
163 Richard Court
Pomona, NY 10970

Camera Mart Inc.
456 West 55th Street
New York, NY 10019

Cine Tech Inc.
7330 NE Fourth Court
Miami, FL 33126

Cine-Pro
1037 North Sycamore Avenue
Hollywood, CA 90038

Comquip Inc.
366 South Maple Avenue
Glen Rock, NJ 07452

F & B/Ceco Inc.
315 West 43rd Street
New York, NY 10036

Ferco
363 Brannan Street
San Francisco, CA 94107

Image Devices Inc.
1825 NE 149th Street
Miami, FL 33181

Ross Gaffney Inc.
21 West 46th Street
New York, NY 10036

SOS Photo-Cine-Optics Inc.
40 Kero Road
Carlstadt, NJ 07072

Victor Duncan Inc.
200 East Ontario
Chicago, IL 60611

Laboratories

Allied Film Laboratories
7375 Woodward Avenue
Detroit, MI 48202

Calvin Productions Inc.
1105 East Truman Road
Kansas City, MO 64106

Capital Film Laboratories
1998 NE 150th Street
North Miami, FL 33161

Capital Film Laboratories Inc.
47 East Street SW
Washington, DC 20024

Cine Craft Laboratories
45 North Texas Avenue
Orlando, FL 32805

Cine Magnetics Inc.
202 East 44th Street
New York, NY 10017

Du Art Film Laboratories
245 West 55th Street
New York, NY 10019

Filmtronics Laboratories
231 West 54th Street
New York, NY 10019

General Film Laboratories
1546 North Argyle
Hollywood, CA 90028

George W. Colburn Laboratories
164 North Wacker
Chicago, IL 60606

Huemark Films Inc.
227 East 44th Street
New York, NY 10017

Movielab Inc.
619 West 54th Street
New York, NY 10019

The Optical House Inc.
25 West 45th Street
New York, NY 10036
(optical effects)

Reverse-O Laboratory Inc.
45 Columbus Avenue
New York, NY 10023

Videart Opticals
39 West 38th Street
New York, NY 10018
(optical effects)

WRS Motion Picture Laboratories
210 Semple Street
Pittsburgh, PA 15213

Miscellaneous

Allied Impex Corporation
168 Glen Cove Road
Carle Place, NY 11514
(projection equipment)

American Photographic Instrument Company Inc.
10 East Clarke Place
The Bronx, NY 10452
(pic stands)

Arriflex Corporation
One Westchester Plaza
Elmsford, NY 10523
(Sachtler support systems)

Cine 60 Inc.
630 Ninth Avenue
New York, NY 10036
(batteries, sun-guns, accessories)

Cinema Products
2037 Granville Avenue
Los Angeles, CA 90025
(lighting, image stabilizers, accessories)

Cinetron Computer Systems Inc.
6700 I-85 N
Atlanta, GA 30093
(computerized optical and animation equipment)

Comprehensive Service Corporation
P.O. Box 881
Times Square Station
New York, NY 10036
(reels, general supplies)

Elemak Movie Making Equipment
Via Poggibonsi, 15
Roma 00148, Italy
(camera dollies)

Fax Company
374 South Fair Avenue
Pasadena, CA 91105
(animation camera stands)

Innovative Television Equipment
P.O. Box 681
Woodland Hills, CA 91365
(tripods, etc.)

Javelin Electronics
6357 Arizona Circle
Los Angeles, CA 90045
(night viewing devices)

Karl Heitz Inc.
979 Third Avenue
New York, NY 10022
(Gitzo tripods)

Kenworthy Snorkel Camera Systems
Los Angeles, CA 90022
(snorkel lenses, etc.)

Magnasync/Moviola Corporation
5539 Riverton Avenue
North Hollywood, CA 91601
(editing, recording, etc.)

Matthews Studio Equipment Inc.
2405 Empire Avenue
Burbank, CA 91504
(lighting and grip equipment)

Motion Picture Enterprises Inc.
Tarrytown, NY 10591
(film and video supplies)

Oxberry Division of Richmark Camera Service
180 Broad Street
Carlstadt, NJ 07072
(animation equipment)

Plastic Reel Corporation
46 Passaic Street
Building 52
Wood Ridge, NJ 07075
(reels, cases, general supplies)

Tyler Camera Systems
14218 Aetna Street
Van Nuys, CA 91401
(helicopter mounts)

W.A. Palmer Films Inc.
611 Howard Street
San Francisco, CA 94105
(projectors, general supplies)

Appendix 1

Sixteen-millimeter camera dataguide

The following descriptive list of 24 cameras is one of the most complete ever published. It includes not only cameras that are being currently manufactured, but also several that are available only used. Ten cameras have been dropped from the survey because information was not available and they had almost completely disappeared even from the used camera marketplace. Among these are six cameras that in many respects were ahead of their time when introduced and that offered some truly superb features: the Beaulieu News 16, Bolex 16 Pro, Canon Sound Scopic, Kodak Reflex 16, Mitchell 16 Pro, and the Beckman & Whitney CM16. The Kodak Cine-Special, an early and dearly loved workhorse, is now, along with the gray and brown Keystones, on the antique collectors' lists. The Dioflex, a Japanese copy of the Arriflex S, never caught on, and the Kodak K-100 is no longer manufactured. Out of respect for their superb quality and importance as basic tools in so many studios over the years the Mitchell 16 and Maurer 16 remain listed; these cameras are among those sometimes available used at bargain prices even today.

Because of inflation, the prices for currently manufactured cameras listed will, of course, be out of date even before this book is published. This is especially true for German and French equipment because of the fluctuation in the dollar against other world currencies. The purpose of the approximate prices given is mainly to provide you with a basis for comparing equipment.

	Aaton 7LTR	Arriflex 16S	Arriflex 16M	Arriflex 16BL	Arriflex 16SR	Auricon Cine-Voice	Auricon Pro-600	Auricon Super 1200
Availability/price body only	new, $13,00	new, $9,000	new, $11,500	new, $15,000	new, $23,000	new, $2,200	new, $2,500	new, $6,200
Weight, less lens and film	13 lb	9 lb	11 lb	14 lb, 6.5 oz	12.5 lb	12 lb	21 lb	42 lb
Type of lens mount	50mm Aaton bayonet	standard Arriflex	standard Arriflex	standard Arriflex with lens blimp	Arri bayonet	"C" mount	"C" mount	"C" mount
Style of turret	single lens port	3 lens divergent	3 lens divergent	single port	single port	3 lens flat	3 lens flat	3 lens flat
Shutter	180° fixed	180° fixed	180° fixed	180° fixed	180° fixed	180° fixed	180° fixed	180° fixed
Registration	single claw	single claw and registration pin	single claw, single registration pin	single claw, single registration pin	single claw, single registration pin	single sinusoidal claw	single sinusoidal claw	single sinusoidal claw
Standard motor	variable speed, crystal sync DC	interchangeable DC	interchangeable DC	governor controlled	crystal sync	constant speed 110v AC	100v AC sync	110v AC sync
Battery	12v DC clip-on pack	8v DC pack	8v DC pack	12v DC pack	12v DC clip-on pack			
Loading style	400' magazine	100' spools in body	400' magazine	400' magazine	400' magazine	100' daylight spools in body	400' and 600' magazine	400', 600', and 1200' magazine
Type of magazine	threaded quick-change coaxial	optional 400' single chamber	quick-change single chamber	quick-change single chamber	threaded quick-change coaxial		double chamber	double chamber
Magazine price	$2,700	$1,000	$1,000	$1,500	$3,400		$325	$350
Type of viewing	mirrored shutter reflex	mirrored shutter reflex	mirrored shutter reflex	mirrored shutter reflex	mirrored shutter reflex	nonreflex monitor viewer	nonreflex with separate telefinders	nonreflex rackover prism and telefinders
Viewfinder optics	fiber optic with L/R swivel	ground glass	ground glass	ground glass	fiber optic with swivel		aerial image	ground glass and aerial
Blimping	self-blimped to 28db	unblimped, optional blimp available	unblimped, optional blimp available	self-blimped to 31db	self-blimped to 28db	self-blimped	self-blimped	self-blimped
Major features and accessories	video viewing, time code marking, auto exposure	numerous quick-change motors, matte boxes, battery styles, lenses	numerous motors, matte boxes, batteries, lenses, 1200' coaxial magazine	sync motors, orientable viewers, single-system sound	video viewing, time code marking, auto exposure, orientable viewer	optical or magnetic single-system sound	optical or magnetic single-system sound	optical or magnetic single-system sound, 1200' capacity, self-heating
Comments	superb studio and location camera, with most advanced features available	the major workhorse location camera, extremely versatile, rugged	rugged 400' reflex location camera popular on helicopter rigs	rugged, dependable studio camera, body brace recommended for hand holding	probably finest made instrument available, with all advanced features	although rare in stock form, functions well with reflex lens	real bargain in sync cameras, use of reflex lens recommended	a famous and reliable studio camera; reflex lens increases usefulness

	Auricon Conversions	Beaulieu R-16	Bell & Howell Filmo	Bolex H16 Rex 5	Bolex H16 EBM	Bolex H16 EL	Canon Scoopic 16	Cinema Products CP-16
Availability/ price body only	used, $2,500±	indefinite, approx. $5,000	new, $800	new, $3,100	new, $3,100	new, $4,800	new, $3,200	new, $4,400
Weight, less lens and film	13.5 lb	3.6 lb	9 lb	7.5 lb	8.7 lb	8.6 lb	7.3 lb	11 lb
Type of lens mount	"C" mount	"C" mount	"C" mount	special "C" mount	Bolex bayonet	Bolex bayonet	noninterchangeable	"C" mount
Style of turret	single port	3 lens flat	3 lens flat	3 lens flat	single port	single port	none	single port
Shutter	180° fixed	144° reciprocating	180° fixed	135° variable	170° fixed	170° fixed	170° fixed	180° fixed
Registration	single claw	single claw	single claw	trailing claw	trailing claw	trailing claw	trailing claw	sinusoidal claw
Standard motor	110v AC sync	DC variable	19-foot spring	5-meter spring	variable speed DC	variable speed DC	variable speed governor DC	DC crystal controlled
Battery		12v DC grip		optional 12v DC pack	12v DC pack or grip	12v DC lid, pack	12v DC, internal	20v DC internal
Loading style	400' magazine	100' spool inside body	100' spool inside body	100' spool inside body	100' spool inside body	100' spool inside body	100' spool inside body	400' magazine
Type of magazine	Mitchell double chamber	optional 200' single chamber	optional 400' double chamber	optional 400' single chamber	optional 400' single chamber	optional 400' single chamber		double chamber
Magazine price	used, $150	$250	$200	$600	$600	$600		$350
Type of viewing	none	oscillating mirror reflex	nonreflex telefinder	beamsplitter reflex	beamsplitter reflex	beamsplitter reflex	beamsplitter reflex	none
Viewfinder optics	provided via reflex lens	ground glass	aerial image	ground glass	ground glass	ground glass	ground glass	as per reflex lens
Blimping	self-blimped	none	none	none	none	none	none	self-blimped
Major features and accessories	single-system sound, DC motors	sync pulse generator, auto exposure	AC motor, 400' magazine, DC motor	DC motor, auto exposure, variable auto shutter, automatic threading	sound blimp, auto exposure, crystal sync, automatic threading	built-in exposure, crystal sync, single frame synchroflash, automatic threading	built-in exposure, permanent mounted macro zoom lens, semiautomatic threading	single system with built-in amp; AC battery eliminator
Comments	popular news and documentary camera	extremely lightweight location camera; easy to hold; fragile	rugged, reliable, silent news and student camera	versatile system with numerous features; good location camera	versatile electric location camera; many quality features	versatile location camera, animation and time-lapse equipped; many extras available	extra-easy-to-use location camera, popular among students	a favorite professional news and documentary camera

	Cinema Products CP16R	Cinema Products GSMO	Eclair NPR	Eclair ACL II	Frezzolini LW-16	Frezzolini FR-16	Mitchell 16/Maurer 16	Photo-Sonics Actionmaster
Availability/price body only	new, $9,500	new, $6,000	new, $16,000	new, $16,000	new, $4,600	new, $8,300	used, $2,000 ±	new, $5,000
Weight, less lens and film	12.75 lb	8.75 lb	11 lb	7.7 lb	11 lb	12.25 lb	35 lb	12 lb
Type of lens mount	CP bayonet	CP bayonet	CA-1 and "C" mount	CA-1 or "C" mount	"C" mount	Frezzi bayonet	Mitchell mount/"C" mount	Arri standard or PS bayonet
Style of turret	single port	single port	single port	single port	single port	single port	4 lens flat/3 lens flat	single port
Shutter	170° fixed	180° fixed	180° variable	175° fixed	180° fixed	170° fixed	235° variable	160° variable
Registration	sinusoidal claw	sinusoidal claw	single claw with registration pin	single claw	sinusoidal claw	sinusoidal claw	double claw and pins/special claw	double claw and pins
Standard motor	DC variable crystal	DC variable crystal	DC variable crystal sync	DC variable crystal sync	DC crystal sync	DC crystal variable	AC synchronous	DC crystal to 500 fps
Battery	20v DC internal pack	20v DC internal pack	12v DC pack	12v DC "mini" module	12v DC clip-on	12v DC clip-on		28v DC belt
Loading style	400' magazine	400' quick-change magazine	400' quick-change magazine	200' and 400' quick-change magazine	400' magazine	400' magazine	400' magazine	400' quick-change magazine
Type of magazine	double chamber	threaded coaxial	threaded coaxial	threaded coaxial	double chamber "Mitchell"	double chamber "Mitchell"	double chamber	threaded coaxial
Magazine price	$350	$2,500	$3,200	$3,200	$350	$350	used, $150	$5,000
Type of viewing	mirrored shutter reflex	mirrored shutter reflex	mirrored shutter reflex	oscillating mirror reflex	none	mirrored shutter reflex	rack-over	beamsplitter reflex
Viewfinder optics	fiber optic	fiber optic	ground glass	ground glass	as per reflex lens	fiber optic	ground glass/aerial image	ground glass
Blimping	self-blimped to 30db	self-blimped to 30db	self-blimped	self-blimped	self-blimped	self-blimped	none	none
Major features and accessories	single-system sound with built-in amp, wireless microphone, orientable viewer	orientable finder, auto exposure	numerous motors, time base coding	auto exposure, anatomic grip, attached battery	single-system sound with side-mounted amp	single-system sound with side-mounted amp, orientable viewer	optional sound blimp for Mitchell; studio monitoring viewfinders; assorted motors	instant switch from standard to preset high-speed pistol grip
Comments	superb documentary and news camera that uses "studio rig" to adapt to studio applications	state-of-the-art all-around production camera; best of new designs	classic French all-around production camera; fully professional	ultracompact, quiet, location documentary camera	popular news camera comparable to CP-16	successful reflex news and documentary camera comparable to CP16R	unequaled quality; classic studio cameras, excellent for optional work and back-up	one of several superb sports and slo-mo cameras

Aaton 7LTR

Arriflex 16S

Arriflex 16M

Arriflex 16BL

Arriflex 16SR

Auricon Cine-Voice

Auricon Pro-600

Auricon Super 1200

Auricon Conversions

Beaulieu R-16

Bell & Howell Filmo

Bolex H16 Rex 5

Bolex H16 EBM

Bolex H16 EL

Canon Scoopic 16

Cinema Products CP-16

Cinema Products CP16R

Cinema Products GSMO

Eclair NPR

Eclair ACL II

Frezzolini LW-16

Frezzolini FR-16

Mitchell 16/Maurer 16

Photo-sonics Actionmaster

Appendix 2
Film dataguide

Until the end of the 1970s at least six film manufacturers contributed 16mm camera films to the production market. But at this writing Agfa Gevacolor, Gevachromes, Gevapans, GAF Anscochromes, the 3M black-and-white reversals and the Ilford black-and-white negative films are no longer being produced. Fuji color negative and reversal films provide the only competition to Eastman Kodak products. Even the Ilford black-and-white emulsions, which are still manufactured, are no longer sold in the United States.

For further information on Eastman Kodak products, contact:

Eastern Region—1187 Ridge Road, West Rochester, NY 14650; (716) 254–1300; Telex 97–8429

Midwestern Region—1901 West 22nd Street, Oak Brook, IL 60521; (313) 654–5335; Telex 25–5156

New York City Region—1133 Avenue of the Americas, New York, NY 10036; (212) 262–6000; Telex 12–5334

Pacific Northern Region—3250 Van Ness Avenue, San Francisco, CA 94109; (415) 928–1300; Telex 34–0892. *Mail address*— P.O. Box 3145 (Rincon Annex), San Francisco, CA 94119

Pacific Southern Region—6706 Santa Monica Boulevard, Hollywood, CA 90038; (213) 464–6131. *Mail address*—P.O. Box 38939, Hollywood, CA 90038

Southeastern Region—1775 Commerce Drive, N.W., Atlanta, GA 30318; (404) 351–6510. *Mail address*—P.O. Box 4778 (Federal Annex), Atlanta, GA 30302

Southwestern Region—6300 Cedar Springs Road, Dallas, TX 75235; (214) 351–3221; Telex 73–0214

For information regarding Fuji Photo Products, contact Fuji Photo Film USA, Inc., 350 Fifth Avenue, New York, NY 10001.

	Manu-facturer	Film Name	Code Numbers		Description*	Color Balance	Exposure Index and Filter Required for Shooting Under:			
			16mm	35mm			Daylight 5,500°K	Tungsten 3,200°K	Tungsten 3,400°K	Cool White Fluores-cent
Black-and-White Negative Films	Kodak	Plus X	7231	5231	medium-speed, fine-grain, general-purpose panchromatic film for high-quality reproduction		80	64	64	70*
	Kodak	Double X	7222	5222	high-speed panchro-matic film for general production use under adverse lighting conditions		250	200	200	225*
	Kodak	4 X	7224	5224	extremely high-speed panchromatic film with moderate grain for available-light cinema-tography and general production with low light levels		500	400	400	450*
Black-and-White Reversal Films	Kodak	Plus X Reversal	7276		slow- to medium-speed panchromatic reversal film intended for gen-eral exterior photogra-phy, news, documen-tary, and kinescope recording		50	40	40	45*
	Kodak	Tri X Reversal	7278		high-speed panchro-matic film for general interior photography or slow-motion/low-light shooting in daylight; sports, news, documen-tary film		200	160	160	180*
	Kodak	4 X Reversal	7277		very high speed and moderate grain for filming under very poor lighting conditions, night sports, available-light documentaries, etc.		400	320	320	360*
Color Negative Films	Eastman	Color Negative	7247	5247	medium-speed, low-contrast, fine-grain emulsion for profes-sional production under all conditions; excellent reproduction "backs up" this superb film	tungsten 3,200°K	64 with #85 filter	100	80 with #81A filter	25 with filters #60R and #10Y
	Eastman	Color High-Speed Negative	7293	5293	exciting breakthrough in speed and quality for production under adverse lighting condi-tions; will intercut with 7247, can be pushed to EI 1000	tungsten 3,200°K	160 with #85 filter	250	200 with #81A filter	60 with filters #60R and #10Y
	Fuji Photo	Fujicolor Negative Film	8527	8517	general-purpose, me-dium-speed, fine-grain film for professional production under all conditions; provides al-ternative to 7247	tungsten 3,200°K	64 with #85 filter	100	80 with #81A filter	25 with filters #60R and #10Y

* estimated; no special recommendation by manufacturer

	Manu-facturer	Film Name	Code Numbers		Description*	Exposure Index and Filter Required for Shooting Under:				
			16mm	35mm		Color Balance	Daylight 5,500°K	Tungsten 3,200°K	Tungsten 3,400°K	Cool White Fluorescent
Color Reversal Films	Eastman	Ektachrome Video News Daylight	7239	5239	intended for news and sports photography under difficult lighting conditions, especially where pushing may be required and direct projection is desired	daylight	160	40 with #80A filter	50 with #80B filter	80 with #30M filter
	Eastman	Ektachrome Video News Tungsten	7240	5240	tungsten balanced	tungsten 3,200°K	80 with #85B filter	125	100 with #81A filter	64 with filters #20R and #20Y
	Eastman	Ektachrome Video News High Speed	7250	5250	very high-speed film intended for use under available low-lighting levels, night sports, etc; may be pushed one stop with little loss of quality; recommended for direct projection	tungsten 3,200°K	250 with #85B filter	400	320 with #81A filter	100 with filters #60R and #10Y
	Eastman	Ektachrome Commercial	7252		slow-speed, fine-grain emulsion for general production that produces a low-contrast original; ideally suited for printing and reproduction	tungsten 3,200°K	16 with #85 filter	25	20 with #81 filter	6 with filters #60R and #10Y
	Kodak	Ektachrome MS	7256	5256	medium-speed, sharp daylight film used in industrial and instrumentation filming where direct projection is desired	daylight	64	16 with #81A filter	20 with #80B filter	32 with #30M filter

Manu-facturer	Film Name	Code Numbers 16mm	Code Numbers 35mm	Description*	Color Balance	Exposure Index and Filter Required for Shooting Under: Daylight 5,500°K	Tungsten 3,200°K	Tungsten 3,400°K	Cool White Fluores-cent
Kodak	Ektachrome EF Daylight	7241	5241	high-speed film recommended for difficult lighting conditions when direct projection is desired; may be pushed and/or flashed to extend versatility	daylight	160	40 with #80A filter	50 with #80B filter	80 with #30M filter
Kodak	Ektachrome EF Tungsten	7242	5242	tungsten balanced; same as above	tungsten 3,200°K	80 with #85B filter	125	100 with #81A filter	32 with filters #60R and #10Y
Kodak	Ektachrome SM	7244 (Super 8 only)		high-speed Super 8 ideally suited for indoor available light; used for news, sports, and industrial filming, especially where direct projection is desired	tungsten 3,400°K	100 with #85 filter	125 with #82A filter	160	40 with #60R filter
Fuji Photo	Fujicolor Reversal Film RT125	8427		fine-grain film designed for general filming, especially TV news, and industrial and scientific purposes where direct projection is intended	tungsten 3,200°K	80 with #85 filter	125	100 with #81A filter	32 with filters #60R and #10Y
Fuji Photo	Fujicolor Reversal Film RT500	8428		very high-speed film intended for available-light, night, and high-speed cinematography, especially where direct projection is desired		320 with #85 filter	500	400 with #81A filter	200 with #50R filter

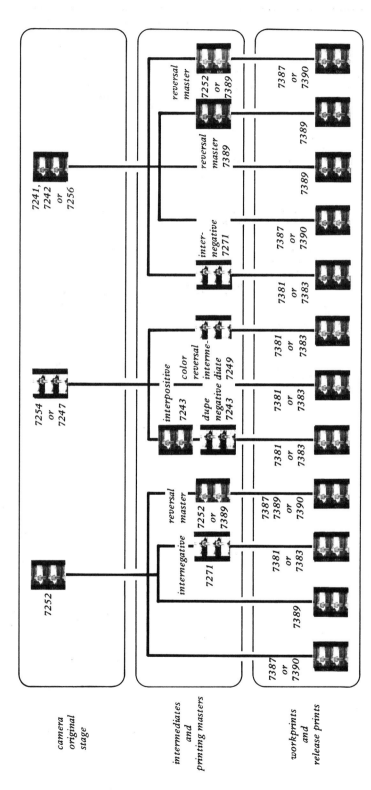

Sixteen-millimeter color prints from 16 mm camera originals: 7241, *Eastman Ektachrome EF Film (daylight);* 7242, *Eastman Ektachrome EF Film (tungsten);* 7243, *Eastman Color Intermediate Film;* 7247, *Eastman Color Negative II Film;* 7249, *Eastman Color Reversal Intermediate Film;* 7252, *Eastman Ektachrome Commercial Film;* 7254, *Eastman Color Negative Film;* 7256, *Eastman Ektachrome MS Film;* 7271, *Eastman Color Internegative Film;* 7381, *Eastman Color Print Film;* 7383, *Eastman Color SP Film;* 7387, *Eastman Reversal Color Print Film;* 7389, *Eastman Ektachrome R Print Film;* 7390, *Eastman Ektachrome Print Film.*

Appendix 3
Lens dataguide

The following list of 120 prime and zoom lenses for 16mm cameras must be introduced with a few qualifiers. First, some rather commonly found lenses are not listed because of their unavailability as new equipment: Kodak Cine-Ektars, Bausch & Lomb Baltars and Elgeet lenses. However, the superb line of Cooke prime lenses is listed even though they are only available used and for rental.

The available mounts listed are those generally shown for given lenses; however, certain lenses may not be available in a given mount, and sometimes adapters and custom modifications by parties other than the manufacturer provide mounts in addition to those listed.

Actual price and availability of all lenses are subject to change at any time. It is interesting to note that virtually any focal length from a 1.9mm "fish eye" to a 1,200mm telephoto is available, at prices ranging from under $100 to over $10,000.

Manufacturer	Model	Type	Focal Length(s)	Maximum Aperture (F-Stop)	T Stop	Available Mounts					Special Attachments and Features	Approximate Cost
						Arri Standard Bayonet	Arri Bayonet	Bolex Bayonet	CP16R	"C"		
Angenieux	R7	fixed	5.9mm	1.8	2					x	fixed focus	$1,900
Angenieux	R21	fixed	10mm	1.8	2					x	available for Bolex Rex	$600
Angenieux	R41	fixed	15mm	1.3	1.5					x	available with finder for Bell & Howell 70	$750
Angenieux	S41	fixed	25mm	1.4	1.5					x	available for Bolex Rex	$600
Angenieux	M1	fixed	25mm	0.95	1.1					x		$1,100
Angenieux	M2	fixed	28mm	1.1	1.2				x	x		$900
Angenieux	S5	fixed	50mm	1.5	1.6					x		$1,000
Angenieux	P3	fixed	75mm	2.5	2.7					x		$700
Angenieux	P2	fixed	100mm	2.5	2.7					x	telephoto	$900
Angenieux	P4	fixed	150mm	2.7	2.9					x	telephoto	$1,100
Angenieux	4 X 17	zoom	17–68mm	2.2	2.5	x			x			$1,800

Manufacturer	Model	Type	Focal Length(s)	Maximum Aperture (F-Stop)	T Stop	Available Mounts					Special Attachments and Features	Approximate Cost
						Arri Standard	Arri Bayonet	Bolex Bayonet	CP16R	"C"		
Angenieux	4 X 17.5	zoom	17.5–70mm	2.2	2.5	x	x		x	x	special for Arri BL and ST	$2,000
Angenieux	6 X 12.5	zoom	12.5–75mm	2.2	2.5	x	x		x	x		$1,800
Angenieux	6 X 9.5	zoom	9.5–57mm	1.6/2.2	1.9/2.4	x	x		x	x		$4,600
Angenieux	10 X 9.5	zoom	9.5–95mm	2.2	2.8	x	x		x	x		$6,100
Angenieux	10 X 12	zoom	12–120mm	2.2	2.5	x	x		x	x		$3,800
Angenieux	15 X 10	zoom	10–150mm	2/2.8	2.3/3.2	x	x	x	x	x		$4,800
Angenieux	20 X 12	zoom	12–240mm	3.5/4.8	4.2	x	x		x	x	greatest zoom range available	$10,400
Canon		fixed	13mm	1.5						x	reasonable price, good quality	$185
Canon		fixed	25mm	1.4						x	reasonable price, good quality	$140
Canon		fixed	50mm	1.4						x	reasonable price, good quality	$195
Canon	Fluorite Super Macro	zoom	12–120mm	2.2		x	x		x	x	reasonable price, good quality	$2,650
Carl Zeiss	Distagon	fixed	8mm	2	2.2	x	x		x	x		$600
Carl Zeiss	Planar	fixed	16mm	2	2.2	x	x		x	x		$250
Carl Zeiss	Distagon	fixed	16mm	2	2.2	x	x		x	x		$650
Carl Zeiss	Distagon	fixed	24mm	2	2.2	x	x		x	x		$600
Carl Zeiss	Planar	fixed	25mm	2	2.2	x	x		x	x		$250
Carl Zeiss	Planar	fixed	32mm	2	2.2	x	x					$250
Carl Zeiss	Planar	fixed	50mm	2	2.2	x	x					$350
Carl Zeiss	Planar	fixed	85mm	2	2.2	x	x					$390
Carl Zeiss	Sonnar	fixed	135mm	4		x	x					$200
Carl Zeiss	Superspeed	fixed	9.5mm		1.3	x	x				extra fast	$3,600
Carl Zeiss	Superspeed	fixed	12mm		1.3	x	x				extra fast	$2,900
Carl Zeiss	Superspeed	fixed	16mm		1.3	x	x				extra fast	$2,700
Carl Zeiss	Superspeed	fixed	25mm		1.3	x	x				extra fast	$2,400
Carl Zeiss	Vario Sonnar	zoom	12.5–75mm	2	2.2	x	x	x		x		$900

Carl Zeiss	Vario Sonnar	zoom	10–100mm	2.8	13.3	x	x	x	x	x		$1,000
Century	Extreme wide-angle	fixed	3.5mm	1.8		x	x	x	x	x	extra wide	$600
Century	Super wide-angle	fixed	5.7mm	1.8		x	x	x	x	x	extra wide	$600
Century	wide-angle	fixed	10mm	1.8		x	x	x	x	x		$400
Century		fixed	150mm	2.8		x	x	x	x	x	telephoto	$500
Century	Tele-Athenar	fixed	230mm	3.8		x	x	x	x	x	telephoto	$500
Century	Tele-Athenar	fixed	300mm	4.2		x	x	x	x	x	telephoto	$500
Century	Tele-Athenar	fixed	385mm	4.5		x	x	x	x	x	telephoto	$500
Century	Tele-Athenar	fixed	500mm	4.5		x	x	x	x	x	telephoto	$1,250
Century	Tele-Athenar	fixed	800mm	4.7		x	x	x	x	x	telephoto	$2,700
Century	Tele-Athenar	fixed	1,000mm	5.6		x	x	x	x	x	telephoto	$2,800
Century	Tele-Athenar	fixed	1,200mm	6.8		x	x	x	x	x	telephoto	$3,000
Cinema Products	Ultra T	fixed	9mm		1.35		x	x	x		ultrafast	$1,600
Cinema Products	Ultra T	fixed	12mm		1.25		x	x	x		ultrafast	$1,400
Cinema Products	Ultra T	fixed	16mm		1.25		x	x	x		ultrafast	$1,250
Cinema Products	Ultra T	fixed	25mm		1.25		x	x	x		ultrafast	$1,150
Kilfitt-Munich	Macro Kilar	fixed	40mm	2.8		x	x			x	macro lens	$600
Kilfitt-Munich	Super-macro Kilar	fixed	90mm	2.8		x	x			x	macro lens	$900
Kilfitt-Munich	Kilar	fixed	150mm	3.5		x	x			x	telephoto	$700

Manufacturer	Model	Type	Focal Length(s)	Maximum Aperture (F-Stop)	T Stop	Arri Standard	Arri Bayonet	Bolex Bayonet	CP16R	"C"	Special Attachments and Features	Approximate Cost
Kilfitt-Munich	Tele-Kilar	fixed	300mm	5.6		x	x			x	telephoto	$800
Kilfitt-Munich	Pan Tele-Kilar	fixed	300mm	4		x	x			x	telephoto	$1,500
Kilfitt-Munich	Dual Pan Tele-Kilar	fixed	300mm	4		x	x			x	telephoto	$2,000
Kilfitt-Munich	Sport Reflectar	fixed	500mm	5.6		x	x			x	telephoto	$1,600
Kilfitt-Munich	Sport Fern Kilar	fixed	600mm	5.6		x	x			x	telephoto	$2,600
Kilfitt-Munich	Icitar Tele Combination	dual	600mm/400mm			x	x			x	includes tele-extender for 1,200mm and 800mm	$3,200
Kinoptik	Super Tegea	fixed	1.9mm	1.9		x	x		x	x	ultrawide fish eye	$2,000
Kinoptik	Tega	fixed	5.7mm	1.8		x	x		x	x	ultrawide	$1,400
Kinoptik	Apochromat	fixed	9mm	1.5		x	x		x	x		$1,000
Kinoptik	Apochromat	fixed	12.5mm	2.5		x	x		x	x		$600
Kinoptik	Apochromat	fixed	12.5mm	1.5		x	x		x	x		$900
Kinoptik	Apochromat	fixed	18mm	1.8		x	x		x	x		$700
Kinoptik	Apochromat	fixed	25mm	2		x	x		x	x		$500
Kinoptik	Apochromat	fixed	32mm	1.9		x	x		x	x		$550
Kinoptik	Apochromat	fixed	35mm	1.3		x	x		x	x		$800
Kinoptik	Apochromat	fixed	40mm	2		x	x		x	x		$700

Manufacturer	Lens	Mount	Focal length	Aperture					Price
Kinoptik	Apochromat	fixed	50mm	2	x	x	x		$500
Kinoptik	Apochromat	fixed	50mm	1.3	x	x	x		$1,200
Kinoptik	Macro Apochromat	fixed	50mm	2	x	x	x	macro lens	$1,200
Kinoptik	Macro Apochromat	fixed	75mm	2	x	x	x	macro lens	$1,200
Kinoptik	Apochromat	fixed	75mm	2	x	x	x		$600
Kinoptik	Apochromat	fixed	100mm	2	x	x	x		$1,000
Kinoptik	Macro Apochromat	fixed	100mm	2	x	x	x	macro lens	$1,400
Kinoptik	Apochromat	fixed	150mm	2.5	x	x	x		$1,200
Kinoptik	Macro Apochromat	fixed	150mm	2.5	x	x	x	macro lens	$1,600
Kinoptik	Special Cine	fixed	210mm	2.5	x	x	x	telephoto	$1,400
Kinoptik	Special Cine	fixed	300mm	3.5	x	x	x	telephoto	$1,400
Kinoptik	Special Cine	fixed	500mm	5.6	x	x	x	telephoto	$1,600
Kinoptik	Kinoptar	fixed	1,000mm	8	x	x	x	telephoto	$7,000
Soligor		fixed	12.5mm	1.3			x		$207
Soligor		fixed	25mm	1.9			x		$86
Soligor		fixed	75mm	1.4			x		$219
Soligor		fixed	75mm	1.9			x		$125
Soligor		zoom	12.5–75mm	2.5			x		$358

Manufacturer	Model	Type	Focal Length(s)	Maximum Aperture (F-Stop)	T Stop	Arri Standard	Arri Bayonet	Bolex Bayonet	CP16R	"C"	Special Attachments and Features	Approximate Cost
Schneider-Kreuznach	Cinegon	fixed	10mm	1.8		x	x		x	x		$970
Schneider-Kreuznach	Cine-Xenon	fixed	16mm	2		x	x		x	x		$813
Schneider-Kreuznach	Cine-Xenon	fixed	25mm	1.4		x	x		x	x		$850
Schneider-Kreuznach	Cine-Xenon	fixed	35mm	2		x	x		x	x		$775
Schneider-Kreuznach	Cine-Xenon	fixed	40mm	2		x	x		x	x		$775
Schneider-Kreuznach	Cine-Xenon	fixed	50mm	2		x	x		x	x		$850
Schneider-Kreuznach	Cine-Xenon	fixed	75mm	2		x	x		x	x		$900
Schneider-Kreuznach	Macro-Tele Xenar	fixed	75mm	2.8		x	x		x	x	macro lens	$900
Schneider-Kreuznach	Cine-Xenon	fixed	100mm	2		x	x		x	x	telephoto	$2,050
Schneider-Kreuznach	Cine-Tele Xenar	fixed	150mm	4		x	x		x	x	telephoto	$1,000
Schneider-Kreuznach	Varigon	zoom	16–80mm	2		x	x		x	x		$3,500
Schneider-Kreuznach	Varigon	zoom	10–100mm	2		x	x		x	x		$8,000
Schneider-Kreuznach	Tele Varigon	zoom	80–240mm	4		x	x		x	x	telephoto zoom	$3,000
Kern	Switar	fixed	10mm	1.6				x		x	5.5mm attachment available	$625
Kern	Macro Switar	fixed	26mm	1.1				x		x	macro	$1,000
Kern	Macro Switar	fixed	75mm	1.9				x		x	macro	$1,000

Manufacturer	Lens	Type	Focal length	f/				Notes	Price
Kern	Vario Switar	zoom	17–85mm	3.5			x		$1,000
Kern	Vario Swi-tar 100 POE	zoom	16–100mm	1.9			x	with auto exposure system	$3,300
Kern	Vario Switar	zoom	12.5–100mm	2		x	x		
Kern	Vario Switar	zoom	12.5–100mm	2		x	x	with 6.5mm wide-angle attachment	
Taylor Hob-son Cooke	Kinetal	fixed	9mm	1.85	x		x	these lenses are no longer manufactured but are among the finest ever made and are sometimes available for rental or as used items	used, $1,200
			12.5mm	1.8					
			17.5mm	1.8					
			25mm	1.8					
			37.5mm	1.8					
			50mm	1.8					
			75mm	2.6					
			100mm	2.6					
			150mm	3.8					
Taylor Hob-son Cooke TVAR	Vario Kinetal	zoom	9–50mm	2.5	x	x	x	this lens currently available	new, $7,000
Macro TVAR		fixed	150	3.3		x	x	macro lens	$600

Appendix 4

Lighting dataguide

The following is a selected listing of available lighting systems. Space does not allow for all currently available new and used lighting systems to be included. Additional products and accessories are available from all manufacturers, as well as manufacturers other than those appearing on this list.

A quick check under Model and Number of Units will determine if units are a series or entire product line.

Grip equipment, such as stands, clamps, gobos, flags, leasers, dots, scrims, and so forth, are available from many manufacturers—most notably Mole-Richardson Company and Matthews Studio Equipment Company, both of Los Angeles, California.

Manufacturer	Model and Number of Units	Type of Housing
Bardwell & McAlister	Slimline II, 1 unit	round open reflector
Bardwell & McAlister	Mini Mats, 2 units	square open reflector
Bardwell & McAlister	Double Broad, 2 units	square double open reflector
Bardwell & McAlister	CYC Strips, 1-6 units	square multiple open reflector
Bardwell & McAlister	Focusing spotlight, 5 units	focusing Fresnel
Bardwell & McAlister	Softlights, 2 units	open indirect flood
Colortran	Mini-Pro, 1 unit	round open reflector
Colortran	Multi-Quartz, 2 units	round open reflector
Colortran	6-Inch Theater Fresnel, 1 unit	focusing Fresnel
Colortran	Soft-Lite, 3 units	indirect reflector
Cinema Products	Sturdy-Lite, 2 units	round open reflector
Cinema Products	Bubblelite, 1 unit	indirect flood
Cine 60	Turbo Lites, 1 unit	air-cooled open reflector
Cine 60	Sun Gun	round open reflector
Lowel	Original Lowel-Light	clip socket and barn door
Lowel	Lowel-Quartz Model D	round open reflector

Style Bulb	Range of Power	Weight Range	Price Range	Intended Use	Studio or Location	Available as Kit
double-end quartz	1,000–2,000w	8.5 lb	$125	broad floodlight	both	2 unit, 4 unit
double-end quartz	650–1,000w	3.5–4 lb	$90–$100	broad floodlight	mostly location	
double-end quartz	500–1,500w		$150–$175	broad flood and fill	both	no
double-end quartz	1,000–6,000w	2.75–18 lb	$150–$300	background illumination	studio	no
2-pin quartz bipost	1,000–10,000w	13–128 lb	$200–$1,000	key, kicker	studio	no
2-pin quartz bipost	2,000–5,000w	18–46 lb	$200–$500	fill lighting	studio	no
2-pin quartz bipost	250–650w	2 lb	$80	key, kicker	location	3 units
double-end quartz	650–1,000w	4–7.5 lb	$200	key, kicker	location	yes
mogul prefocus	500–750w	10 lb	$100	key, kicker	both	no
double-end quartz	1,000–4,000w	22–30 lb	$250–$500	fill lighting	both	no
double-end quartz	650–1,000w	4–6 lb	$75–$100	key, kicker	location	yes
bipost prefocus	600–1,200w	5 lb	$225	fill lighting	both	yes
2-pin quartz bipost	850w	28 oz	$125	key, kicker	location	yes
bipost quartz	100–250w	1 lb	$180	battery-operated news light	location	no
R-40 reflector flood	75–500w	8 oz	NA	key, kicker	studio	no
bipost quartz	500–1,000w	2.5 lb	$375	key, kicker	both	yes

Manufacturer	Model and Number of Units	Type of Housing	Style Bulb	Range of Power	Weight Range	Price Range
Lowel	Lowel Softlight	folding in-direct soft reflector	double-end quartz	1,000w	7 lb	$375
LTM	Luxarc, 6 units	focusing Fresnel	HMI daylight	200–4,000w	5–30*kg	$1,800–$7,500
LTM	Ambiarc, 6 units	open round reflector	HMI daylight	200–2,500w	4.5–27 kg*	$1,800–$7,000
Mole-Richardson	Solar-Arc, 4 units	focusing Fresnel	HMI daylight	575–4,000w	13–59 lb*	$3,000–$6,000
Mole-Richardson	Solar Spot, 8 units	focusing Fresnel	bipost quartz	200–10,000w	3–131 lb	$60–$1,475
Mole-Richardson	Molequartz, 4 units	round open reflector	double-end quartz	600–2,000w	1.75–6.5 lb	$123–$207
Mole-Richardson	Mole Solar Arc, 4 units	round closed dif-fuser, focusable	HMI daylight	575–4,000w	15.25–48 lb*	$2,750–$5,500
Mole-Richardson	Brute Mole-arcs, 2 units	focusing Fresnel	carbon arc	225 amp, DC	126–152 lb**	$8,800–$9,000
Mole-Richardson	Mole Fay, 6 units	variable multiple sealed beam	quartz-sealed Fay reflector floods	250–7,700w	2.25–22 lb	$112–$650
Mole-Richardson	Soft Lites, 7 units	indirect re-flector fill	double-end quartz	750–8,000w	5–99 lb	$210–$1,235
Mole-Richardson	Cinelite, Bell & Scoop, 6 units	direct re-flector fill	mogul screw quartz	300–2,000w	5.25–12.75 lb	$180–$200
Mole-Richardson	CYC-Strips, 9 units	multiple open square reflector	double-end quartz	500–12,000w	3–26 lb	$107–$475
Strand Century	Bambinos, 3 units	focusing Fresnel	bipost quartz	2,000–10,000w	13–37 lb	$400–$1,300
Strand Century	Ianiro HMI Fresnels	focusing Fresnels	HMI daylight	575–4,000w	22–63 lb*	$4,000–$8,000

* not including ballast or stand
** not including grid or stand

Intended Use	Studio or Location	Available as Kit
key, flood	location	yes
key, kicker	location	yes
fill	location	yes
daylight key, fill	both	no
daylight key, fill	both	no
daylight key, fill	both	no
key, daylight boost	both	no
key, sun-light, moon-light, day-light fill	both	no
daylight and studio booster, fill, punch	both	yes
tungsten fill	both	no
tungsten fill	both	no
CYC and background illumination	studio	no
key, kicker	studio	no
key, kicker, daylight boost	both	no

Appendix 5

Exposure dataguide

As with other equipment guides in this book, there has been no attempt to list all of the many models available. The exposure meters listed represent a sampling of the most popular, classic, and widely used instruments. They are among the smaller and less expensive filmmaking accessories and, as such, are more prone to model and price changes than some of the larger equipment reviewed previously.

Since the total outcome of at least one day's shooting rests on the reliability of these items, the selection and use of exposure meters is always a critical task.

Manufacturer	Model	Primary Use
Fotometer	HSZ-5	spot reading reflected light
Honeywell Pentax	1°/21° Spot Meter	spot reading reflected light
Sekonic	Studio Deluxe	incident light
Sekonic	Apex	reflected light
Gossen	Luna Pro	reflected light
Gossen	Luna Pro SBC	reflected light
Gossen	Sixticolor	color temperature
Spectra	Combi-500	incident light
Spectra	Professional	incident light
Spectra	Candela	footcandles and incident light
Spectra	Tricolor	color temperature
Spectra	Combi II	incident light
Minolta	Auto Spot II	spot reading reflected light
Minolta	3 Color	color temperature
Rebikoff	Color Temp Meter	color temperature

Adapts to	Design	Battery/Type	Range	Special Features	Approximate Price
		mercury	2.5–20,000 ASA	2° measurement in 20° field of view	$300
	CdS element	1.3v DC and 9v DC	6–6,400 ASA	low light booster button	$190
reflected light	selenium		6–12,000 ASA	dual range slides, movie scale	$65
incident light	CdS	mercury	6–12,000 ASA	moonlight sensitivity, movie scale	$60
incident light	CdS	mercury	6–25,000 ASA	spot and microscope attachments; versatile	$90
incident light	CdS	mercury	6–25,000 ASA	many attachments; pro model	$150
			2,600°K– 20,000°K	supplementary filters for camera	$125
reflected light	selenium and CdS	2 PX-13	3,000,000 to 1 ratio	ASA slides for direct reading	$170
reflected light	selenium		10–320	ASA slides for direct reading; individually calibrated	$120
	selenium		0–30,000 footcandles	basic accurate luminance meter	$650
	red, blue, and green scales	2 TR 113R	full spectrum	filter sets available	$170
reflected light	blue silicon		25,000,000 to 1 ratio	1° spot accessory	$170
	CdS	9v DC		1° angle of view	$350
incident light	red, blue, and green sensitivity		2,500°K– 12,500°K	incident exposure readings	$500
	red-blue scale only		2,000°K– 10,000°K	pack size	$80

Bibliography

Alton, John. *Painting with Light.* New York: Macmillan, 1949

Baddeley, W. Hugh. *Documentary Film Production.* 2nd revised ed. New York: Hastings House, 1969.

Bluem, William A. and Squire, Jason E., eds. *The Movie Business.* New York: Hastings House, 1972.

Brown, William O. *Low Budget Features.* Hollywood: William O. Brown, 1971.

Camera Mart Film and Video Sales Catalog. New York: Camera Mart, 1981.

Campbell, Russell, ed. *Photographic Theory for the Motion Picture Cameraman.* New York: A.S. Barnes & Co., 1970.

Campbell, Russell, ed. *Practical Motion Picture Photography.* New York: A.S. Barnes & Co., 1970.

Carlson, Verne and Sylvia. *Professional 16/35mm Cameraman's Handbook.* New York: Amphoto, 1970.

Clarke, Charles G., ed. *American Cinematographer Manual.* 5th ed. Hollywood: American Society of Cinematographers, 1980.

Eastman Kodak, *The Business of Filmmaking.* Rochester: Eastman Kodak Co., 1978.

————. *Cinematographer's Field Guide.* 2nd ed. Rochester: Eastman Kodak Motion Picture and Audiovisual Markets Division, 1978.

————. *Kodak Filters.* Rochester: Eastman Kodak Co., 1972.

————. *The Selection and Use of Kodak and Eastman Motion Picture Films.* 3rd ed. Rochester: Eastman Kodak Co., 1976.

Fuji Film, *Photographic Properties of Fuji Motion Picture Films.* Tokyo: Fuji Photo Film Co., 1980.

Gilmour, Edwin. *Photographer's Guide to Movie Making.* New York: A.S. Barnes & Co., 1963.

Hardy, Arthur C., and Perrin, Fred H. *The Principles of Optics.* New York: McGraw-Hill, 1932.

Hurst, Walter E.; Minus, Johnny; and Hale, William Storm. *Your Introduction to Film, TV, Copyright, Contracts, and Other Law.* Hollywood: Seven Arts Press, 1973.

Jacobs, Lewis. *Introduction to the Art of the Movies.* New York: Farrar, Straus and Giroux, 1960.

Life Library of Photography. *The Camera.* New York: Time-Life Books, 1970.

————. *Color.* New York: Time-Life Books, 1970.

————. *Light and Film.* New York: Time-Life Books, 1970.

Lipton, Lenny. *Independent Filmmaking.* San Francisco: Straight Arrow Books, 1972.

Malkiewicz, J. Kris. *Cinematography.* New York: Van Nostrand Reinhold, 1973.

Mascelli, Joseph V. *The Five C's of Cinematography.* Hollywood: Cine/Graphic Publications, 1965.

——————. *Mascelli's Cine Workbook.* Hollywood: Cine/Graphic Publications, 1973.

Millerson, Gerald. *The Technique of Lighting for Television and Motion Pictures.* New York: Hastings House, 1972.

——————. *The Technique of Television Production.* New York: Hastings House, 1961.

Mole-Richardson Co. *Catalog.* Hollywood: Mole-Richardson Co., 1980.

Morgan, Willard D. gen. ed. *The Encyclopedia of Photography.* New York: Greystone Press, 1963.

Pincus, Edward. *Guide to Filmmaking.* New York: New American Library, 1969.

Quick, John, and LaBau, Tom. *Handbook of Film Production.* New York: Macmillan, 1972.

Ritsko, Allen J. *Lighting for Motion Pictures.* New York: Van Nostrand Reinhold, 1979.

Roberts, Kenneth H., and Sharples, Win Jr. *A Primer for Filmmaking.* New York: Bobbs-Merrill, 1971.

Smallman, Kirk. *Creative Filmmaking.* New York: Macmillan, Inc., 1969.

Society of Motion Picture and Television Engineers. *Elements of Color in Professional Motion Pictures.* New York: SMPTE, 1957.

Souto, H. Mario Raimondo. *The Technique of the Motion Picture Camera.* Revised ed. New York: Hastings House, 1969.

Spottiswoode, Raymond. *Film and Its Techniques.* Berkeley: University of California Press, 1963.

——————, ed. *The Focal Encyclopedia of Film and Television Techniques.* New York: Hastings House, 1969.

——————. *A Grammar of the Film.* Berkeley: University of California Press, 1967.

Sylvania. *Lighting Handbook.* 3rd ed. Danvers, MA: General Telephone & Electronics, 1969.

Wheeler, Leslie J. *Principles of Cinematography.* New York: Morgan and Morgan, 1953.

Index